Pas

Passion

PASSIONATE SCANDAL
by
Michelle Reid

MISTRESS OF DECEPTION
by
Miranda Lee

THE CRUELLEST LIE
by
Susan Napier

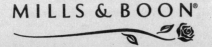

MILLS & BOON®

MILLS & BOON and MILLS & BOON with the Rose Device are registered trademarks of the publisher.
Harlequin Mills & Boon Limited,
Eton House, 18-24 Paradise Road, Richmond, Surrey, TW9 1SR

PASSION
© by Harlequin Enterprises II B.V., 1999

Passionate Scandal, Mistress of Deception and *The Cruellest Lie* were first published in Great Britain by Mills & Boon Limited in separate, single volumes.

Passionate Scandal © Michelle Reid 1994
Mistress of Deception © Miranda Lee 1993
The Cruellest Lie © Susan Napier 1993

ISBN 0 263 81540 4

05-9908

Printed and bound in Spain
by Litografía Rosés S.A., Barcelona

Michelle Reid grew up on the southern edges of Manchester, the youngest in a family of five lively children. But now she lives in the beautiful county of Cheshire with her busy executive husband and two grown-up daughters.

She loves reading, the ballet, and playing tennis when she gets the chance. She hates cooking, cleaning, and despises ironing! Sleep she can do without and produces some of her best written work during the early hours of the morning. Michelle had her first book published by Mills & Boon® in 1988 and has since written nearly twenty romances, which have been sold all over the world.

PASSIONATE SCANDAL

by

MICHELLE REID

CHAPTER ONE

SEATBELT securely fastened. Seat in its upright position. That distinctive humming sensation in the head that always happened when the cabin slowly depressurised along with their steady descent. And that other very familiar growling sound which said the huge Boeing was throttling back on its final approach into London's Heathrow Airport at last. And suddenly panic erupted from nowhere, drying Madeline's mouth, closing her eyes, catching at her breath and jerking her hands into white-knuckled fists on her trembling lap.

Was she really ready for this?

What a question! she chided herself angrily. What a useless, stupid question to ask herself now, of all times!

Of course she was ready. And even if she wasn't, she would still have come!

Nothing—nothing would stop her from attending Nina's wedding. Not even the reawakening of a sick panic she had thought she'd spent the last four years combating!

Four years, she thought painfully. Surely four years had been quite long enough to spend in exile for her sins, without her having to feel like this? Four years ago she had been just too young and ill-equipped to deal with the pain and humiliation of it all. She had been her own worst enemy then. But she was four years older now, she reminded herself sternly, four years the wiser, and she had gained four full years' much needed maturity and sophistication to help armour herself against whatever waited for her down there beneath those familiar grey clouds of London.

'All right, darling?'

Part of her armour, Madeline admitted as she forced a reassuring smile for her travelling companion. Perry had invited himself along on this trip, and she had hesitated only slightly before accepting his company—whether through conceit or cowardice she wasn't sure. Conceit certainly played a part in her need to show them all at home just how well she could do for herself. And cowardice because she was uncomfortably aware that she was using Perry as an elegant prop for her new image.

An image that was the complete antithesis of her old one.

Perry, she supposed, could be called her latest beau! He was one of the Boston Linburghs. The eldest son and heir in fact to that highly influential and wealthy family. And looked it too, she noted fondly as she studied his smooth lean profile. Hair the colour of wood ash, worn fashionably short, styled to the good shape of his head. His eyes were a warm shade of hazelnut, and his smile the unaffected kind which made him so easy to like.

She and Perry had been a 'thing' for several months now. Their relationship—warmly platonic, she decided, described it best—was useful to both of them, because behind their friendly intimacy they were each nursing the wounds of a broken engagement.

So, when Nina's letter had arrived begging Madeline to come to her wedding, Perry had immediately suggested he come with her.

'I can combine the trip with some business my father needs attending to at our London office. That way, at least I'll be able to to be with you at weekends.' And give you any support you may find you'll need, was his silent addition. She and Perry understood each other very well.

'What's this stepsister of yours like?' he enquired now,

turning teasing eyes on her. 'Not one of the wicked kind, is she?'

'Nina?' Madeline gasped. 'Good grief, no!'

If anything, she thought ruefully, she was the wicked stepsister; Nina was the angel.

Madeline was the only child from Edward Gilburn's first marriage, a marriage that had lasted only six stormy years before ending up in a surprisingly amicable divorce considering her parents' track record for doing nothing amicable for each other. The then five-year-old Madeline had remained in England with her father when her mother decided to return to the States to live. Dee, her Boston-born-and-bred mother, had possessed just enough sensitivity to see that parting Madeline from her father would have been nothing short of first-degree murder, since they both doted so much on each other. Dee had not been offended, just philosophical about the situation. Madeline and her father had needed each other more than they needed Dee. So she had packed her lorry loads of baggage and shipped herself back to Boston, where Madeline had commuted on a regular visiting basis ever since.

She had been just eight years old when her father announced his intention to remarry, and she could still remember how determined she had been to hate this unexpected competitor for her father's affections. Then in walked Louise, a vision of fair and gentle loveliness. And by her side, with her small hand clinging to her mother's, stood Nina, tiny will-o'-the-wisp Nina, with her mother's anxious cornflower blue eyes and soft vulnerable mouth. And the very spoiled and wilful Madeline Gilburn had been captivated right there and then.

On looking that far back as the plane's wheels touched smoothly down to earth, Madeline wondered why everyone had been so surprised by her immediate capitulation when over the years she and her father had proved time and time again how much in harmony were their thoughts and feelings. Where one loved, the other invariably loved also.

Which had made it doubly painful for both of them when she and Dominic broke up...

Dominic. Thoughts of Dominic Stanton brought her full circle and back to the very roots of her moment's panic. It was because of him that she had run away to Boston four years ago. And, she acknowledged secretly, it was also because of him that she had decided to come back.

She needed to lay the ghosts of a love long dead.

Customs clearance took ages, but eventually she emerged into the mad crush of the arrivals lounge with her loaded luggage trolley, her blue eyes scanning the sea of faces she encountered, looking for the one she was expecting to see and completely oblivious to the interested glances she was receiving for herself alone.

She was tall and beautifully slender in her tailored suit of pure silk knit, its electric blue colour an exact match to her wide-spaced eyes. Her skin was a little pale after the long hours cooped up in an aeroplane, but nothing could dim its natural purity. Her long blue-black hair had been confined in a braided coronet for the journey, and had arrived at the end of it looking as sleek and sophisticated as it had when she'd set off more than twelve hours ago. She was the kind of woman who stood out in a crowd. Destined to belong to someone special. Exclusive.

The man walking at her side suited her. His air of high breeding and easy sophistication showed clearly. His smooth fairness complemented her dark sleekness. Two very sophisticated people.

'Madeline!'

Her head twisted, blue eyes alighting on the tall distinguished figure of her father, and on a soft cry she moved eagerly into his arms.

'You're late,' he complained after releasing her from a suffocating bear-hug of an embrace. 'Over an hour late coming in, and another hour getting through those infernal Customs!'

Madeline smiled and kissed his cheek. 'Don't knock the tight security,' she scolded him. 'It's all done for our own safety.'

'Hmph,' was his only answer to that as he held her out at arm's length so he could look at her. 'You're looking good enough to eat,' he decided, 'though how you manage to after that lousy journey confounds me.'

'Mummy comes in useful for some things, you know,' she grinned. Expecting and getting another disparaging 'Hmph'.

There was very little love lost between her parents. Her father saw Dee as a very beautiful but empty-headed social doll, and Dee saw her father as a brusque, insensitive tyrant. The only place they met in any harmony was where their daughter was concerned, and even there they begged to differ—over all points but her happiness.

'Now, where's this young man your mother's been telling me so much about?'

Turning in her father's arms, Madeline searched Perry out, to find he had been joined by a big dark-haired man who was greeting him like an old friend.

'Forman!' she cried in surprise.

The newcomer grinned and came over to kiss her cheek. She had met Forman Goulding several times in Boston. He was a big dark man with the kind of hard masculine looks she tended to shy away from these days. He was also Perry's cousin and the member of the family who took care of their European interests.

It was with Forman that Perry was going to stay during his stay in London, coming to Madeline in Lambourn during the weekends only. By the time all the introductions had been made, her father had invited Forman down to Lambourn with Perry whenever he wished to join them, then they were all moving outside to her father's Bentley, with Rogers his chauffeur standing by the boot waiting to receive her luggage, and in front of it a long low growling monster of a car which could only belong to Forman Goulding.

Perry took Madeline in his arms and kissed her gently, promising to be with her in Lambourn by Saturday lunchtime.

'That was a fine show of affection,' her father commented once they were seated in the car and on their way.

'Was it?' Madeline murmured, then subtly turned the conversation by demanding to know how everyone was, her eyes warm on him as she listened to all the latest news.

At fifty-five he was still a strikingly attractive man with his head of thick wavy hair which had gone prematurely white in his twenties. He was a man who carried the power he wielded around with him like a banner. Dominic had once described him as a man who totally lacked caution but possessed the luck of the devil to compensate. Reluctant though Madeline was to agree with anything Dominic Stanton said, she had to agree with that particular observation. Her father took risks in business guaranteed to rock the City back on its heels in horror. The fact that he invariably made the right move placed him high on the respect rating with people in the speculative business. Few scoffed at a Gilburn idea. Nobody dared underestimate him. He was just too sharp, too shrewd.

'And what's this Charles Waverley like?' she asked when her father concluded the local news without mentioning Nina's new fiancé. 'I can't imagine our own little Nina getting married and leaving the fold,' she added drily. 'She was always such a timid little home bird.'

'Charles is perfect for Nina,' her father assured her. 'He possesses a natural desire to love and cherish, which is all we can ever ask of the man who wins our Nina. Their marriage will be a good one,' he asserted confidently.

A weight pressing down on her heart kept Madeline silent while she diminished it. It was nothing new to her to feel this terrible burden constricting her chest whenever she thought of love and marriage. It was something she'd had to learn to live with—and control so no one else knew it was there. Love held only bitter memories for her, painful experiences she wouldn't wish on her worst enemy. Marriage meant commitment. An honest declaration of love undying. She had once known love, thought the offer of marriage gave her that commitment. But she had been wrong. And she never wanted Nina to know that same pain, that same anguished desolation.

'And Louise—how is she?' she asked next.

'Very well,' her father said positively. 'Beautiful and well,' he added with all the satisfaction of a man who adored his lovely wife to distraction. Louise suited the blustery Edward Gilburn far better than Madeline's own mother had. With Louise he had a chance to utilise that softer side of his nature which otherwise would never be seen. No one would think of being cruel or tyrannical towards Louise. She was just too soft and vulnerable. 'And eager to have you back home,' he finished warmly.

Madeline didn't doubt it. Louise had been a wonderful surrogate mother to her throughout her formative years. And she had done it without coming between daughter and father or outlawing Dee.

'She had your rooms completely refurbished as a surprise for you—then sat down and worried herself silly that she should have left them as you remembered them, and had us all frantic in case she decided to change them back again in the hopes that you wouldn't notice! Nina managed to stop her.' He sounded heartily relieved. 'She told her that the new Madeline I've been telling them all about would hate to sleep in a candy-pink room with frills and flounces!'

Would she? Madeline laughed dutifully, but felt a heavy sense of loss inside, as if the old Madeline had died, and this new one was just a stand-in. Would other people see her as a stranger now, someone they had to learn to know all over again? She shuddered at the thought. She had just grown up, that was all. Albeit late.

Watching her covertly, Edward Gilburn read more in his daughter's studiously placid features than she would like. He had worried terribly about her when she first went to Boston four years ago. Dee had been marvellous with her, he had to admit. She'd refused to let their daughter mope, dragging her—literally sometimes—protesting miserably out to face the human race and learn to deal with it again. But he had feared what kind of person was going to emerge from the ashes of this brutal kind of therapy. He had been relieved to find Madeline slowly learning to cope during his regular visits to see her in Boston. But he could not say he was exactly happy with the final result of the four-year influence of her rather superficial mother.

Where had all that sparkling eagerness to meet life full on gone? he wondered in grim exasperation. That wild and wonderful love of life which made her the captivating creature she was at eighteen? Trust Dee to bleed it all out of her, he thought grimly.

And, not for the first time, he cursed Dominic Stanton

for making it necessary for his baby to place herself in the hands of her mother.

'Nina was worried you might not come,' he put in quietly.

'Because of Dominic, you mean?' As usual, Madeline went directly for the point, and Edward smiled to himself. Dee obviously hadn't managed to curb that natural habit. Then the smile went awry when he remembered how that painfully open honesty of hers had made her broken love affair with Dominic all the harder for her to bear. She had not been able to seek solace in lying to herself, and the truth had been so dreadfully hard to endure. 'I didn't know I'd given such a feeble impression of myself.'

'You didn't, darling, and you know it.' Her father's hand came out to take hers, squeezing it gently.

'What Dominic did to me was cruel.' Madeline said flatly. 'But what I did to him was unforgivable. Neither of us came out of it well. It took me a whole year to acknowledge that,' she admitted on a small smile. 'And a bit of brutal talking from Mummy,' she added drily. 'She was brutal all around, when I come to think of it.' She shrugged, slender shoulders moving up and down beneath the immaculate silk jacket. 'Was that your doing?' She looked enquiringly at her father. 'Did you advise her not to let me wallow?'

His face gave him away, and Madeline smiled again. If anyone knew how best to deal with her, then it was this man. 'Thank you,' she leaned over to kiss his cheek. 'Your instincts rarely let you down, do they?'

'They did where Dominic was concerned,' he muttered gruffly. He had liked and respected Dominic Stanton. So much so that he'd encouraged his love affair with Madeline from its conception. Everyone concerned had, the Stantons just as eagerly as the Gilburns. It had been a

beautiful dream while it lasted. 'I'll never forgive myself
for my part in encouraging you.' He voiced his grim
thoughts out loud.

'You really had no say in what I did, you know,'
Madeline drily pointed out. And he grinned because he
knew as well as she did that when Madeline wanted something badly enough she went all out to get it. And she had
wanted Dominic, so badly that it still hurt just to remember. 'We were simply wrong for each other,' she stated
flatly. 'And we should perhaps be thankful that we found
out soon enough. Does Charles Waverley run a successful
racing stable?' Once again, she deftly changed the subject.

'Very. He trained last year's Derby winner...'

There were going to be some surprised faces around
Lambourn in the near future, Edward Gilburn ruefully
judged as he watched the sleek mask of sophistication drop
smoothly into place on his daughter's face. And found
himself yearning for a time when a black-haired, wicked-
eyed gypsy had danced all over his peace of mind. A time
when Nina had captivated, and Madeline shocked. While
Nina had sat sewing her fine seam, filling his heart with a
gentle gladness for being allowed to take the place of her
dead father, Madeline would be off on some wild prank
or other which would inevitably bring his wrath tumbling
down on her unrepentant head—followed by his secret respect. She rode like the devil, played every sport there was
going with panache. And later, when she grew into a wild
and wilful young woman, she'd run rings around all the
poor besotted young men who fell for a pair of wicked
blue eyes and a mane of wild black hair.

Dee had despaired of ever taming her then, he recalled.
She would send letters home with Madeline after one of
her Boston visits, enquiring in her oh, so sarcastic way if
Edward was raising their daughter as a delinquent for any

specific reason. But even Dee had had to admit that Madeline drew the opposite sex to her like bees to honey, that she was exciting to be with. Madeline possessed a fierce will of her own, but she was also able to laugh at herself, and not many could do that.

Dominic hadn't laughed, the damned fool! If he had—if only he had laughed that fateful night of the country club ball, then maybe Madeline wouldn't have run away, and maybe she would not be sitting next to him now, talking with the bland aplomb of the well trained socialite.

He preferred the other girl, the one who would have been bouncing up and down beside him right now, brimming with excitement, plans, driving him demented with the pranks she intended pulling on her friends.

Or maybe she wouldn't, he then revised thoughtfully. Maybe time alone would have taken the spirited child out of Madeline. Perhaps Dominic Stanton had only accelerated a natural progression—though he didn't think so. He knew his daughter well, knew what kind of devil drove her, because the self-same one had driven him. It had taken him over forty years to learn to tame his own. He hadn't expected Madeline to do it any quicker.

No, Dominic had done that, taught her how to think before she acted; hide instead of being her true exciting self!

They stood like a formal reception party, Madeline noted drily as the car slowed and stopped in front of the grey-stoned country manor house where Louise, Nina and a serious-faced man stood waiting for them at the bottom of the wide stone steps.

Louise looked no different than she had the last time Madeline had seen her four years ago now. Small, and neat-figured, she still had hair that shone that wonderful spun-gold colour, and her smile was still that infinitely gentle one Madeline had first encountered at the age of eight. Nina had altered, though, she noted with a small shock. Her stepsister had grown more beautiful in the four intervening years, her pale gold hair a short cap of enchanting curls around her angelic face. And that had to be Charles Waverley, she decided as she turned her attention to the only stranger in their midst. Tall, weatherbeaten, with the whipcord-lean frame of a working farmer, he stood head and shoulders above both women. There was an expression of solemn reserve about his chocolate-brown eyes.

And it was at him that she smiled first. Why, she wasn't quite sure, except that she knew somehow that it was what Nina would want her to do, make this man she had fallen in love with know she welcomed him into their small family fold.

She saw the uncertain glance he sent Nina before he levelled his gaze back on her, and also saw the hint of relief, as if he'd just taken some terribly important test and was now glad it was over.

'Maddie, darling!' It was Louise who came forward to envelop her in her warm embrace. 'Oh, it's so wonderful to have you home!' She pushed her to arm's length in much the same way her father had done earlier at the airport, her smile rather watery. 'And looking so different, too!' she exclaimed. 'So frightfully sophisticated!'

'Nice to be back, Louise,' she answered earnestly, somehow unable to return the effusive greeting. It'll come back, she told herself firmly, frowning inwardly at her own reticence. It was only now as she stood here with these people she had spent many years of her life with that she noticed the restraint she had learnt to apply on herself. 'And you haven't changed in the slightest,' she made an effort to sound natural. 'I hope Nina won't mind if I tell you I had to take a second look to tell which of you was which!'

'You've earned yourself a kiss for that,' Nina said promptly, coming to replace her mother in Madeline's arms. 'I can't think of a better compliment than to know I look like Mummy. Hello, Maddie,' she added huskily, looking up at her with gentle, loving eyes. 'Have you missed us?'

'Every single day,' she assured, unwilling to tell the truth and admit that she had found it necessary to her own survival to dismiss all that was even vaguely English from her mind for those first few years. 'And you look wonderful. Would that have anything to do with this rather dishy man I see standing guard behind you?' she teased.

Nina blushed, and turned to draw Charles Waverley closer. 'This is Charles, Madeline,' she gravely introduced. 'And you have to like each other on sight, or I shall be miserable.'

Madeline found herself looking once again into those serious brown eyes, and held out her hand. 'Well,' she said frankly, 'I shall promise to like you on sight, Charles, so long as you can promise me you'll take precious care of Nina.'

'A promise I won't find it difficult to keep.' He smiled, and took her outstretched hand.

'Let's get inside, shall we?' Edward Gilburn's gruff voice broke in. 'Come on, Charles,' he took his future son-in-law's arm. 'Women are notoriously silly when it comes to hellos and goodbyes. Let's you and I go and find a nice glass of something while they talk each other's tails off.'

With a laugh, the three women followed them indoors, and proceeded to do exactly what Edward Gilburn had predicted by chatting madly—or, more correctly, Nina and Louise did the chattering. Madeline simply smiled a lot and put the odd word in now and then when required. They didn't seem to notice her reserve, though she did.

It will come, she repeated to herself on a small frown. It was only natural that she should feel strange with them after a four-year separation. The old natural camaraderie would return soon enough once she'd settled back in…

CHAPTER TWO

BUT it didn't. And it was a relief to escape.

Madeline turned Minty, her chestnut mare, towards the river and cantered off. The clouds which had welcomed her home to England had all but cleared away now, leaving a bright full April moon shining in the night sky above her. It wasn't late, barely nine o'clock, but it was cold, cold enough to warrant the big sheepskin jacket she had pulled on over her jeans and sweater.

Her decision to take a ride alone had been met with consternation, but they'd let her go. It wasn't as if they were concerned for her safety. Madeline had been riding over this part of the countryside since she was old enough to climb on to the back of a horse. It was just that they were hurt by her need to get away from them so soon after her arrival home.

But she could not have taken any more tonight.

Within an hour of arriving she'd begun to feel like an invalid home on convalescence because of the way they all seemed to tiptoe around her, around subjects they'd obviously decided between them were strictly taboo, watching her with guarded if loving eyes. By the time another hour had gone by, she had been straining at the leash to escape. Dinner had been an ordeal, her tension and their uncertainty of her acting against each other to make conversation strained and stilted.

She'd blamed her restlessness on jet-lag when she saw their expressions. And they'd smiled, bright, false, tension-packed smiles. 'Of course!' her father had exclaimed—too heartily. 'A ride is just what you need to make you feel at home again!' Louise had agreed, while Nina just looked at her with huge eyes.

Madeline's soft mouth tightened. So, she'd hurt them all, but she couldn't do a single thing about it just yet. Four years was a long time. They all had adjustments to make—her family more than herself, because she was what she was, and nothing like the girl who had left here four years ago.

They were all exactly the same, though, she told herself heavily. They hadn't changed at all.

Minty's hoofs pounded on the frozen ground, and Madeline crouched down low on her back, giving herself up to the sheer exhilaration of the ride as they galloped across the dark countryside. The further she got away from the house, the more relaxed she began to feel, as if the distance weakened the family strings that had been busily trying to wrap themselves around her aching heart.

She didn't know why she felt this way, only that she did. From the moment she'd stepped out of the car, she'd felt stifled, haunted almost, by memories none of them could even begin to contemplate.

A sharp bend in the river was marked by a thick clump of trees standing big and dark against a navy blue sky. She skirted the wood until she found the old path which led down to the river itself, allowing Minty to pick her own way to what was one of their old haunts: a small clearing among the trees, where the springy turf grew to the edge of the steep riverbank.

She loved this place, she thought with a sigh, sliding down from Minty's back to stand, simply absorbing the peace and tranquillity of her surroundings. Especially at night, when the river ran dark and silent, and the trees stood like sentinels, big and brooding. Her father had used to call her a creature of the night. 'An owl,' he used to say, 'while Nina is a lark.'

The full moon was blanching the colour out of everything, surrounding her in tones of black and grey, except for the river, where it formed slinky silver patterns on the silent mass as it moved with a ghostly kind of grace.

Letting the bridle fall so that Minty could put down her head to graze, Madeline shoved her hands into the pockets of her old sheepskin coat and sucked in a deep breath of sharp, crisp, clean air then let it out again slowly, feeling little by little the tension leave her body. It wasn't fair—she knew she was being unfair. They were good, kind, loving people who only wanted the best for her and for her to be happy.

But how could she tell them that she'd forgotten what happiness was? Real happiness at any rate, the kind she had once embraced without really bothering to think about it.

Sighing, she moved towards the edge of the bank where she could hear the water softly lapping the pebbly ground several feet below her.

On the other side of the river, hidden behind another thick clump of trees, the old Courtney place stood dark and intimidating. She could just make out its crooked chimneystacks as the moon slid lazily over them. It was an old Elizabethan thing, let to go over the years until it had gained the reputation of being haunted. Its owner, Major Courtney, had done nothing to refute the claims. He was a recluse, an eccentric straight out of the Victorian era who had guarded his privacy so fiercely that in her mad youth Madeline had loved to torment him by creeping into his overgrown garden just so he would come running out with his shotgun at the ready.

Shocking creature! she scolded herself now, but with a smile which was pure 'old' Madeline.

The silence was acting like a balm, soothing away a bleakness she had been struggling with from the moment she had stepped into the house this afternoon. She knew exactly why it was there. Her problem was how to come to terms with it.

She had not expected Dominic's presence to be so forcefully stamped into everything she rested her eyes upon.

'Damn him,' she whispered softly to the night, and huddled deeper into her coat.

'Another step, and you'll fall down the bank,' a quiet voice warned from somewhere behind her.

The moon slid behind a lonely cloud. Blackness engulfed her suddenly, and Madeline let out a strangled cry, her heart leaping to her mouth as she jumped, almost doing exactly what that voice warned against and plunging down the riverbank in sheer fright.

Heart hammering, the breath stripped clean from her body, she spun around, eyes wide and frightened as they searched the inky blackness for a glimpse of a body to go with the voice.

Another horse stood calmly beside Minty. And Madeline realised that she had been so engrossed in her own thoughts that she hadn't heard the other rider come up. But she could see no one, and a fine chilling thread of alarm began slinking along her spine while she stood there breathless and still, the sudden deathly silence filling her ears, drying her mouth while her eyes flicked anxiously around the dark clearing.

By legend, this was highwayman country. And she could conjure up at least three gruesome tales of ghostly sightings in these parts. She'd always laughed them off before—while secretly wishing she could witness something supernatural. Now, she was rueing that foolish wish.

The horses shifted, bridles jingling as they nudged against each other. Madeline blinked, her eyes stinging with the effort it took to pierce the pitch-blackness.

'Who's there?' she demanded shakily.

'Who do you think?' drawled a mocking voice.

It was then, as she caught the lazy mockery, the dark velvet resonance of the voice, that the fear went flying as a new and far more disturbing emotion took over, making her hands clench in her pockets as she saw a movement over to the right of the horses.

A tall figure of a man detached itself from the shadow of a tree, looking more wicked than any highwayman could to Madeline's agitated mind. She had known him to come upon her like this many times, using shock tactics to heighten her awareness of him. He was that kind of man. A man who thrived on others' uncertainty.

'So, the prodigal has returned at last.'

'Hello, Dom,' she said, forcing herself to sound cool and unaffected by his sudden presence, even as her nerve-ends scrambled desperately for something she refused to acknowledge. 'What brings you out here tonight of all nights?'

The moon came out from behind its cloud, and his smile flashed white in his shadowed face. 'The same thing as you, I should imagine,' he answered, close enough for her to see the clean taut lines of his handsome face. 'Hello, Maddie,' he belatedly responded.

He seemed to loom like the trees, tall and dark, black jeans and a heavy black sweater exaggerating the muscled power of his body. Everything about Dominic Stanton was in general larger than life, she mused acidly. Including his vows of undying love.

Abruptly she turned away from him, a hard pang of pain twisting in her ribs. They had used to meet here often once. It had been their place—among several others along this eerie riverbank. She would always arrive first, the more eager, she bitterly recalled. And he would come out of the darkness to take her in his—

A hand touched her shoulder. She reacted violently, his unexpected touch coinciding so closely with her thoughts that she took a jerky step back, and felt the riverbank tilt dangerously beneath her feet.

'You stupid fool!' he growled, fingers digging into her shoulders as he yanked her on to safer ground. 'What do you think I'm going to do—rape you?'

Rape? A noise left her throat like a hysterical choke. Since when had he had to resort to rape with her? Surely it had been the other way around.

'Let go of me,' she insisted, disgusted with herself because even now, after four long years, one look at him and everything she had in her was clamouring in hungry greeting, sending her pulses leaping wildly.

His eyes still looked down at her with that same passionate intensity; his mouth was still firm-lipped and sensual. He still stood eight inches above her, still exuded that same hardcore sexuality that had always driven her mad with wanting—and still had the ability to stir her wayward nature.

She hated him for that. Hated him for making it happen.

His hands left her instantly, and she almost sagged in groaning relief. 'Don't worry,' he said tightly. 'I want to touch you probably less than you want to feel my touch on you.'

'W-what are you doing here?' she demanded, wanting to rub her arms where his fingers had dug in—not because he'd hurt her, but because her flesh was stinging as if she'd just been burned.

'To see you, what else?' He moved back a step to thrust his own hands out of sight in the tight pockets of his jeans. 'Four years is a long time not to set eyes on the woman who made a public spectacle of me.'

She had made a public spectacle of him? Madeline almost laughed out loud. 'As I remember it,' she smiled bitterly, 'it was the other way around.'

'Not from where I was standing, it wasn't,' he grunted. 'Humiliated by a spoiled if beautiful black-haired brat who has never given a care for anyone but herself!'

'Thank you,' she drawled. 'It's so nice to know how fondly my then fiancé thought of me.'

'As nice as it was for me to find out what a faithless fiancée you were to me?'

Madeline visibly flinched, guilt and shame four years in the nurturing holding the breath congealed inside her lungs. And she had to look away from him, unable to defend herself against that ruthless thrust. There was just too much truth in it.

Silence fell hard and tight between them, and they stood stiffly in the moonlit clearing, neither seeming to know what to say next to hurt the other. It was amazing how the antipathy was still there throbbing like a war drum between them. It should have dulled a little by now, at least withered into a mutual dislike maybe, but it hadn't. And this meeting could be happening the night after the country club ball for the way they were reacting to one another, and the intervening years might as well as not have gone by.

The moon hung like a silver lantern above their heads, etching out each harshly handsome line of his smooth lean face: the silky black bars of his eyebrows, almost touching as he glowered down at her; his eyes glinting at her from beneath those dark thick lashes; his slender nose, long and arrogant, just like the man. And his mouth, she noted lastly. Just a thin taut line of contempt which even then could not disguise its in-built sensuality.

'Four years,' Dominic muttered suddenly. 'And you still look the same bewitching child. Still more beautiful than any woman ought to be.'

Something inside her twisted in pained yearning, and she went to turn away from him, only to find her arms caught once again in his bruising grip. 'Not yet,' he bit out. 'You're not going to escape again just yet. Tell me, Madeline…' He pushed his angry face closer to her own so that she could see the bitterness burning in his eyes, feel it pulsing right through him. 'Did you do it just to punish me? Or was it that you simply did not care?'

'Your desire to know comes four years too late,' she threw back, lifting her chin to let her cool gaze clash with his angry one.

He looked ready to shake her out of her coolness, and certainly his fingers tightened their grip on her arms. Then he suddenly seemed to think better of it. 'You're right,' he agreed. 'Four years is a long time to await an answer which really does not interest me. But what does interest me, Madeline,' he persisted harshly, 'is whether Boston and those damned four years have managed to make a woman out of the wilful child I thought I loved!'

She should have expected it, Madeline realised a moment later. She should have read it in the sudden flash of those coldly burning eyes, seen it in the tension of his hard mouth just before it landed punishingly on top of her own. But she hadn't, too shaken by her own disturbing reactions accurately to interpret his, and his warm breath rasped against her cold mouth as he went from the verbal attack to the physical in one swift angry movement.

Stunned into total stillness, she just stood in front of him, his fingers biting into her arms through the padded warmth of her sheepskin coat as he held her tight against him. And the angry pressure of his mouth crushed her lips back against her teeth, forcing them apart and drawing memories from her that she would far rather have left banished to the dark recesses of her mind.

And as each lonely sense began to stir inside her, awakening to the only source ever to bring them to life, she began to fight, fight like hell for release—aware of his angry passion, of her own reaching up to match it, and wanting neither.

Never again! she told herself desperately as she strained frantically away from him. Never again!

'Home half a day,' he muttered, lifting his head to glare at her through eyes shot silver with a strange mixture of rage and anguish. 'And already I can't—'

The words died, choked off by a thickened throat as his mouth came back to hers. He lifted a hand to bury his fingers in the silken softness of her hair, drawing her head back, forcing her face up to his own. His other arm was like steel around her waist, clamping her to him, and the helpless groan he gave against her mouth wrenched an answering one from herself.

The kiss went on and on, nothing kind or loving in the cruel assault, but slowly she felt her control slipping away from her, felt her senses begin to hum with a need to respond. And suddenly they were kissing frenziedly, straining against each other, lost in the turmoil which had always been an exciting part of their relationship four years ago. When Dominic had allowed it to happen, that was, which wasn't often.

Reality came crashing back with the memory, and she dragged her mouth away from his, her own bitterness aimed entirely at herself because once again she had fallen for his easy passion—a passion she knew from experience he could switch on and off like a tap.

'It's funny how we should both end up on this particular spot by the river tonight of all nights,' he murmured against the heated smoothness of her cheek. 'I seem to still possess that special antenna where you're concerned, Madeline. I think I knew the moment you stepped back on to British soil. What does that admission do to your quaking heart, I wonder?' he taunted silkily. 'Does it make it beat all the faster?'

The flat of his hand suddenly came out to press firmly against the heaving mound of her breast where her heart was racing madly beneath the thick padding of her sheepskin coat. And she gasped.

'Stop it,' she hissed, trying to push him away. 'Stop it, Dominic—please!'

'Why?' he taunted. 'You love it! You always did!'

His mouth crushed down on to hers again with one last angry kiss, then suddenly she was free, standing dazed and swaying in front of him as he pushed himself away from her as violently as he had taken hold.

'The next plane to Boston leaves in the morning,' she heard him say quite coldly. 'If you aren't on it, Madeline, I shall take it that you're prepared to stay and fight this time, instead of running away like the coward I never thought you to be.'

Then he was gone, striding away and leaping on to his horse before she had a chance to absorb the full meaning of his words.

The dull throb of galloping hoofs kept time with the thud of her pounding heart as she remained standing there, staring blankly at the spot he had last been standing in, her confused mind half wondering if she had imagined the whole incredible scene!

God knew, she'd dreamed of confrontations similar to this one often enough in the last four years—struggled with the same emotions clamouring inside her now. But never had she thought of Dominic being the one throwing out ultimatums. It had always been the other way around, she the injured one and he the one to grovel and plead.

Was she going to run away again?

The idea certainly appealed to her as she forced her quivering body to move. Meeting him unexpectedly like this had shaken her to the very core. And the knowledge that she was no more invulnerable to him now than she had been four years ago frightened her into seriously considering going back to Boston before he could really manage to hurt her.

Revenge, she realised grimly as she climbed on to Minty's back. Dominic had just warned her that he was out for revenge, for what he called her humiliation of him.

Surely he had to see that he'd already had his revenge on her? In her mind they were quits. And this angry meeting should never have taken place.

'Damn you, Dominic Stanton,' she whispered into the icy darkness, her heart aching in so many different ways. 'Damn you to hell.'

Damn him, she was still cursing him over an hour later as she restlessly paced her bedroom floor, her hands dug into the pockets of her blue satin robe.

Louise had showed her usual good taste in the refurbishment of her rooms, she acknowledged on a defiant snub to her troubled thoughts. Gone were the hearts and flowers, and soft toning blues and greys had replaced childish pinks, with the occasional splash of deep violet in acknowledgement of her own love of passionate colours. The walls were plain-painted instead of pattern-papered, the furnishings either replaced or re-covered to reflect the more mature woman, yet the touch of femininity was here, in the dozens of lace-edged satin cushions scattered about the place. Her old single bed had been replaced by a grand-looking double one with a beautiful silver-grey satin quilt thrown over it, appliquéd in blue and lilac silks. The carpet was grey and thick beneath her bare feet, the drapes the palest blue with tie-backs to match the bedcover.

Madeline sat down on her dressing stool, absently picking up her brush to stroke it through the tangled mass of recently wind-blown hair. She looked tired; dark smudges were spoiling the soft skin around her eyes. Her body felt heavy with fatigue, yet her limbs refused to stay still, twitching and forcing her to keep moving when she really wanted to flop into a blissfully deep sleep.

She was experienced enough in the side-effects of long-distance travel to know it was going to take her several days to adjust. But it wasn't jet-lag bothering her tonight, she admitted heavily to herself. It was Dominic.

He hadn't changed, not one small inch of him, inside or out. He was still big and lean and powerfully attractive. He still possessed that strong sexual allure about him that had always drawn her to him.

Could still kiss like the devil.

Her body responded, curling up into a tight tingling coil then springing open to spray those tingles all over her, and she sucked in a sharp breath, half impatience, half desperation.

It would have been better if Dominic had never seen her as anything but his sister's best friend; then he would not have become the bitter man she had met down by the river tonight, and she would not be suffering the same old calamity of emotions he had always managed to stir inside her from that first moment he had looked at her and seen Madeline the woman and not the aggravating child.

She had scampered in and out of his life for years before that, seeing him as nothing more than Vicky's big brother whose ten-year age difference placed him on a different plane from that which she had existed on. He had been one of them—the grown-up set she so loved to torment. And Vicky had loved to watch her do it because she herself was so in awe of her big brother that she didn't dare antagonise him as Maddie had no qualms about doing.

Then the change had come. Circumstances had meant that she and Dominic hadn't seen each other for almost two years, Dom because he was busy at his father's bank, travelling the world as high-stepping financiers did, and she because she was busy studying for exams or commuting more often to Boston. And they had just seemed to miss—like ships in the night, she thought now with bitter wryness.

It was during the month of her eighteenth birthday that they met for the first time as adults. It was one of those long, lazy June days when the sun blazed down from an unblemished sky and the air lay so hot and still that she and Vicky had decided to laze around the Stanton swimming-pool for the afternoon.

Madeline's skin already glowed with the rich golden tan from a recent Florida holiday with her family—her American family, that was—her mother, Lincoln, her second husband, and his two teenage children from his first marriage. She enjoyed being with them all for the month she spent there, but, as always, was glad to come home to Lambourn, and had been back only a few days when she donned her black and white striped one-piece swimsuit which showed more flesh than it hid and made Vicky green with envy for her luscious tan.

'That figure of yours should be censored,' her friend complained, eyeing the way the fashionable suit moulded Madeline's slender frame from the firm fullness of her breasts to the high cutaway sides which made an open statement about the long sleek length of her legs.

'Pocket Venuses bring out the male instinct to protect,' she answered soothingly, studying Vicky's demure little frame with her own brand of envy. Next to Vicky—and Nina, come to that—Madeline had always felt a bit like an Amazon. She had what Louise called an exotic figure. It didn't inure her much to the softly rounded curves she had, but, never the type to chew on her lip in yearning for what she saw as too much of everything, she accepted her lot and got on with life in her usual happy-go-lucky way.

She had just got up from her padded lounger and executed a neat dive into the pool, and was swimming lazily up and down when another splash alerted her to the fact that she was no longer alone in the pool. She expected to see Vicky's streaky brown head emerge beside her, and was therefore surprised when the dark, attractive features of Dominic grinned white-toothed at her instead, water streaming down his tanned body, muscles rippling everywhere, cording his strong neck where it met broad shoulders.

'Now, what have we here?' he murmured silkily, his warm grey eyes glinting with mischief. 'A real live water nymph in our pool? Does she cast wicked spells, I wonder?'

For all Madeline had been the one to torment Dominic over the years, he wasn't averse to giving her a taste of her own medicine when in the mood—and he was clearly in the mood that day.

'Wicked ones,' she grinned, surprised to feel so pleased to see him. 'So watch it,' she warned, wagging a lazy finger his way. 'Or I may decide to turn you into a frog. And then what would all the lovely Lambourn ladies do without the rakish Dominic Stanton to send their poor hearts all a-flutter?'

He grinned and so did she—then with her usual impulsiveness she turned a somersault and dived beneath the water, grabbing at his foot as she went so that she could trail him down with her, watching the disconcertment on his face as he tried to tug his captured foot free, air bubbles escaping all around them.

He was a big man, but Madeline was strong and determined. In the end, he had to grab her wrist and make her release him, and they both came to the surface gasping for air.

'God, you haven't changed much, have you?' he choked, flinging back his head to clear his soaked hair from his face.

Madeline saw the measuring glint in his eyes, squealed when she correctly interpreted its vengeful meaning, and made a flailing dive for the side of the pool. She didn't make it. Dominic caught her by the waist and lifted her up high above him, laughing at her helplessness as water streamed down her sun-browned skin.

Then he wasn't laughing but looking, those piercing grey eyes of his warm on her body, taking in its new maturity, the unconscious sensuality in the way she arched away from him in an attempt to free herself, her breasts thrusting up and outwards, the hard press of her extended nipples clearly etched against the fine Lycra material of her suit, her head thrown back so her hair turned into a thick curtain of wet black silk which trailed in the water behind her.

He muttered something beneath his breath, and Madeline stopped struggling to glance questioningly at him.

It was then that she saw it—the change from teasing big brother to sexually stimulated male. His eyes were narrowed and his body tense. And slowly—slowly he lowered her down the length of him, letting her feel—and feeling for himself—the electric response as their wet bodies brushed enticingly against each other.

Their faces came level, and Madeline stared in blushing confusion at him. His mouth twisted, a self-mockery masking out the sensual awareness. Yet he did not immediately release her, Instead his hands went on an outrageous exploration of her body beneath the surface of the water. Breathlessly, she let him, her eyes fixed on his face as awareness began to pulse between them.

'When did you get back?' Vicky's sleep-slurred voice broke into their absorption in each other, breaking them apart with an abruptness that was a message in itself. They glanced up to find her yawning lazily, completely unaware of the sudden tension fizzing in her pool. She blinked at her brother, then repeated the question, adding, 'Daddy said you wouldn't be back until tomorrow.'

He turned away from Madeline, and instantly she dived below the surface of the water, swimming quickly away until she had put the full width of the pool between them, her senses in turmoil, a confusion over what had just happened making her feel peculiarly dizzy.

'I finished quicker than I thought I would, so I caught an earlier flight home.' He answered his sister levelly enough. 'How are you, pug-face?' he enquired teasingly as he levered himself out of the pool.

Suddenly and disturbingly aware of her own body, Madeline found that it took all her courage to make her climb out of the pool. And the fact that she was actually blushing made Dominic's eyes glint mockingly at her as he watched her fumble with her towelling wrap while seemingly totally engrossed in a conversation with his sister.

'Have dinner with me tonight,' he murmured later under cover of Vicky's light chatter.

Feeling shy for perhaps the very first time in her life, she shook her head, not at all sure she wanted to continue what had begun in the pool. 'I don't—'

'Please.' His hand curled about her wrist, stopping her mid-refusal. His touch acted like a bee-sting to her system and she gasped as the blood began to burn in her veins. Even Vicky had gone silent, watching with growing comprehension what was happening between her best friend and her big brother.

'Dinner, that's all,' he repeated, then added in a soft-voiced challenge, 'Where's that spirit of adventure you're so famous for?'

Well, it was dead now, thought the four-years-older Madeline. Killed by the hand that had once loved to feed it. Ruthlessly crushed by a man who took his revenge on a stupid impulsive child in a way which had instantly cured her of a lot of things. But most of all it had cured her of her silly belief that love conquered all. And she no longer believed in love at all now—not the all-consuming passionate kind, anyway.

CHAPTER THREE

MADELINE rang Vicky the next day.

'You're back!' came the excited proclamation.

'I think so,' she murmured drily, 'although I'm not certain all of me is here, if you know what I mean.'

'Jet-lag,' Vicky recognised. 'Are you too tired to meet me today?'

'Do you mean you may manage to fit me in?' Madeline teased. 'I believe you have certain—commitments which curtail your freedom these days.'

'You've heard,' Vicky grunted. 'Who told you—Nina?'

'My father, actually,' Madeline corrected, unaware of the sudden tension on the other end of the line. 'He's rather proud of you, Vicky,' she went on oblivious. 'Said you're making quite a name for yourself at the bank.'

'Against all the odds,' Vicky added drily, knowing Madeline was aware of how determined she had been to join the family bank—and how equally determined her father had been to keep her out of it. 'It took me three years' hard graft at the uni and a lot of rows before he caved in. But even he couldn't turn a blind eye to the distinctions I got with my degree. I have been an official Stanton bank employee for just over a year now,' she proudly announced. 'Dom says I...' Her voice trailed off, silent horror singing down the line between them.

Madeline sighed inwardly, seeing the irony in the way everyone seemed determined to skirt around all mention of Dominic Stanton while the man himself felt no qualms in making his presence more than felt! 'Dom says—what?' she prompted gently.

'He—he says it's my sexy behind that draws in the new accounts,' Vicky mumbled uncomfortably.

'Why, do you wriggle it at every potential client?' Madeline asked, damning the odd tightness she felt in her chest when she visualised Dominic's flashing grin as he issued that small tease to his sister.

'Only at the male ones,' Vicky chuckled, the tension easing out of her voice again. 'What about Saturday night on the town if you don't fancy making the trip into London today?'

'No can do, I'm afraid.' Madeline apologised. 'I have a friend coming to stay.'

'Perry Linburgh?' Vicky quizzed.

'How did you find that out so quickly?' Madeline gasped, fine brows arching above wide-spaced eyes so darkly circled by thick black lashes.

'With a grapevine like we have here?' her friend scoffed. 'I could probably describe him better than you could do yourself! A Linburgh, no less,' she went on mockingly. 'The name legends are made of. You do move in exclusive circles these days, Madeline.

'Don't I just?' she agreed, then added on a burst of inspiration. 'Hey—why don't you come to lunch here on Sunday! You could meet Perry yourself then, and maybe give your honest opinion of the real thing rather than the legend!'

The suggestion met with utter silence. A sudden tension buzzing so strongly down the line that it was impossible to miss it, though she did not understand the reason for it.

'I'm afraid I can't do that,' she heard Vicky say coolly.

'Why?' She frowned. 'Got a date?'

There was another small silence, then, 'Don't you know, Madeline?' Vicky asked curiously.

'Know what?' Her tone alone said she had no idea what Vicky was referring to.

The other girl sighed, muttered something not very ladylike which had Madeline's eyebrows arching all over again, then lowering into an incredulous frown as Vicky curtly explained, 'The Gilburns and the Stantons no longer acknowledge each other, dear,' she was informed with a shivering derision. 'They haven't since you and my brother split up.'

Louise walked into the room just as Madeline was slowly replacing the telephone receiver.

'Your young man, dear?' she enquired.

'No.' Madeline was still frowning. 'Vicky,' she said grimly, then looked up at Louise. 'Is it true?' she demanded. 'Have our two families been involved in a feud for the last four years?'

'Oh, dear,' Louise sighed and sat down next to Madeline on the sofa. 'I wondered how soon you would find out.'

Horrified, Madeline jerked to her feet. 'I can't believe it!' she exclaimed.

'No, neither could I when it first began,' Louise agreed. 'Men are such children sometimes, Madeline!' she sighed. 'And I've been warning your father for weeks that he ought to put a stop to it before you came home. But he refuses to listen. He blames James Stanton for starting it— after Dominic, of course, that is—and I can only assume that James blames your father—after you. Am I being too honest, Madeline?' she broke off to ask anxiously when she saw Madeline's face grow steadily more distressed as she went on. 'I have no wish to upset you with all of this, but it is a problem which has to be taken note of simply because you will sense it the moment we all get together in the same room.'

'Oh, so you do actually move in the same company,' Madeline scowled. 'I suppose that has to mean something.'

'Not much,' Louise grunted. 'We may attend the same things but we never acknowledge one another.'

'Good grief!' Madeline exploded. 'But that's positively—archaic!'

'I entirely agree with you, dear.' Louise nodded. 'But it's there and has to be faced. And I wouldn't like you to make some terrible gaffe by speaking to the Stantons this Saturday night at the Lassiters' only to find yourself cut dead where you stand.'

'Y-you mean, they would actually do that?' Her blue eyes widened in pained disbelief. 'No wonder Vicky was so damned touchy whenever we mentioned family! My God,' she breathed, utterly appalled by it all.

'Your father felt sure you would be able to cope,' Louise was looking pensive at Madeline's paste-white face, 'but if you don't feel you can face it all just yet, Madeline, we would understand if you preferred not to attend…'

'Oh, I'm going,' Madeline murmured ominously. 'And don't think for one moment that I shall be joining in your petty feud!'

'I thought you might say that,' Louise grimaced.

Another sudden thought brought Madeline's gaze arrowing on to her stepmother. 'Does this also mean that the Stantons have not been invited to Nina's wedding?' she demanded, saw the answer in Louise's uncomfortable face and was furious. 'Vicky is my best friend!' she cried. 'We—all three of us—Nina, Vicky and I planned to be bridesmaids at each other's wedding! Are you now telling me that even poor Vicky has been made a pariah by this family?'

'I'm so sorry, dear.'

'I should hope you jolly well are!' Madeline snapped, so angry her eyes were flashing in a way that they hadn't done once since she'd returned home. 'For the first time, I feel heartily glad that I've come back! It's time it stopped, Louise,' she stated grimly. 'And you can tell Daddy that I'm going to see to it that it does!'

'You can tell him that yourself, Madeline,' Louise drily declined the offer as she came gracefully to her feet. 'The subject has been made taboo between your father and me ever since we fell out over it for a whole month! I don't ever intend to put myself through that kind of purgatory again.' She shuddered at the mere memory of it. 'No,' she reached up to pat Madeline's shoulder, 'any sorting of this problem will have to come from you, darling, since you're the one who is at the root of it.'

And Dominic, Madeline added crossly to herself as Louise left her to seethe alone. How could he have allowed things to deteriorate into this state? And how darned petty!

She needed to talk to Vicky, she decided. And urgently if something wasn't to be done before Nina's wedding-day. Grimly, she picked up the phone and dialled the Stanton home number, crossing her fingers that she would catch Vicky before she left for the day.

She did just. 'I've changed my mind about today,' she told her friend. 'What time do you usually have lunch?'

Loath though she was to admit it, it was with great reluctance that Madeline rode the Stanton Bank lift to the executive floor later that morning.

On the face of it, meeting Vicky at her place of work had seemed logical since it was Madeline who was flexible with her time and Vicky restricted by what might require attention on her desk. But even with the assurance that both Vicky's father and Dominic were to be out of the building all day today, she was still finding it difficult to be here, in the enemy camp so to speak, she thought with feudal dryness.

Still. At least she knew she looked good. Her taupe jacquard suit was elegant, and reacted well with the deep purple accessories she'd teamed with it. Her hair was plaited in a single thick braid down her back, and her newly acquired self-awareness—forced on her by her mother—helped her maintain an air of cool self-possession—even if it didn't go more than skin-deep.

Four years ago she wouldn't have given a second thought to how others might see her. She had used to wear what she enjoyed wearing rather than what was considered appropriate for the occasion—but then, she mused rather heavily, she had used to laugh infectiously when she thought something funny, cry real tears at the drop of a hat! The old Madeline had flitted her way through life on a restless ever-changing spirit. This new one tempered every move and gesture to suit the status quo.

Her composure was now inscrutable, her sophistication an indisputable fact. She walked, talked, behaved as the daughter of a prominent man of the City should do. She never revealed ruffled nerves, wouldn't dream of putting on a show of temperament like the old Madeline had used to do often—and to her ruin, she reminded herself. Her dress sense was superb, her personal grooming impeccable, and her manner serene. And if those closest to her were surprised to the point of dismay in the change in her, they had to agree, surely, that this new Madeline was far more acceptable than the old one?

That wretched girl who had run away four years ago was now back, and determined to make a point. She had begun with her family, and intended continuing by facing the people who had hurt her the most. The Stantons mainly, bar Vicky, and really only one Stanton in particular who was going to be made to eat those bitter words he'd thrown at her four years ago—even if he had set her off balance slightly with their unexpected meeting last night.

And she intended to do it by calmly smoothing out the quarrel between their two families. How, she wasn't sure yet. She only knew that she was going to do it, and show them all that Madeline Gilburn had matured into a cool sensible woman at last.

The lift doors slid open, and she stepped gracefully out into the luxurious foyer of the Stanton directors' floor, pausing for only a moment to collect herself as old memories hit out at her senses.

Once upon a time, she had rode that lift and bounced out here like an inmate, blithely trotting past the disgruntled receptionist of the day to walk right into Dominic's office without knocking—just so she could surprise him with a kiss before walking blithely out again!

Now she cringed at the very idea of doing such a thing. So gauche—so adolescent.

The walls of panelled walnut still looked the same, and the same deep-pile grey Wilton carpet still covered the floor. Everything, in fact, was just as she remembered it— except the smiling face of the receptionist already on her feet and waiting to greet her.

Madeline flicked a brief glance at the several closed doors she knew led to the plush offices of the individual Stanton Bank directors, James Stanton's dead centre, Dominic to the right of his and the rest belonging to lesser members of powerful family. She had no idea which door belonged to Vicky. Four years ago, the family had been dismayed at their daughter's desire to join the firm. Now things were different. Vicky would be different, Madeline reminded herself. She too was older, would be more self-assured now that she held a responsible position in the bank.

'Miss Stanton is expecting me,' Madeline informed the waiting receptionist. 'I'm Madeline Gilburn.'

The woman's smile warmed into rueful humour. 'She's been jumping about like a demented flea all morning because you were coming. If you'll just take a seat for a moment, I'll put her out of her misery and let her know you've arrived.'

But the receptionist didn't get the chance to inform Vicky of anything, because just at that moment a door further along the row flew open and out bounced Victoria Stanton—who came to a jerking halt when she saw Madeline standing there.

Grey eyes so like her brother's gazed at her transfixed, thickening Madeline's throat with tears as she stared into the pretty diminutive face of her closest friend. She had been wrong about Vicky, she acknowledged tearfully. She hadn't changed, not one single iota.

'Maddie—!' she cried, coming back to life with a stunned blinking of her eyes. 'Good God,' she gasped. 'It is you, isn't it?' then, before Madeline had a chance to say anything at all, Vicky was rushing across the room to fling herself into her arms. 'Oh, you beautiful, beautiful creature! I have missed you so!' She pressed a satisfying kiss on Madeline's cheek, then leaned back to stare at her again. 'Goodness me, but you've changed,' she told her. 'You look so—so…'

'Grown-up?' Madeline solemnly supplied when at last Vicky floundered. 'You too,' she smiled. 'You look quite the hot-shot executive in that pin-striped suit!

'It comes with the job,' Vicky explained the severe tailoring of the suit which accentuated every nuance of her hour-glass figure. 'Specially made for bottom-wiggling at the—'

'Judith, have you heard from—?'

Silence fell like a stone. Vicky's excitement switched off like a light as she spun round to stare in horror at her brother while he fixed his narrowed gaze on her best friend.

The very air in the foyer began to tingle. And so did Madeline's senses as she stared at him without even managing to breathe.

Meeting Dominic on a dark moonlit night bore no resemblance to meeting him like this, in broad daylight, where there was nothing—nothing to help mute the effect he had upon her senses.

Four years, she thought desperately, four years of quelling the aches, sealing up the wounds, learning to come to terms with the public rejection and humiliation he had forced on her, and it had all been for nothing. She had suspected it last night when he had caught her so unawares. But it was only now, as she stood face to face with him in the cruel light of day, that she had to accept that no amount of self-discipline was ever going to erase the profound effect he'd always had on her. And all she could think, and bitterly at that, was—thank God for Boston! Because she knew that, whatever turmoil was wringing at her insides, her face remained supremely calm and composed.

'Hello, Dominic,' she greeted quietly, accepting that it was for her to break the silence since nobody else seemed capable of it. 'You're looking—well.'

'Madeline,' he acknowledged huskily, running his narrowed gaze over her as if he couldn't believe what he was seeing. 'And you,' he returned equably. 'Very different, in fact,' he added on a note which told her he was talking about last night, not four years ago.

'M-Maddie is taking me out to lunch!' Vicky put in with a voice so high-pitched that it hovered just this side of hysterical. Then her poor friend began talking quickly, saying things that no one else listened to. Even Judith, the receptionist, was too busy flicking her eyes from Dominic's face to Madeline's in wide-eyed curiosity to hear a word Vicky said.

'You've not returned to Boston yet, then,' Dominic drawled across his sister's nervous chatter.

Instantly recognising the dig, she moved her chin upwards in mild defiance. 'Since I only arrived home yesterday, I'm not likely to be rushing straight back, am I? Though,' she added exclusively for his benefit, 'once England begins to pall, no doubt I shall go back—home.'

In his turn, Dominic did not miss her own subtle meaning in the final word. And his mouth tightened on it.

'I th-thought you were out today,' Vicky rushed in agitatedly. 'Y-you said you were—all day—out at some meeting.'

'I changed my mind,' Dominic informed Vicky while not removing his eyes from Madeline. 'And aren't I glad I did?' he added silkily. 'A Gilburn in our bank again; quite a surprise, Vicky. How did you manage to do it?'

It was time to put a stop to this, Madeline decided angrily as she saw Vicky's hands clench convulsively at her stomach. It was one thing him wishing to mock her, but quite another to use his sister as a tool to do it with.

With a slight lifting of her chin, she held Dominic's gaze for a short second which felt more like an hour in the throbbing tension, then slowly closed her dark lashes over her eyes. When she opened them again, she was looking directly at Vicky. 'We'll lose our table if you don't hurry,' she reminded her friend softly.

With a silent 'O' formed by two Cupid's bow lips and a pair of rounded eyes which showed a horrified appreciation of the way Madeline had just discarded her brother, Vicky turned and shot back into her office. She must have dived for her bag, because she was back with them before anyone had a chance to move.

With all the cool aplomb her mother had instilled into her, Madeline smiled pleasantly at the hovering receptionist, sent Dominic a cool nod, then was turning towards the lift, ignoring the hot needles of fury that impaled her as she went, chatting lightly to a wholly absorbed Vicky.

'God in heaven!' Vicky literally wilted against the panelled lift wall. 'That was just awful!'

'Not—pleasant,' Madeline drily agreed.

'He's an arrogant swine!' Dominic's sister ground out. 'Sometimes I—'

'He was taken by surprise, that's all,' Madeline put in, surprised by her instant rise to Dominic's defence.

'Taken by surprise, my foot!' scoffed Vicky. 'He knew damned well that you were coming here today—I told him! Made him promise to stay out of the way! God,' she choked, 'I could kill him for doing that, the rotten devil!'

The lunch was not the resounding success it should have been. Madeline's confrontation with Dominic had helped spoil it, but it was the feud between their two families which completely ruined the day.

'It's crazy,' Vicky agreed. 'They don't seem to mind that you and I stay friends. But my father will have nothing to do with yours, and vice versa.' She grimaced, 'It's made the last four years damned difficult for me if you must know. I daren't speak to your family because it would upset my lot, but I can't just snub people who have always been warm and caring towards me. So I stay out of the local social scene for most of the time. That way I don't get pulled in two different directions.'

'Is there no way you can think of that would put an end to it?' Madeline asked anxiously.

Vicky lifted her face and smiled rather cynically. 'Not unless you and Dominic fancy getting back together again— No,' she then said quickly when Madeline stiffened up. 'I didn't mean that seriously. It's just that…' She sighed, frowning. 'He was sorry afterwards you know. He tried to see you, but…'

'I don't wish to know.' Had he? Had he tried to see her? she wondered. He can't have tried very hard, then, she stubbornly dismissed the weak sensation Vicky's claim touched her with.

'He was appalled at himself. He…'

'Vicky!' she warned.

'All right—all right.' The other girl waved a placatory hand. 'I just wanted to understand, that's all. I never did. Nobody did.'

'It was no one else's business.' Madeline flatly pointed out. 'Yet they all made it their business by starting this silly feud!' she added impatiently.

'They all hurt for their respective chicks, Madeline; surely you can understand that? When you went off to Boston you left one big hornets' nest of bottled-up emotion behind you. Even Dominic shot off out of it to our sister bank in Australia for six months. By the time he got back, they'd quarrelled so badly that nothing was going to shift either your father or mine.'

'Did he try?' Madeline asked wryly.

'Of course he tried!' Vicky bristled instantly in her brother's defence. 'We all tried! Even the timid Nina, for all the good it did her,' she muttered.

'How?' Madeline asked, surprised to hear that Nina could even find the courage to intervene in any dispute— she had used to run out of the room when Madeline had one of her spats with her father.

'She insisted we be invited to her wedding,' Vicky said. 'Apparently, your father said he was quite happy to see me walk behind Nina down the aisle as one of her brides-maids—but the rest of 'em could go to hell!' Vicky's gruff mimic of her father's rasping voice was very good, but while doing it she also revealed her own disgust.

'And Nina actually told you that?' She was beginning to wonder if her stepsister had changed beyond all rec-ognition if she could repeat something as cruel as that to Vicky.

'Of course she didn't!' Vicky denied, to Madeline's re-lief. 'Annie, your housekeeper, told Clara, our house-keeper, and she was so affronted on our behalf that she told us.'

'And the feud worsened,' Madeline added heavily. 'God, what a mess.'

'Anyway, it was all so much hot air over nothing,' Vicky finished grimly. 'Because there was no way I was going to be able to be bridesmaid at Nina's wedding while my own family remained in exile.'

It was a mess, and one Madeline saw no way out of. She left Vicky feeling as dissatisfied with their meeting as she had been with anything for a long time. It seemed so damned unfair that Vicky, the innocent in all of it, should be the one to lose out! She wanted Vicky at Nina's wed-ding, but she had backed off from inviting her personally, because of the strain she saw it would place on Vicky's loyalty to her own family. To attend without them would be disloyal. Yet her not being there seemed equally dis-loyal to her friendship with Madeline.

It was a dilemma, and one Madeline saw no answer to as she went home that afternoon. And for the first time, she seriously considered calling Dominic to see if he could come up with a solution.

So she wasn't so surprised when he took it upon himself to ring her instead.

CHAPTER FOUR

'WE HAVE to talk. Have dinner with me.'

'W-what did you say?' The sound of his voice, washing deep and seductively over her via the telephone earpiece, was enough on its own to make her deaf to the words he actually said.

'Have dinner with me,' he repeated huskily. And her throat closed up on a wave of nostalgia those few gruff words resurrected from years ago when he had asked her the selfsame question in the exact same intimate tone. Was it done deliberately? She couldn't tell. 'We must talk.'

'How dare you ring me here!' she whispered, glancing furtively around the empty hallway, She was alone, thank God! But it was only by fluke that she had happened to answer the phone because she was expecting a call from Perry.

'Why, will your father beat you if he finds out you've been talking to me?' he drawled.

'Probably,' she grimaced, remembering the stand-up row she'd had with her father over the Stanton affair. It hadn't got her anywhere, and she was beginning to realise just how impossible the situation had become.

'He wouldn't harm a hair on your lovely head, and you know it,' came the sardonic reply. 'Now, about dinner.'

'I can't,' she answered bluntly, searching her mind for an adequate excuse why not, then realising that she didn't need one when the truth was clear enough. 'I don't want to, actually.'

'Actually,' he mocked, 'I don't think either of us has

much choice. Not if you don't want to see Vicky hurt more than she has been already over this damned wedding of Nina's.'

'All right, I accept that something has to be done and perhaps you and I are the only ones to do it,' she agreed. 'But I am not prepared to share another slanging match with you, Dominic,' she warned him coolly.

'No?' he murmured provocatively. 'What a shame. We used to have such fun throwing insults at each other...'

'Well, not any more,' she said coldly, hurt that he could be so cruel as to taunt her about their row four years ago.

'So, when can we meet?' he enquired more briskly, obviously deciding he had provoked her enough for one day.

Not at all if I had any choice, Madeline thought heavily. 'Not before next week,' she told him out loud. 'Today is Friday, and my weekend is fully booked.'

'The Lassiter thing?'

'Yes,' she said. 'The Lassiter thing.'

'We could meet there,' he suggested. 'You know, sneak off somewhere to some secret location and have a little pow-wow all on our own...?'

Madeline closed her eyes, her pulses automatically beginning to race as a trace of the old Madeline fondness for intrigue pierced its way through her armour. Was that why he'd made that outrageous suggestion, she wondered agitatedly, because he knew it would appeal to her old wayward nature?

But not her new careful nature it didn't. So, 'Sorry,' she drawled. 'But my—partner wouldn't like me sneaking off like that.'

'Partner?' Madeline had the satisfaction of hearing his voice sharpen. 'What partner?'

'The one I brought with me from Boston,' she informed him coolly. 'Perry Linburgh.'

'Ah,' he breathed, pretending no knowledge of Perry when she was sure as dammit that if Vicky knew about Perry, then Dominic surely did. 'Byron Linburgh's son and heir.' He sounded suitably impressed. 'My, but we do move in exalted circles, do we not?'

'Thank you.' She refused to take up the bait, and Dominic's own short sigh of acknowledgement to that whispered down the line to shiver right through her.

'Dinner next week, then,' he said, dropping the sarcasm.

'Not dinner, no,' she refused. 'I don't think it—'

'Lunch, then, in London,' he cut in.

'No.' Madeline bit down on her bottom lip. 'Dominic, I—'

'A drink,' he thrust curtly at her. 'Meet me for a drink in Newbury one evening, and we'll…'

'Dominic,' she broke in gently, softening her tone because in this particular case she had no wish to wound him. 'You just have to understand that I can't afford to be seen anywhere alone with you. The cost will run too high.'

'What cost?' His anger whipped at her, and Madeline flinched, accepting his right to it. 'What's wrong with being seen with me? I don't have some dreaded social disease, you know.'

'I never meant to imply that you—'

'Look—' he bit out tightly, then heaved in a deep breath to control the sudden flare of temper. 'You'll meet me, Madeline, out in the open, and for dinner one evening, or I come around to your home to see you tonight. Which will it be?' he asked tightly. 'A civilised dinner for two, or a very uncivilised confrontation at your home with your damned family as witness!'

'Dinner, then,' she reluctantly agreed, not even bothering to call his bluff. Dominic was quite capable of carrying out any threat he uttered.

'Where?' He shot the question at her like a bullet.

'In Newbury— No.' That was too close to home. 'I have to be in London on Wednesday next week.' For gown fittings with Nina. It should be easy enough to find a convincing excuse why she couldn't come back home with Nina in the evening. Nina had a function to attend with Charles that night, so there should be no chance of her stepsister deciding to stay in the City with her. 'At least there we have less of a chance of being recognised,' she added drily.

'I am quite prepared to meet you anywhere and in front of anyone, Madeline,' he said grimly. 'Since when have you become so damned protective of your so-called reputation?'

'My father would tell you, Dominic, that for all my sins I only needed teaching a lesson once before it sank indelibly in.'

'He might, if he was speaking to me,' he ruefully agreed. 'But since he isn't—and hasn't for four years—it seems pointless to remark upon it, don't you think?'

Perry arrived on Saturday in a dashing red Lotus sports car. Madeline met him in the driveway with a warm hug.

'That was nice,' he murmured, smiling down at her. 'But I wonder why there was a hint of desperation about it?'

'Oh…' She shook her dark head. 'It's all been a bit of a strain here, that's all,' she dismissed, turning within the curve of his arm to walk with him into the house. 'I'm still feeling like a visitor after being away for so long.'

'Good,' he said. 'Keep feeling like that. Then perhaps you won't be tempted to stay too long before coming home to us in Boston.'

'Why?' she murmured provocatively. 'Will you miss me when you have to go back?'

'You know I will.' He squeezed her closer to him. 'If I have to return without you,' he then added meaningfully.

'And what about the lovely Christina?' she reminded him. 'I'm sure she won't like you arriving back in Boston with me on your arm.'

'Christina knows how I feel,' he stated coolly. But Madeline wasn't fooled in the slightest by his offhand reply.

Madeline was quite aware that Perry used her as protection against the beautiful but very spoiled Christina van Neilson. One of the reasons why she and Perry had gravitated towards each other in the first place was because they were both hiding a broken heart, and recognised the struggle in each other. Madeline didn't like the Boston beauty, but she could understand why Perry did. Christina was probably the closest you could get to American royalty, a tall willowy golden beauty with the van Neilson billions to give her everything she wanted in her overindulged life.

She wanted Perry, royalty himself if it was wealth that made the distinction. But she wanted him on her own terms—and those terms did not include Perry working for his living when she wanted to play. Christina had been a fool when she challenged that inbred sense of responsibility Perry possessed with her 'get out from under the family wing and live the kind of jet-setting life I'm used to, or no Christina' ultimatum. It was no contest. Christina had lost, but at the expense of poor Perry's heart.

Whether or not the beauty's own heart was involved was difficult to say with someone as superficial as Christina. She certainly did not like the closeness there was between

Madeline and Perry. But that could just be spoiled possessiveness.

'Forman didn't take up my father's invitation to come
with you, then,' she noted, wisely changing the subject.

'He's in Brussels,' Perry informed her. 'Maybe I can
talk him into coming next weekend.'

'That would be nice,' she murmured casually.

'Why?' He glanced frowningly at her. 'You aren't fan-
cying him, are you?'

Madeline laughed. 'He's not my type,' she assured him.
'Too big and brooding for my taste. I'll stick to you if you
don't mind.'

'I don't mind in the least,' he grinned, dropping a light
kiss upon her cheek, 'but watch it, if Forman does come,'
he warned. 'A real rake if I ever knew one.'

'Has a way with the ladies, does he?' she murmured
curiously.

'Makes me jumpy just to have him around,' Perry
mocked. 'Safety in numbers is Forman's motto, and my
God, does he live by it!'

Madeline just laughed again, and took him in to meet
her family. By the time he had spent an hour talking City
business with her father, complimented Louise on her
lovely home, and gently teased Nina into blushing, her
family were ready to announce Perry great!

She dressed with a care that told her just how apprehensive she was about this first airing of the new Madeline
in Lambourn society. Four years ago she had made a public clown of herself, and most of the people present tonight
would have been present that night too. It was that last
humiliating appearance they would have carried around in
their memories ever since. Which meant this appearance
had to so overshadow it that would only see this one—
and not the clown.

So instead of the palest lime silk she had worn to her downfall, she wore black. Dramatic-lined, simple sheathed matt black. The fine silk crêpe had been exclusively designed for her to follow each subtle line of her tall and slender shape. It covered her from throat to wrist to ankle, its only adornment a wine-red silk cord circling her narrow waist and tied loosely so it draped her slender hips to hang low on the flat of her stomach. Severely gothic in style, the skirt fluted very slightly from the knees to swirl gently around her ankles.

She clipped dark rubies to her wrists and ears, added a matching choker to her throat—the whole set a present from her mother and Lincoln for her twenty-first birthday.

She slipped her feet into high black satin mules then turned to view the finished affect in the long dressing mirror. Her hair she had swept up into a simple knot to leave her creamy neck exposed for her glinting rubies. Her make-up had been applied to add drama to her eyes and mouth, the long thickness of her lashes a lush frame to the vivid blue of her eyes, mouth the same dark red as the rubies. Studying herself, Madeline saw what she wanted to see, the complete antithesis of that other frilled and flounced girl they would remember. And with herself alone knowing how much nervousness she was suffering inside, she turned and left her room.

'Goodness me!' her father exclaimed as she entered the drawing-room to find them all waiting for her. 'Is that really my girl?' He brought all the other heads swinging around to stare at her in several expressions of amazement. Except Perry, dear Perry who only knew this elegantly sophisticated creature and could not understand everyone else's awe.

'Perfect, darling.' He came towards her with a smile

which said how lovely he found her. 'Dee would be proud of you tonight if she could see you.'

'Thank you,' she murmured softly. Uncanny though it was, Perry always knew exactly what to say to her to put her at ease. The agitated flutters in her stomach eased and her pulses calmed. 'Quite the handsome beau yourself tonight, Perry,' she returned.

'Thank you, ma'am.' He offered her a mocking bow, looking very attractive in his black dinner suit, his hazelnut eyes twinkling at her.

Despite her confidence that she'd hidden it well, her family must have all known how nervous she felt, Madeline acknowledged hours later when the Lassiter party was in full swing and she was at last beginning to relax—mainly because there was no sign of a single Stanton in evidence.

'They love you dearly, don't they?' Perry remarked at her side. She turned to look at him to find him studying her gravely. 'You have a wonderful family, Madeline. Each one of them—including your future brother-in-law— have taken it in turns to stay close by your side... Why is that, I wonder?' His gaze left her studiedly bland face to wander slowly around the crowded room. 'There isn't a person here tonight who hasn't at some point or another stood staring at you in disbelief.' That shrewd gaze came back to her. 'And again, I wonder why I get the feeling that they see you as some very unpredictable explosive substance they just daren't trust, no matter how utterly serene you look.' Hazel eyes studied her narrowly. 'I've heard the Stanton name bandied about like crazy,' he went on, 'picked up on little remarks about Boston and the changes it has wreaked. I have even overheard my own name being bantered about with a kind of delicious awe, and seriously wondered if the tension sizzling in this place tonight is actually going to catch fire… Why, I again wonder?' His hand came up to lightly brush the satin smoothness of her cheek. 'Was *he* supposed to be present here tonight, darling,' he murmured huskily, 'the man you were once engaged to?'

It was her turn to let her gaze drift around the Lassiters' packed drawing-room. 'The Stantons had a—prior engagement, it seems, that they could not get out of,' she told him with only the slightest hint of cynicism for the effect that excuse had on her. Looking back at him, she added drily, 'Dominic Stanton and I did not part gracefully, I suppose you could say.'

'You were engaged to Dominic Stanton?' His surprise made her smile, and her mocking nod made his fair brows arch. 'I never did ask you his name, did I?' he murmured ruefully.

'I suppose I should have warned you what to expect here tonight, but…' Her sigh was heavy. 'I think to have explained it all to you would have been like having to admit to myself that the nightmare I created four years ago actually existed, and I was still hoping, right up until we arrived here, that it was all just my own silly imagination.'

'You caused something of a scene?' he suggested shrewdly.

'What would probably best be described as a humdinger of one,' Madeline drily admitted. 'Since then our two families have not been on the best of terms.'

'And have all these people come here tonight expecting the Stantons to show up also?'

'What do you think?' she drawled.

'I think,' he said grimly, 'the place is full of bitches—men and women alike.'

Madeline just smiled. 'You won't believe it, Perry, but they have a right to expect trouble when I'm around. And to be fair to the Stantons,' she added quietly, 'their absence will not be meant as a slight to me, but their way of defusing a potentially awkward situation.'

'I've met him, you know,' Perry said suddenly, studying her look of wary surprise. 'Once and only briefly, the other day at a bank meeting I attended. He seems quite a man.'

'Dominic always was the dynamic businessman,' Madeline oh, so drily agreed.

'I was not referring to his business acumen, darling,' Perry drawled.

'No?' she mocked, not taking him on.

'No,' he said, and laughed because he knew that expression of old. 'There's music in the other room. Let's go and dance.'

'What a lovely idea!' she cried, allowing him to take her arm. 'You know,' she drawled, 'I could become a trifle bored with this provincial crowd if I stay around them too long.'

'That's my girl.' He patted her hand where it lay in the crook of his arm. 'Show them all how truly sophisticated you are.'

'You see too much,' she grumbled.

'And you, my darling Madeline, hide too much.'

'I promise to tell all later,' she vowed as she went into his arms for the dance.

'I'll keep you to that,' he warned.

And he did, once they were back home and left alone after everyone else had gone off to bed. Madeline sighed, wondered where to start, then decided the beginning was the only sensible place, which was exactly where she began, leaving hardly anything out, and by the time her voice faltered to a husky halt Perry's face had gone pale with anger.

'The bastard!' he rasped.

'No,' Madeline wearily protested. 'Believe me, Perry, when I tell you that I deserved all I got.' She dragged in a deep breath then let it out again. 'You can't begin to know the kind of person I was then. So spoiled, so criminally wilful! I must have driven Dominic to the point of insanity several times before he eventually snapped. I was an absolute terror. There was no controlling me once I got an idea into my head. I was a danger to myself—and to those people around me. I don't blame Dominic for what he did to me that night—God knows,' she sighed, 'I'd had it coming. I just—just wish he'd found a kinder way of putting me in my place, that's all.'

'Rubbish!' Perry dismissed. 'You were young and foolhardly, but that gave him no excuse to humiliate you in that brutal way!'

How could Perry be expected to understand things as they had been then when he could only see the new cool and self-disciplined Madeline? she wondered heavily as she lay awake in bed later than night. Even that tiny hint of impishness at the Lassisters' had stunned him, he was so unused to seeing it. A headstrong and ungovernable Madeline was quite beyond his comprehension.

Nor had she told him about the less obvious pressures brought to bear upon herself and Dominic. From the moment they had shown an interest in each other, they had been picked up and carried along by their families' mutual enthusiasm for a match.

It had felt as if they were under constant surveillance from both family and friends. Everywhere they went there had always seemed to be someone more than willing to monitor their every move and gesture towards one another, eager to encourage, to tease, to automatically assume that if they were together they had to be in love—which, Madeline had to admit, she'd thought too at the time.

They had been engaged within a month of their first dinner date, and there was hardly a person living in Lambourn who hadn't wanted to celebrate it with them in some way or another. So much so that she and Dominic had hardly ever found time to be on their own.

Maybe if they had been left alone to allow the relationship to develop at its own pace things would not have got so out of hand. But as it was, and like everything else to do with the old Madeline, she had thrown herself into the excitement of it all as eagerly as everyone else had. Only Dominic had remained calm and unaffected throughout it all. He had seemed more amused by her than anything else, quite happy to indulge her crazy love of secret assignations, meeting her down by the river somewhere for a private hour or so of gentle lovemaking, willing to tease her, play with her emotions with light kisses and mild petting, but any sign of things flaring out of control and he had been quick to curtail things, leaving her feeling only more restless and frustrated as the weeks went by.

She had known he wanted her—she wasn't so innocent that she didn't known what desire looked like when it glowed in a man's eyes—but his self-control had infuriated her, so, in typical Madeline style, she had gone all out to seduce him, and Dominic, though slowly beginning to reveal cracks in his impressive control, had continued to resist her every lure until the tension growing between them had meant they started to argue more than kiss, and she'd harboured a suspicion that Dominic had actually been relieved when he'd had to go away on a week-long business trip to Bonn.

The night he had been due back was also the same night the whole family were supposed to be going to see the latest musical block-buster currently playing in the West

End. And Madeline had found herself in the rare position of having Dominic all to herself for a whole evening.

Dominic had arrived at the house, dressed in casual jeans and a pale blue shirt, ready to spend a rare evening alone with his fiancée. And had found a surprise waiting for him....

CHAPTER FIVE

'WHAT the hell are you playing at coming to the door dressed like that?' Dominic's rasping bark came rattling down the years to make Madeline wince even now, four years on. He had stared at her as if he couldn't believe his eyes.

'Don't you like it?' Wearing her father's best dress shirt—and nothing else bar the flimsiest pair of lacy briefs—she'd thought then that she looked far more seductive than any Mata Hari could do. But, looking back now, she could only cringe in horror now at her own brazenness. It was no wonder Dominic was appalled at her.

'Go and get some clothes on,' he commanded, thrusting her ungently inside so that he could close the front door.

Instead, she moved in close to wind her arms around his neck, 'Without even a kiss from my loving fiancé?' She widened her deep blue eyes at him, seducing him with every lure she possessed.

'Madeline…'

'It's all right,' she murmured huskily, 'we're completely alone,' and stopped his protests with her mouth, taking the initiative and kissing him with a hunger that had been building steadily over the weeks. He returned the kiss with an angry reluctance that made him growl, but he parted her lips so that he could deepen the kiss himself. She could still recall the heat of his body as she pressed against him, and the quivering rush of excitement that flooded through her as his arms came wrapping convulsively around her. It was her first real experience of sexual ignition, a light-

ning that sparked into a flame that began to lick right
through her. And her body melted against him, her need
so strong that it blanked out everything else.

He picked her up in his arms, and she clung to him, her
mouth refusing to let his go as he carried her up the stairs.
The pounding of his heart against her breast, the gasping
sound of his laboured breathing, the fiery touch of his
hands where he held her cradled to him, all culminated to
make her unprepared for what Dominic really intended.

She was so drunk on her own success at getting him
this far that she never even noticed his own lack of response to everything but the kiss. While her hands ran
urgently over his shoulders and his back, revelling in the
rippling muscle beneath her fingers, Dominic was grimly
planning her punishment.

They reached her room. He sat down on her bed with
her still cradled in his arms—and the next moment, he had
flipped her over and was issuing her with her very first
and only bottom-beating of her entire life!

Deaf to her cries of outrage, he delivered his punishment
quite ruthlessly before tossing her off his lap on to the bed
so he could get up and stride angrily for the door.

'You've been asking for that for years,' he growled as
he turned to glare at her. 'You are a totally unprincipled,
ungovernable brat, Madeline!' he snapped. 'And I'm beginning to wonder if I've gone mad wanting to marry myself to a sex-crazed little minx like you!'

Sex-crazed! 'I wouldn't marry you if you were the last
man on earth!' she screamed at him, so wild with hurt and
humiliation she could barely breathe. She knelt among the
fluffy pink and white flowered duvet, her hair a mad tangle
of black around her flushed face, eyes spitting a hatred at
him that only made Dominic's mouth curl in deriding contempt. 'And you won't get another chance to lay a finger

on me, you brute! I hate you, Dominic Stanton—I hate you!'

'You can come and apologise to me tomorrow,' he said, looking so incredibly aloof, so damned arrogantly pompous that her temper flew right out of control.

'I'll burn in hell first!' she vowed. And with a yank she dragged the lovely sapphire and diamond ring off her finger. 'I need a real man in my life,' she spat at him. 'Not some old has-been who's incapable of responding with any passion!'

The ring hit his back as he turned abruptly away from her. Now, on looking back on that awful scene, she could see that Dominic had been desperate to get away from the house before he retaliated to that unforgivable gibe. He had always been too sensitive to the gap in their ages, and, saying what she had, Madeline knew now that she had been lucky he hadn't jumped on her for a reply. As it was, the feel of something hitting his back brought him to a halt, and he turned slowly, looking down at the exquisite ring lying on the rose-pink carpet at his feet.

'I'm warning you, Madeline,' he said huskily as he lifted his grim gaze back to her. 'Stop right there before this gets entirely out of hand.'

Too furious to listen, too humiliated to care, and in the unusual position of being out of control of a situation, she couldn't stop the bitter words tumbling from her trembling lips. 'And I'm warning you,' she breathed. The sobs already racking her distraught frame, she delivered an ultimatum which really should have put an end to it all. 'You walk out of here now, and I shall have your replacement here before you even reach home!'

'Is that so?' he drawled, and suddenly she was afraid of him, cringing back against the pillows, thinking he was going to murder her by the look she saw glinting in those hard grey eyes. But all he did was bend and pick up the ring, then stand there twisting it thoughtfully between finger and thumb before glancing back at her. 'You know where to find me—and this, Madeline, when you're ready to apologise.' And he pocketed the ring and turned away.

'I mean it—*I mean it*!' she screamed at his retreating back.

'So do I,' she heard him mutter grimly as he disappeared from view.

As threatened, too proud to back down, and just too stupid to recognise when she was beaten, within the hour Madeline had the house full of friends, throwing herself into the gaiety of the party with an inflamed defiance spurring her on.

Perhaps, by morning, the bitter flames would have burned themselves out. Perhaps, if she'd been allowed to work off the terrible devils gnawing inside her, then she could have gone cap in hand to Dominic and begged forgiveness. But things didn't turn out that way. Instead, it was Dominic who took the initiative to return that night, Dominic who walked in to find the Gilburn house in the throes of a party even Madeline's long-suffering family would have been shocked by.

The front door was off the latch so Dominic only had to walk in, enter the dimly lit drawing-room where the reek of cigarette smoke and alcohol told its own story. He only had to flick on the overhead light and see a dozen or so bewildered faces turn his way, see Madeline stretched out on the sofa with the young man she had been dating before Dominic, her face flushed, her soft mouth swollen from another man's kisses, the incriminating shirt riding high on her silken thighs. His oddly blank gaze remained fixed on her for a long nerve-crackling moment, then he simply turned around and walked right out of the house again.

She rushed after him, knowing with a cold feeling that struck deep into the core of her that this time she had sunk beyond redemption with this last defiance. She caught him at his car, and it was there, in the quiet darkness of the night, with the width of the black Ferrari between them, that Dominic delivered the utter and complete slaying of her character. He did it without pause for breath, or by raising his voice beyond a harsh whisper. And she received it all without offering a single word in her own defence.

She had no defence. She had realised that even as she'd run desperately after him. She knew it as she stood there staring at his cold, contemptuous face and listened to the words spilling out from his hard, ruthless lips.

By the time her family returned home, they found her so sunk in misery that it took some urgent sleuthing to find out what had happened.

Conscience alone would not allow her to leave things there. She tried to ring him, only to be told he had gone away again and wasn't expected back until the night of the country club ball.

Within days, everyone in the area knew how Madeline Gilburn had been caught red-handed by Dominic Stanton in the arms of another man. The scandal was sensational. She didn't dare go out of the house because of the accusing looks she received. In everyone's eyes she had, of course, run true to form and behaved appallingly. And she suspected that most were pleased to have their worst expectations about her confirmed.

'Wait until the ball; he'll be ready to listen then,' those who cared about her advised. 'He loves you, Madeline. Dominic will come around eventually.'

So she spent the following week living for the night of the ball, knowing Dominic would have to be there since his parents had taken on the task of organising it all this year.

Perhaps if Vicky had been home and able to talk some sense into her then she would not have walked herself right into her own public crucifixion. But Vicky was away at university—a thing Madeline had turned down when she fell in love with Dominic. So Vicky was blithely unaware of the utter mess her best friend had made of her romance with her brother.

The night of the ball arrived, and Edward Gilburn worriedly watched his daughter as she came down the stairs towards him, dressed like a princess in a ballgown of the palest lime silk. Its fitted heart-shaped bodice curved the sensual swell of her breasts and nipped in to her narrow waist. And the full-length skirt was just a fine billow of layer upon layer of fine silk chiffon. She had left her hair down so it fell in glistening waves around her shoulders. She looked beautiful, frighteningly fragile, with no amount of make-up managing to hide the ravages of the last week. The only part of her seeming to be alive were her eyes, which glowed wide and dark in her pale face.

They arrived at the club to find they were one of the last to do so. And the first thing she saw was Dominic dancing with a beautiful blonde creature dressed in blood-red velvet.

Jealousy ripped through her. Nina's hand closing tightly on her own icy cold one made her aware of the avid looks she was receiving. The air was as tight as a drum, everyone expecting a spectacular Madeline Gilburn scene, maliciously hoping she would run true to form and challenge Dominic right there in the ballroom.

'It's all right,' she murmured to Nina at her worried glance. 'I'm not going to do anything.'

And, to be fair, she didn't. Ignoring the tension which

eddied around with her, she mingled with the crowd, chatted lightly, smiled a lot, and made a point of going to say hello to Dominic's parents, who were equally determined to pretend nothing untoward had happened. They welcomed her with hugs and kisses as they always did, and she stood beside them for several minutes talking about God knew what—she had an idea that even the Stantons didn't know what passed between them.

Slowly the room began to relax, and she continued to circulate with all the light-hearted innocence of an unexploded bomb. All the time, her consciousness was fixed on Dominic—where he was, what he was doing—her heart beating hectically, her lungs aching with the effort it took to drag air past her constricted throat.

She was therefore limp with relief when after a dreadful hour of him completely ignoring her presence he came over to her and coolly drew her on to the dance-floor.

She went in his arms without a single word, mouth dry, eyes over-bright, skin tingling where his hands rested upon her.

'I am dancing with you only because my father requested I do it to avoid more scandal,' he informed her bluntly as he swung her away. 'So don't read anything into this which is not there.'

'I love you, Dominic,' she whispered huskily.

'You don't know the first meaning of the word!' he jeered. 'It's over between us, Madeline,' he informed her coldly, 'so just be a good girl for once in your wretched life, and don't cause a scene—for our families' sake if not for our own.'

'Won't you at least let me say I'm sorry?' she pleaded with him, terrified at the look of granite-hard coldness on his face. 'I think I went a little mad the other night, I—'

'I don't wish to know,' he cut in. 'I find your juvenile

antics wearying to say the least. Stick to your own kind from now on, Madeline, is my advice to you. Leave the big boys alone and go and play with the young ones like the one you were offering yourself to the other night. They may fumble and have little finesse, but they'll give you the quick kind of thrill that's all you seem to need before moving on to the next experience, the next new kick!'

'That's a terrible thing to say!' His revulsion at her sent her emotions swinging into a violent downward spiral, the bitter words thrashing against her wretched senses as he twirled her around the dance-floor, his hand biting into her as cruelly as his words were doing, restricting her ability to breathe, think, to even notice the tears filling her eyes.

'I didn't promise to be nice to you, Madeline,' he gritted. 'Only to dance one damned dance with you!'

'Then let me go.' She tried to pull away from him, but his grip only tightened. 'I don't need your benevolence.'

'Oh, no,' he refused through clenched white teeth. 'You'll stay right here and see this through! I've been humiliated enough by you already!'

'And you didn't humiliate me the other night?' she shot back, the tears gone now, replaced with an anger that always came alongside pain for her.

'Because I wouldn't take what was so—cheaply offered?' he scoffed. 'Behave like a whore and you get treated like one, Madeline. And you were playing the whore to the bloody hilt! Don't!' he warned when her head came up, eyes like midnight fire in her paste-white face. 'Don't cause that scene, or you'll get more than you bargained for from me.'

'Revenge, Dominic?' she suggested shrilly. 'Is that what this is really all about: you want revenge on me, so you've decided to give me my one conciliatory dance then intend to walk away so everyone will know exactly why you danced with me at all!'

'That's your problem to deal with, Madeline, not mine,' he threw back carelessly. 'You could have stayed away tonight and saved us all this, but you didn't, so now you have the choice of either finishing it with a bit of class or doing what these people have come to expect from you, and showing yourself up for the crazy fool you really are!'

'Oh, by all means, let's not disappoint the punters by not giving them what they expect,' she drawled, her eyes brilliant with intent, heart cracking wide like an egg slowly seeping its dying contents. 'Now, what should it be, Dominic? Would you prefer me to dash out of here in a flood of tears, or would it be rather more amusing if I prostrate myself at your feet and humbly beg forgiveness?'

With a violent jerk, Madeline removed herself from his arms, and lifted her chin to send him a final glinting look from her pain-darkened eyes. 'I think the latter, don't you?' she murmured, and, with an odd twist spoiling the perfect contours of her mouth, she dropped into a low, deep and humbling curtsy at his feet, pale lime silk billowing around her, her gleaming black head bowed in mute contrition.

It was dramatic. It was utterly diabolical of her to do it. But as a country club ball stopper, it threw the whole room into total silence. And now, Madeline could actually find it in her to smile a little at her own wicked temerity.

Dominic could have laughed, but he didn't. He could have seen the humour in the precocious Madeline Gilburn abasing herself in front of him like some lowly serf, but he didn't. He could even have dragged her up by the hair and given her another beating for causing the scene he had specifically warned her against! But he did none of these things. Instead, and on a filthy curse which only reached as far as Madeline's ears, he derided, 'Why don't you just grow up, Madeline? For God's sake grow up!' and walked angrily away.

To everyone watching the little scene from the sidelines, they saw Dominic get his revenge that night, because Madeline's dramatic little gesture looked like a desperate plea for forgiveness—not given. And in true Madeline Gilburn style, she begged with optimum impact—or that was how it appeared to the onlookers. In truth—and as Dominic had known—she was mocking him, and he walked away because he could see no other way of dealing with the situation without appearing the fool once again.

Madeline, by contrast, remained exactly where she was, dying a little more with each second that passed, taking with it all her brave defiance, her mind going over and over every cruel word he had thrown at her, adding them to the long list of criticisms he had hurled at her the week before, and by the time her father gently lifted her back to her feet and led her out of the room the old Madeline was already dead, and the new one floundering somewhere close to hell. It took six months in Boston before the new woman began to form any real substance, and years to build her into the person she was today.

No one, Madeline had vowed often since, was going to find a single thing to criticise about her again.

She and Perry spent Sunday morning on horseback, riding across the lovely spring-green countryside to stop for lunch at a small riverside inn.

Afterwards, they went for a walk by the river, drawing the eyes of other Sunday strollers by the sheer balance one made against the other, Madeline long-legged and slender in her buff riding breeches and brown check tweed jacket, with her long hair caught up on a simple coil high on the crown of her head, and Perry dressed similarly, tall and lean, with his light brown hair and classically clean features.

They had been walking for a good ten minutes before Madeline plucked up enough courage to ask him the question which had been gnawing at her all weekend. 'Perry…' she murmured carefully. 'Can I ask a favour of you?'

'Of course,' he said agreeably. 'Anything you want.'

Just like that. Madeline smiled a little ruefully to herself. That was not going to be his attitude in a moment. 'If I tell my parents I am dining with you in London on Wednesday night, will you cover for me?'

He stopped walking. 'Why?' he demanded. 'Why do you need cover?'

Madeline ran her tongue around her suddenly dry lips. 'Because I've arranged to meet someone,' she explained. 'And they're going to disapprove thoroughly if they know who.'

'Who?'

Logical next question, she acknowledged. Oh, gosh! She took a deep breath. 'Dominic,' she said, then cringed when he turned angrily on her.

'Are you losing your mind?' he cried. 'The man virtually crucified you in public four years ago, and now you calmly tell me that you've arranged to have dinner with him!'

There was nothing calm about the decision, Madeline thought drily. 'I crucified him first, Perry,' she pointed out. 'This community is small and tightly knit. For as long as this stupid feud between our two families goes on, that dual crucifixion will never be forgotten. And it's hurting people who have no right to be hurt by it. I am meeting Dominic because we both accept that something has to be done to bring it all to an end, and it seems that we are the only ones who can do it.'

'How?' he jeered. 'By seeing each other again? Pretending the past never existed?'

'Yes,' she answered, then more fiercely, 'Yes! If that is what it takes!'

'Then you're a fool!' he muttered gruffly. 'Because the past did exist! And you've spent the last four years of your life recovering from the wounds it inflicted on you! He inflicted on you! For God's sake, woman,' he muttered harshly, 'see sense! Steer well clear of him. Protect yourself and let the rest of them sort themselves out!'

'I'm not intending jumping all over him, you know!' she said defensively. 'Just meeting him for dinner and discussing family problems!'

'How do you know?' he shot back. 'The way I read it, he led you around by the nose four years ago. What makes you think he won't have the same power over you now?'

That stung—mainly because it was so near to the truth—and forced her to respond accordingly. 'That's a bit like the pot calling the kettle black, isn't it?'

He had the grace to flush. 'All right. Point taken,' he grunted. Christina van Neilson had made a fool of him several times with other men before Perry had eventually snapped.

'But that doesn't answer my question,' he pointed out. 'You haven't so much as set eyes on him in four years, so how do you know how you're going to feel about him?'

Madeline lowered her face—but not quickly enough for Perry's sharp gaze. 'Ah,' he concluded tightly. 'So you have seen him.'

She didn't answer. It was too late anyway. Perry had already seen the truth written in her eyes. 'When?' he demanded gruffly. 'Where?'

'One evening,' she told him. 'When I was out riding and we happened to meet up.' She didn't tell him which night. She didn't dare.

'And what happened?'

'Oh, don't worry about it, Perry,' she mocked the sudden concern in his eyes. 'We picked up from where we left off four years ago—throwing insults at each other.' She smiled cynically at the memory. Even Dom's kiss had been an insult, harsh and punishing.

'So what makes you think this next meeting with him will be any different?'

'Because this business between our families means something to both of us,' she answered. 'We are both capable of putting our own animosity aside in an effort to find a solution.'

'Really?' His arched brow mocked her along with the tone he used. And Madeline sighed impatiently then began walking again on a sudden burst of restlessness, his perception of her just too uncomfortable to take standing still. It was a minute or two before Perry came up beside her again, and they didn't speak for a while, both seemingly lost in their own heavy thoughts as they walked on, the ice-cold water moving swiftly by beside them.

Then Perry muttered suddenly, 'I wish he'd walk by here right now. I would enjoy throwing the swine in the river.'

Madeline smiled, linking her arm through his and giving it a kind hug. 'You don't know how many times I've felt the same urge about Christina,' she confessed, remembering how, after Perry had finally broken off his engagement, Christina had enjoyed taunting him with a different man at every social gathering they attended. 'Only it was the nearest swimming-pool I used to want her to tumble into.'

His smile was rueful. 'Pair of idiots, aren't we?' he mused.

'Hmm,' Madeline agreed. 'Will you cover for me on Wednesday?'

Perry stopped walking so he could take her by the shoulders and turn her to stand in front of him. 'Will you promise to be very, very careful?' he demanded by return.

Madeline nodded. 'I promise to be the model of my mother's daughter,' she vowed gravely.

He laughed out loud at that, because Dee was such a coolly upright and serene member of Boston society. 'I suppose I can't get a better promise than that!' he conceded.

No, thought Madeline. She only hoped she had the power to live up to it.

'Having dinner with Perry, dear?' Louise repeated with the kind of smile growing in her eyes which made Madeline want to grind her teeth. 'That will be nice! He's a nice young man. Your father likes him too. He has a way with him that makes him easy to be with.'

'I thought I'd use the London apartment to change,' she suggested.

'By all means do,' Louise approved, smiling slightly as Madeline's smooth change of subject told Louise that she was not going to get response to her subtle curiosity as to where Madeline's relationship with Perry was going. 'It may be sensible of you to stay over if it means a late night. Shall I let the Crowthers know you're coming?'

'Oh, would you?' She sounded suitably grateful. But really, she found it irritating the way Louise was so eager to help her so-called relationship with Perry.

Shades of the past, she noted heavily. It sent a cold little shiver chasing down her spine.

Nina was in a dreamy mood on Wednesday. And the ostensible reason for the shopping spree fizzled out into a schmaltzy trip down fantasy lane when Madeline couldn't seem to divert Nina from drooling over anything even vaguely babyish!

'Is there something you've not told us?' Madeline quizzed her stepsister when at last she'd talked her into stopping for coffee in one of the many small bistros scattered around London. 'Like—the premature pattering of tiny feet for instance?'

'Maddie!' Nina was shocked. She even went bright red with embarrassment. 'Charles hasn't—wouldn't—couldn't…'

'All right,' Madeline let her off the hook, 'I was only teasing. But brides don't usually spend a whole afternoon drooling over baby cribs and teddy bears.'

'Charles…' The Cupid's bow mouth quivered, and Madeline felt ashamed of herself. 'Charles wants our wedding-day to be absolutely perfect. He said he wants me to walk down the aisle in my gown of white with no hypocrisy to mar my day. My day, Maddie,' she sighed out dreamily, and went off into a world of her own while Madeline remembered another time and another place where a very different man had said those selfsame things to her. She, of course, being what she had been then, had scoffed at such silly, outmoded ideals. And now? she wondered thoughtfully. She would still scoff, she decided. When a man and a woman loved and desired each other, intended to bless that love with marriage vows, Madeline saw no reason to hold back on the rest just because of some old-fashioned custom which said the bride must be a virgin to wear white. Anyway, she'd intended to marry in pink—blush-pink—virgin or not. So what use would Dominic's grand gesture have been then? No one at the wedding would have thought him honourable to the last seeing his bride come to him dressed in pink! But then, she mused drily, by the time it actually came to ordering her wedding-gown, the two families would probably have manoeuvred her into changing her mind and wearing white instead. Just as they'd manoeuvred their whole relationship along the lines they'd wanted it to take.

And there, she recognised, was the real problem that had haunted her during her stormy relationship with Dominic. She had never been really sure whether he hadn't just been jostled along on everyone else's enthusiasm. The fact that he had always managed to draw back from making love to her had only added to her fear that maybe he was only marrying her because everyone else seemed to think it perfect—and because she seemed to amuse him. And even that had palled in the end. In the end, Dominic hadn't found her funny at all.

CHAPTER SIX

MADELINE appeared in the entrance to one of London's most exclusive dining clubs, too busy trying to hide the sudden bout of anxiety that had attacked her to notice the way every male present in the grand foyer turned to stare at her in open appreciation.

She was wearing a knee-length gown of aquamarine silk. Little more than a drape of fabric which crossed smoothly over her breast then fastened at her waist with two aquamarine-studded buttons, it really was a more daring dress than she would normally have worn. But she'd wanted to shock, show Dominic in some crazy twisted way just what he had turned down four years ago. Because she knew—without vanity—that the woman she had developed into by far outstripped the child with whom he had once considered himself to be in love.

Acquiring what her mother called mirror awareness had taught her to be self-aware—and how therefore to make the best of what she had.

So the dress accentuated the long curving grace of her slender legs, moved with the sensual sway of her body, skimming her breasts in a deep cutting V which gave tantalising glimpses of her shadowed cleavage, and hugging her narrow waist before draping itself almost lovingly around her rounded hips and long silken thighs.

Her hair had been left loose for a change, brushed until the dark waves gleamed and crackled around her shoulders, then lifted away from her temples by two sparkling combs. Her make-up, severely plain as always, was just a simple touch of dusky grey-blue to her lids, and a rasp-berry-coloured lipstick that made the onlooker yearn to lick it off. Possessing eyelashes so long dark and naturally curling made it difficult for others to believe they were actually her own. So she rarely put herself out to further accentuate them.

But they were real enough. As Dominic Stanton well remembered as he stood, momentarily stunned into still-ness by the vision she presented, hovering by the entrance. And even as her gaze settled on him and he watched those same lashes flutter downwards to hide whatever thoughts were going through her mind, his senses were being jolted by the exquisite memory of what those long lashes had felt like brushing against his skin when he kissed her.

Madeline took in a controlled breath of air and smiled a cool greeting as he approached. Her heart was bumping, her hands trembling a little, but she hid her nervousness by turning to hand over her jacket to the hovering *maître d'*, the smile she sent him blinding out any hint of tension in her.

'Still slaying them with your smile, I see,' Dominic drawled as he came up beside her, his mocking gaze fol-lowing the *maître d'* as he hurried away, flushing.

Madeline turned slowly back to face him, her own ex-pression under tight control.

He looked fantastic. His dinner suit was conventional black, his shirt just plain white, bow-tie slim and black. Nothing extravagant about him, yet through it all he ex-uded the natural magnetism which made him Dominic Stanton, the compelling person he was, the dynamic busi-nessman he was. A hard man to ignore at any time, he hadn't changed in that direction in four years, she decided. His hair was still as dark and sleek as it had always been, and cut in that neat, short, conventional style he had favoured then. His face was still handsome, strong-boned, smooth-lined—but perhaps in a harder kind of way—his body still that perfect male frame of tightly packed muscle and long strong bones. He would be thirty-two years old now—going on thirty-three, and showed four years more cynicism in the curve of his slightly smiling mouth.

But other than that, he was still the only man she had ever met who could make her senses pulse in awareness.

'Madeline,' he murmured. 'You look beautiful.'

Simply said, and all the more disturbing for it.

'Thank you,' she replied in a quiet, flat little voice that gave nothing away of what she was experiencing inside. Meeting him under cover of darkness had disturbed her deeply. And at the bank she had been too concerned for Vicky's feelings to allow herself the indulgence of studying him in the better light. But seeing him here, with nothing else to do other than absorb every single detail of him, made her want to turn and run from the turmoil of response he was creating inside her.

He took her arm. And in sheer instinctive response to his touch, she started, pulling free of his grasp before she'd realised what she had done. Dominic frowned, his mouth hardening as he glanced sharply at her. Then, determinedly, he took hold of her arm again, watching narrowly as she had to quell the urge to pull away from him a second time.

'We did a lot of things to hurt each other four years ago, Madeline,' he said grimly. 'But I don't recall ever giving you cause to flinch at my touch.'

He didn't? But then, Dominic was misunderstanding the reason why she pulled away. Which perhaps was better for her.

'Then I apologise for the—unnecessary reaction,' she

murmured, 'you'll have to put it down to nervous anticipation,' using the truth to cloak itself.

A dark brow lifted at that. 'Did I catch a hint of acid
on that smooth tongue just then?' he drawled.

He really was the most beautiful man, she thought with
a sudden sense of overwhelming loss. 'You could have
done,' she acknowledged, holding his mocking gaze with
one of her own, 'but I do hope not.'

Her drawl seemed to irritate him further because his
fingers tightened on her arm as he turned her abruptly towards the wide curving staircase which led up to the club's
exclusive dining-room. 'So calm,' he mocked as they
climbed the stairs side by side. 'So exquisitely beautiful,
so very sophisticated. You know,' he said quietly, 'I was
prepared to find you changed. Four years is a long time
after all. But I never once considered the possibility that
you would give in to Dee's ambition to turn you into one
of her kind.'

'So you don't approve,' she concluded, though the derision she'd picked up in his tone rankled. She had, after
all, only acquired what he himself had accused her of lacking badly.

He shrugged. 'In some ways the transformation is both
delightful and rather challenging, but…'

'Ah,' she smiled, 'there has to be a but, I suppose.'

'The hair, for instance,' he observed. 'I saw the other
Madeline marching directly to the nearest stylist's and having the lot shorn off as a defiant gesture aimed directly at
me.'

'Ceremonially, of course,' she assumed, understanding
him exactly. Dominic and her hair had once enjoyed a
private love affair all their own. He had loved to bury his
face in its silken mass and she had loved to feel his fingers

combing through it, reacting to his touch with a shivering pleasure that had used to stir her blood.

His hand moved to her waist in an attentive gesture meant to guide her through the pair of open doors into the dining-room. And, unintentionally maybe, his fingers touched the silken edges of her hair. That instant tingling response on her scalp forced her to smother a gasp.

'I'm sorry to disillusion you, Dominic,' she murmured coolly in an effort to cover up her reaction, 'but I really wasn't that stricken.'

His step faltered. And Madeline gained the small satisfaction of knowing her reply had thrown him.

'You were,' he muttered. Then, before she could form any kind of protest, he added, 'We both were.'

She was saved from having to defend herself against that potentially provoking remark by the waiter, who was eager to see them both comfortably settled at their corner table. Dominic took her by surprise by refusing to take the seat opposite her and instead slipping into the one to her right.

'I hate talking across two dinner plates,' he explained the move as the waiter quickly rearranged the dinner placings, then disappeared, leaving the menus behind. 'If I am wining and dining a beautiful woman, then I want to enjoy her, not to peer at her over the top of some stupid table decoration.'

'This woman has not come here simply so that you can enjoy looking at her,' she said, dampeningly. 'You wished to talk. About Vicky, I believe you said.'

'Not yet,' he refused. 'First I want to know about you. What you've been doing with yourself, how you are—how you really are, Madeline.'

'I'm fine,' she said, then gave him a brief résumé of her life in Boston. 'It feels strange being back in England, but

I expected it,' she concluded. 'Boston is my home now and I feel more comfortable there—'

His hand coming to cover one of her own where it lay on the table brought her to a breathless halt. 'Stop it, Maddie,' he commanded grimly. 'Stop trying to show me how wonderfully cool and sophisticated you've become, and cut out all that blasé spiel you've managed to fool everyone else with.'

'I don't know what you're talking about,' she denied, trying to remove her hand from beneath his, but he wouldn't let her, so she stopped the undignified struggle, gathered together all that impressive sang-froid he was being so scornful of and turned blandly patient eyes on him instead. His face was very close to hers. She could see the silver flecks lightening his slate-grey eyes, and remembered on a wave of sad nostalgia how once she had used to provoke the whole iris to turn black with passion. Angry passion, sexual passion; she'd never used to mind so long as she got a passionate response from him.

The silence between them grew, and slowly Madeline ceased to breathe as tension began to inch itself along her spine, watching his gaze flicker over her face, relearning, taking in the changes and reacquainting himself with those things about her that would never change: the classical structure of her bones, for instance, and the creamy smoothness of her skin; the sensual fullness of her mouth, slightly parted now as she tried to breathe evenly; the small straight line of her nose, and those once so expressive eyes which now hid everything.

Slowly, as the silence stretched, and the tension altered to a fine buzz of awareness, the rest of the room began to lose itself in a blurred haze on the periphery of their tunnel vision, no mockery evident in either of them because for some reason they had both discarded it in this long private communion.

This, Madeline recalled achingly, was the Dominic she'd only ever seen when they were alone with each other—which had been so rarely. This was the one who could probe through the bright glittering girl she had been and home right in on the sensitive and vulnerable creature who hid within.

His hand was warm on hers. They were sitting close enough for their thighs to touch. She could feel the power in those corded muscles cloaked in expensive cloth, feel the ever-present animal magnetism of him. And old, forgotten sensations began to tingle just beneath the surface of her skin.

We once spent hours just gazing at each other like this, she remembered sadly. Her hand resting in his, the only real contact other than their eyes, the link to something so deep and meaningful that suddenly she wanted to cry for the loss of it.

'Boston was good for me,' she heard herself say, then blinked to break the disturbing eye contact. Dangerous, this, she warned herself with an inner shiver. Dangerous. 'I grew up there, Dominic. Don't try looking for that other foolish creature you once knew; she no longer exists.'

Something dark passed over his face—a hint of a sadness one felt with the fleeting memory of a loved one long gone from this life. 'And are you content with this new—image you project?' His voice was oddly gentle, and his eyes showed an alarming understanding.

Madeline removed her hand from his, and so withdrew spiritually away from him. Content? 'Yes,' she said. 'I'm content.' Happy? No. Alive? No. She took in a deep breath. 'And you?' she threw the conversational ball back at him. 'Are you—satisfied with your life? Vicky tells me you've outstroked your father in the money-making race. Success must taste sweet at that level.'

His mouth went awry in recognition of what she was doing. And at last he relaxed back into his seat as his own urbane mask slid smoothly into place. 'We all have our— successes to savour and our…failures to rue.' He looked directly at her, and Madeline knew that she had been one of his failures.

As if by tacit agreement, they both picked up their menus. Rocky ground was always best avoided whenever possible, Madeline mused ruefully. Their conversation had been drawing perilously close to rocky ground. And with an atmosphere tempered better to suit the occasion, they ordered and ate, using trivia to carry them through the interminable meal, and no one looking at them would ever guess that once they had been so closely in tune that it was sometimes impossible to distinguish where one spirit ended and the other began.

'I'm worried about Vicky,' Dominic said when at last they reached the coffee stage. A frown pulled his brows together.

'Yes, I am too,' Madeline agreed. 'Something has to be done about the situation, Dom,' she said grimly, too intent to notice the way she had shortened his name the way she'd used to do. 'It appalled me to come home and dis- cover there was a feud in progress between our two fam- ilies.' She turned an apologetic look on him. 'No one so much as mentioned it in their letters to me. And, quite frankly, I was annoyed to learn that the situation has been allowed to develop just because of our—our…'

'Stupidity,' he supplied for her. Madeline grimaced her dissatisfaction with the word but offered no other. She hadn't got one. And in any case, if she had, it would only have led to a discussion on their 'stupidity' which she had no wish for.

'Poor Vicky is caught right in the middle. And I'm afraid I can see no solution to the problem. She knows without my having to say it that she's more than welcome in my home, that Nina wants her to be bridesmaid at her wedding. Just as we understand that she can't do that without feeling she's letting her own family down.' Madeline gave an impotent shrug. 'I wish...' She sighed, forgetting for the moment to keep her guards in place. 'I wish...'

'What do you wish for, Madeline?' Dominic prompted gently, his gaze fixed on her wistful face. She didn't answer him, lost in those same wishes in a way the old Madeline used to do. 'Do you wish the last four years had never happened?' he suggested, his hand going up to touch her hair as though it couldn't help itself, eyes suddenly dark on her. 'That we could turn back the clock to a time when we were all happy, and everyone loved everyone else with no dissension anywhere in sight?'

But there had been dissension, she remembered with a hardening of her heart. 'It's easy to look back and remember only the good times,' she declared. 'But only dreamers and fools do that.' She reached out for her coffee-cup and in doing so dislodged his hand from her hair. 'No,' she said firmly. 'I don't wish the last four years away. I only wish I could end this silly feud.'

'There is a way,' Dominic said quietly.

Slowly, Madeline replaced her coffee-cup. That tone was shiveringly familiar to her. Her father had used to use it when he was about to suggest something unpleasant. Dominic had too under similar circumstances. It usually accompanied the turning of their quick-calculating brains—and augured ill for all those involved.

'Whatever you're about to say,' she drawled, 'I'm sure I'm not going to like it.'

His smile acknowledged the point. 'I think I can positively say that you're going to hate it,' he drily agreed, then took her entirely by surprise by standing up. 'Come on,' he said, taking hold of her hand. 'Let's get out of here.'

It was automatic that she stood up too. 'But—where are we going?' she demanded as he began drawing her towards the exit.

'To my apartment,' he announced, tightening his grip when she instantly pulled against it.

'I'm going nowhere near your apartment with you!' she protested.

'Why? Too many fond memories there for you to stomach?' he mocked.

'Because I have my reputation to consider,' she informed him coldly.

'You never worried about silly things like that before.'

'I was a besotted child then.' They'd reached the curve on the upper landing where it joined the stairs before Madeline managed to pull him to a stop, tugging him around to see her anger. 'I am not going to your apartment with you,' she insisted on a driven whisper.

He stared at her flashing eyes for a moment, then simply turned without a word and began tugging her down the stairs.

'Dominic—!' Angry frustration almost made her stamp her foot, but then she remembered where she was, and with a tight firming of her mouth she slipped back into her cool shell. 'I refuse to let you cause a scene,' she informed him stonily, and let him lead her towards the exit.

'I was relying on that,' he said, glinting a mocking look at her flushed cheeks and gleaming eyes. 'Although,' he added ruefully as they reached the door where the *maître d'* was already waiting, Madeline's jacket at the ready, 'you worried me for a moment there.' Dominic took the jacket and slipped it around her shoulders. 'I really thought the old Madeline was going to jump out from behind the cool façade of hers, and land me a slap on the face!'

Her cheeks heated at memories of an incident when she had done just that to him and slapped his arrogant cheek. He'd been teasing her mercilessly all evening about a lovely blonde creature he'd spied across the room, mocking, taunting, downright provoking about how he'd like to put his shoes under her bed, or some such equally inflammatory remark. Until, in the end, the lid had come off her temper, and she had taken a swing at him, catching him unawares so that the flat of her hand made stinging contact with the side of his face. He had gone very still. The room had gone silent, every face turned in their direction as they recognised another Madeline Gilburn scene on the way. Then, quite calmly, quite dispassionately he had slapped her back.

The shocked gasps had rustled around the room. Dominic had stood very casually in front of her, waiting for her next response, all hint of teasing gone from his face. The silence had begun to throb all around them, and you could have heard a pin drop as Madeline stood trembling, her wounded eyes slowly filling with tears. Her mouth had begun to quiver, her hand going up to cover the mark on her cheek where his fingers had stung her. And, without a single word, she had just turned away from him and walked out of the room, leaving him standing there.

He had caught her at the door, his fingers curling around her wrist and tugging her roughly around to face him. He had glowered at her reddened cheek, at the tears streaming

unchecked down it, and on a husky groan had pulled her
into his arms.

'Forgive me,' he'd said. That was all, but he had said
it with such a wealth of urgent emotion that it had shaken
her.

'I'll come,' she told him quietly now.

Dominic frowned, surprised by her sudden climb-down.
But then, she thought as they moved outside, he hadn't
been inside her head just then, remembering a moment
when her love for him would have had her following him
to the ends of the earth without question.

The Stanton town apartment was situated on the very top
floor of the bank itself. It was a rather unattainable place,
huge, big enough to accommodate a whole convention of
Stantons if the need arose. But because of the necessary
tight security around the bank itself the family rarely used
it, preferring to stay at one of the good hotels if a stop-
over was required.

Except for Dominic. He, being the penny-pinching
banker he was, saw no sense in paying out for hotel rooms
when they had a perfectly good apartment going to waste
right here.

He drove them up to the rear gates and allowed the night
guard to check them out before he could open the huge
gates which led to the private car park.

'Fort Knox,' he murmured as they climbed out of the
car and had to wait yet again for security to operate the
locking system securing the rear doors. 'Cold?' he asked
when she shivered. He touched his fingertips to her cheek,
eyes almost black in the half-light of the security light.

Startled by the unexpected caress, she glanced up at
him, their gazes locked once again, and fine threads of
electric tension began swirling around them.

'Madeline,' he murmured huskily, 'I...'

The doors swung inwards, bright fluorescent lighting flooding over them, cutting off whatever he had been about to say, and she experienced a profound sense of relief when he let it go, and instead guided her into the building, and straight into the waiting lift.

It took them swiftly upwards, ejecting them directly into the main foyer of the palatial apartment. Softly glowing table lamps greeted them, electronically switched on by the movement of the lift itself. Madeline allowed Dominic to guide her down the wide hallway to a door to the left which housed a room disturbingly familiar to her.

It was Dominic's own private sitting-room—more a den than anything else. It contained nothing fancy, only the creature comforts a man liked to have around him when he relaxed. And Dominic often relaxed here when pressure of work meant it wasn't worth him making the trip back to Lambourn in the evening. There was a desk, of course, untidily scattered with papers, two huge and chunky red velvet sofas, a comprehensively stocked drinks bar, a television set and expensive hi-fi stack, and the ever-present computer link with the bank.

Other than that, it contained all Dominic's personal bits and pieces, like the books on the shelves and the magazines scattered about. It wasn't a tidy room, but then Dominic never let anyone in here to 'mess' with it, and she had always liked coming here with him—mainly because it was one of the only places they had ever managed to be alone in comfort.

'That wasn't here the last time I came,' she observed, covering her nervousness at being here again by remarking on a gold-framed painting she'd spied hanging on the wall opposite.

Dominic sent her a hooded look as he walked over to the drinks bar. 'No,' he murmured. 'It's a recent addition.'

Madeline walked over to take a closer look at it. It reminded her or something…

Unaware of Dominic's stillness as he watched her, she ran her eyes over the rather grand-looking black and white manor house standing within its own beautifully laid out grounds. Its grey-slated roof was shining as if a recent shower of rain had just washed it clean, the tiny diamond-leaded windows glinting in the new sunlight.

It reminded her of the old Courtney place that stood about halfway between her own home and the Stantons'. But where the years had been very kind and loving to the house in the painting, the Courtney place had been allowed to deteriorate badly over the years, its beauty lost.

A small sigh whispered from her lips. She had always shared a sad kind of sympathy with Courtney Manor. And seeing this lovely house looking as Courtney Manor should look brought those feelings back to her now.

'Who does it belong to?'

'What, the house or the painting?' Dominic quizzed, coming over to stand beside her and handing her a glass. 'The painting is mine,' he said. 'I just happened to come across it one day covered in the filth of centuries and looking nothing like it does now…it was the frame which initially caught my attention.'

'A junk shop?' Madeline could remember how Dominic couldn't resist rummaging around old junk shops. He had a passion for the old and unusual—not necessarily the valuable either, but things, objects which captured his interest—an addiction inherited from his mother, the family liked to tease. The Stanton house was filled with old curiosities, not all of them collected by his mother.

'You could say that,' he smiled rather cryptically. 'Once

I got a closer look at the canvas, I decided it might be worth renovating—and as you see…' he indicated with his glass to the picture '…it was.'

'Can I buy it from you?' she asked impulsively, turning hopeful eyes on him. 'I'll pay you the full market price for it,' she added quickly when she saw the way he suddenly closed her out.

'Why do you want it?' He wasn't looking at her, but at the painting. But Madeline detected a tension in him that hadn't been there a few minutes ago.

'It—it reminds me of the Courtney place,' she admitted, shrugging because she was uncomfortably aware that she was revealing more than she liked of her inner feelings. Dominic knew all about her attraction to the Courtney place.

He said nothing though, narrowing his eyes on the picture as if trying to catch the resemblance himself. And they both stood in silent contemplation for a while.

'How serious is it between you and Linburgh?' he asked suddenly, and she jerked her head around to stare at him in surprise.

'What has that got to do with the painting?' she wanted to know.

He didn't reply, his gaze still fixed on the painting, a brooding quality about his stillness. Madeline frowned at him, wondering what was going on in that complicated mind of his.

After another long pause, he turned to look at her, his grey eyes dark and intent. 'You can have what's in the frame the day you can come and tell me that you've given Linburgh up for good.'

Her eyes widened in bewilderment. 'Why should you want me to do that?' she asked.

His crooked smile gave her her answer, and Madeline dropped her gaze from his, a sudden ball tightening the muscles in her stomach. Dominic still wanted her. He had just told her so.

CHAPTER SEVEN

SHAKEN, Madeline moved away from Dominic, going to sit down on one of the chunky sofas, struggling to hide what that revelation did to her.

It had taken four years to get over her last encounter with this man, and in just three short meetings she was sweeping those four years away as if they had never been!

She took a sip at her drink, eyes lowered because she was aware that he was watching her, waiting for her to say something, acknowledge what he had just so casually announced.

Over in one corner, the soft steady tick of one of Dominic's junk shop buys began winding up to chime the quarter. And automatically, Madeline checked the time on her own slender gold wrist watch. Ten-thirty, she saw just as the warm resonant sound of a Westminster chime began filling the room.

She glanced up at him, and their eyes caught and held, an old remembered heat washing right through her. He had undone his bow-tie, and it was hanging loose at his throat. The top few buttons of his shirt were open, too, allowing her a glimpse of his strong tanned throat. Her mouth went dry, and she swallowed some more of her drink, but the light white wine only agitated the commotion already going on inside her.

She took in a controlled breath, feeling her heart pumping heavily against her ribs. 'My relationship with Perry is none of your business,' she managed to say eventually.

'Perhaps not,' he conceded. 'But I would be obliged if you would tell me anyway.'

She should never have sat down. At least when she was on her feet she felt almost on a level with him, but down here, with him standing over her like that, she felt—diminished, under threat almost.

'We're still exploring the possibilities,' she told him, and left him to make of that what he liked.

'And Christina van Neilson?' he put in smoothly, bringing her fine brows arching upwards as she glanced at him.

'Been playing the sleuth, Dom?' she drawled, feeling the commotion going on in her stomach increase with the implications that idea offered.

His rueful smile committed him. 'The Linburgh-van Neilson affair was pretty well publicised, even over here. And the way I read it, Linburgh was not the one to call it off.'

Did he expect her to remark on Perry's broken engagement? 'As I said, we're still exploring the possibilities.' She refused to improve on her original answer.

Dominic gave an impatient sigh and at last moved from his stance by the painting. 'All I am trying to ascertain, Madeline, is whether or not he has a right to feel possessive of you.'

'No one has the right to feel like that about me,' she made quite clear.

He studied her for a moment, taking in the cool blueness of her stare, before saying quietly, 'I said earlier that I knew of a way to end this feud between our families.' And he smoothly shifted the conversation to the reason why they were supposed to be here at all. 'The way I see it,' he went on, 'is that since it all began because of you and I, then really it is up to us to make things right again.'

'Yes?' she said warily, prompting him to go on.

'By trying—as best we can—to put the clocks back four years.'

Madeline felt her composure slip, but she hid it quickly. 'Now, how am I supposed to respond to that, I wonder?' she questioned wryly. 'You know, I think I had better let you continue before making any response.'

Her mockery made his mouth twitch in appreciation. 'I thought,' he took up her challenge, using the lightness of his tone to keep her guessing as to his seriousness, 'I thought, that a—public reconciliation maybe—at the Prestons' this weekend, would—'

Anger flared briefly, the sheer cruelty of the idea stabbing into a wound so deep that it was still raw. 'And how are we supposed to stage this—wonderful reconciliation?' Her voice was so dry that it was brittle. 'Am I supposed to—demean myself at your feet again, so that perhaps you could graciously give your forgiveness this time and— *voilà*! Everything will be just fine and dandy again!'

Dom had the gall to smile. 'I rather saw it as my turn to do the begging this time,' he suggested. 'After all, the lady I see here tonight would not, I think, demean herself to anyone.'

True, Madeline agreed, only slightly mollified by the fact that he had at least noticed that *this* Madeline would cut off her nose rather than make a public spectacle of herself.

'Then how do you see us performing this—reconciliation?' She was curious, genuinely curious to know what dastardly plan he had cooked up for her. She knew Dominic, and the way his conniving mind worked. He had never approached a problem in a nice straightforward manner in his life!

But apparently he was still pondering over the theme Madeline had just so sarcastically discarded. 'I could pros-

trate myself at *your* feet, I suppose,' he murmured thoughtfully. 'And allow you to do the gracious forgiving. But...'
He let out a pensive little sigh. 'Like you, I can't see myself in the role of humble supplicant.'

Neither could Madeline. Dominic was too proud a man
to grovel to anyone.

'So, I wondered how you would feel,' he went on
slowly, gauging his words, it seemed, to a very wary
Madeline, for maximum effect, 'about us playing a little
game of—now how shall I put it?' he murmured thoughtfully, eyeing her assessingly. 'Dalliance seems to say it
well enough, but it's such an old-fashioned word, and I
think *flirtation* probably says it better,' he decided. 'Do
you fancy having a light flirtation with me, Madeline?' he
invited, daring her with the mocking glint in his eyes.

The dreadful cheek of him alone made her smile. 'Oh,'
she pouted, an affectation she had learned from her Boston
contemporaries but rarely used. It just seemed appropriate
here in this very false discussion. 'Flirting sounds so
dreadfully capricious, Dominic.' Her voice was loaded
with *savoir-faire* as she made a lazy gesture with her hand.
'We could, of course, just shake hands and pretend to
make friends?' she suggested. 'Much more civilised than
a flirtation. Shall we pretend to be *just good friends*,
Dominic?' she said, aping his own lightly mocking tone.

'You aren't taking me seriously,' he accused gravely.

'Why?' She opened her blue eyes wide to him. 'Are you
trying to be serious?'

He was the first to snap. 'My God,' he breathed. 'You
really have it all off pat, don't you?'

With a deep sense of triumph stinging the blood to life
in her veins, Madeline maintained the satirical air. 'You
are being serious!' she gasped, shocked, and Dominic muttered something nasty beneath his breath.

He took an angry gulp at his drink. 'They didn't exaggerate, did they, when they said you'd changed beyond all recognition?' His mouth gave a bitter twist of disgust. 'I had hoped they meant just on the outside, but it goes all the way through, doesn't it?'

'What does?' she willingly took the bait.

'The blasé sophistication!'

'Why, thank you!' she drawled Boston-style, seething inside. 'It's so good to know that four years of my life have not been wasted!'

'Stop it!' he snapped, spinning away from her to slam down his glass in an act of burgeoning frustration. His spine was taut, the muscles in his shoulders bunching as he struggled to contain his anger.

Madeline watched him for a while, feeling oddly like crying when really she should be pleased at managing to better him so easily.

A sigh whispered from her. 'I'm sorry,' she relinquished heavily. 'I would like us to be friends, Dominic. For Vicky's sake if not for our own. But I don't know whether a friendship between you and me would ever work.' Too much bitter-tasting water had swirled under the bridge to support a rocky boat of friendship. And anyway, she added grimly to herself, he could still affect her emotions too easily. It was dangerous to so much as contemplate letting Dominic in close again.

She'd been hurt enough the first time.

She thought he wasn't going to bother replying, then he took in a deep breath and let it out again slowly. 'No,' he sighed. 'I do tend to agree with you on that point.'

He turned to face her, and they found themselves staring sombrely at each other again, the vibrations between them an odd mixture of remembered pain and a beautiful loving.

'Why did you do it, Madeline?' he said suddenly, his

voice pitched low and thick. 'Why did you run away like that?'

She dropped her gaze. 'Let's not go back over old ground,' she advised heavily. 'I was very young and foolish, and you were...'

'What was I?' he muttered when she hesitated. Reaching for her, he grasped her by the shoulders and drew her to her feet. His expression was harsh, the dark glitter in his eyes burning wretchedly into hers. 'What was my excuse for what happened four years ago?' he demanded, giving her a small shake as if he couldn't help himself, his fingers clenching into the tender pads of her shoulders. 'It's all so easy for you to use your youth and impulsiveness as your excuse for your behaviour. But what excuse did I have? Tell me,' he growled, 'if you know, because it would certainly help me to understand something I've never been able to justify in four long miserable years!'

Tears sprang to her eyes. 'I don't know,' she whispered, shaken by the depths of his self-contempt. 'I just don't know what you thought or felt then, Dominic! How could I, when you never allowed me to know?' Her mouth turned down on a bitterness and frustration she had allowed to fester for four long years.

Clenching her teeth, she forced herself to calm down, sending him a smile that was every bit as blasé as he'd just accused her of being. 'Why not count your blessings and just be thankful for the lucky escape you had,' she drily suggested, 'instead of trying to understand what was, when all's said and done, a disaster?'

Instead of becoming angrier as she expected him to, Dominic surprised her with a rueful smile, his fingers slackening on her so that she was able to move away from him a little. 'Disaster covers it quite nicely, doesn't it?' he said. 'But,' he continued more seriously, 'as with all disasters, it's the confusion it leaves in its wake which causes the real problems.' He leaned back against the drinks bar, his hands sliding into the pocket of his black silk trousers, his expression grave. 'The confusion we left behind us, Madeline, has affected and still is affecting everyone attached to us. We have a responsibility to them to do something about it,' he concluded firmly.

'I'll get Nina to write out invitations to all the Stantons, inviting them to her wedding,' she suggested, 'and personally deliver them myself—I have no intention of joining this feud, Dominic,' she warned him. 'And both your family and my own will know that the first time I get the chance to show it—if, that is,' she then added ruefully, 'your family ever place themselves in my company again.'

'They stayed away from the Lassiters' to give you time to readjust, Madeline. It was not a personal message to you.'

'I know,' she said. 'I had managed to work that out for myself.' She lifted cool eyes to him. 'It isn't me who has gotten into the habit of reading an insult into everything, Dominic,' she pointed out. 'I can still remember how warm and caring your parents were to me.'

'They love you,' he said softly.

Her heart gave a painful squeeze. 'Yes,' she nodded. 'And I love them. And tomorrow evening I shall pay them a visit to tell them so—with Nina's invitations to sweeten the pill of having Madeline Gilburn threaten their peaceful lives again,' she added drily.

Dominic just smiled. 'And what do you think your father will have to say about that?'

Madeline made an impatient gesture with her hand. 'He shall just have to accept it,' she said stubbornly, then turned her impatient glance on him. 'I can't understand why you've let this go on for so long, Dominic! If I'd been at home, I would have made sure this silliness stopped long ago!'

'Would you?' he clipped. 'Then it just goes to show how little you know about the problem.' He eyed her thoughtfully from his casual stance. 'Did you know, for instance, that your father and mine almost came to blows over our break-up? That your father went as far as withdrawing all his accounts from our bank at a very awkward period for us—and he knew it? Did you also know,' he went on ruthlessly, 'that at this very moment your father is trying to get one of the big banks to back his latest brainwave but, as usual, everyone is wary of touching a Gilburn idea?' She was looking so bewildered that Dominic knew he was telling her fresh news. 'I'd finance him, Madeline,' he told her huskily. 'At the drop of a hat, I'd put the money up he needs to get his idea off the ground. But he's so damned pigheaded, he won't even discuss it with me!'

'Have you tried to approach him?' She was visibly shaken, her face gone pale beneath its smooth covering of make-up.

'Twice,' he nodded, turning grimly away to retrieve his glass. 'He didn't even bother to acknowledge my calls,' he informed her bitterly.

'The stubborn old so-and-so,' she muttered. Dominic was right. Her father was pigheaded! 'So, what do you suggest we do?' she asked, accepting at last that they were not going to solve anything the easy way.

He turned back to face her. 'We have to give an impression that you and I are considering making a go of it again,' he told her. 'It's the only thing I can think of which will melt the ice around them. They always did love the idea of you and me being a pair. Hell!' he rasped. 'I would even go as far as saying they took rather a large role in pushing you towards me! We all rushed at you when I come to think of it,' he added grimly. 'We were all guilty of hunting and cornering the spirited prey, forgetting that she had a habit of coming back spitting.'

'I seem to remember thinking you were the one cornered,' she murmured, remembering that awful night she had tried to seduce him.

'I was old enough to know my own mind.' Dominic dismissed. 'You weren't.'

'I don't flirt, Dom,' she made coolly clear, telling him two things in that brief statement: Firstly that she was at last beginning to take his suggestion seriously, and secondly that she had no wish to rake over the past. It resurrected too many bad memories.

'No, I do remember that,' he said soberly, eyes momentarily turned inwards on some private memory. He flicked a measuring glance at her, then grinned, the mockery back in his expression. 'How about a romance, then?' he offered.

'What…?' Madeline drawled, matching his tone. 'Another one?'

'Oh, but this time it will be different,' he assured her. 'I mean, neither of us is in danger of making the same mistakes a second time, are we? You told me yourself on the phone only the other day that you learned your lessons thoroughly the first time around, and I…' His smile was something only he understood. 'The circumstances will be different for me. So what's to stop us indulging in a bit of romance? We surely are not immune to each other, so there should be no difficulty making it believable.'

A challenge? she wondered, and felt her nerve-ends tingle in temptation. The old Madeline had always possessed a weakness for challenges.

'And just think how it would throw all those vicious gossips into a flat spin seeing you and me together again.'

'All those poor matchmaking mamas,' she derided, 'groaning in despair.' Nina had told her about the way Dominic was haunted by ambitious mothers pushing their pretty daughters at him.

'Vicky as pleased as punch,' he went on after sending her a withering look for that remark. He always had hated his 'eligible bachelor' status. 'The parents would be so afraid that we might fall out again before they could get us married off that they would be around at each other's houses planning the wedding before either of us could draw breath! It could be—'

'Quite frightening.' Madeline said dampeningly. 'The next thing you'll be suggesting is that we got engaged again!'

'Why not?' he said, and it was his turn to be withered with a look.

'And what do we do when all the fuss is over, and everybody is liking everybody else again? When Nina is safely married—in the presence of the whole Stanton clan,' she mocked, 'and Vicky no longer feels pulled in two directions. Which just leaves you and me, with a sham of a romance to wriggle ourselves out of.'

'Can't we cross that bridge when we come to it?' he dismissed carelessly. 'Unless of course,' he then added silkily, 'you're afraid you may fall in love with me all over again.'

Madeline bristled instantly, lifting her fine brows at him in haughty disdain. 'Do you want this—pretend romance to go ahead or not?' she demanded.

'Sorry,' he smiled, 'but I just couldn't resist the taunt— I expected you to throw it right back in my face, but you didn't, did you?' Her tight-lipped refusal to make any comment on that last gibe made him laugh softly. 'Do we have a pact to play the besotted lovers to make our families comfortable again, or not?'

Madeline eyed him levelly for a moment. He was playing with her like a big cat with a defenceless little mouse. But she wasn't defenceless. Never had been, and Dominic knew that. So, what was he actually trying to manoeuvre her into here? She knew he still wanted her; he had said as much when he'd offered her the painting. And she knew that if she had any sense at all she should be turning around and walking right out of here before she found herself flailing in some very dangerous water. The trouble was, though, she couldn't help but feel a tingling buzz of excitement for the game.

It could be worth the risks, just to see all those condescending masks slip.

She took a deep breath. 'How do you propose to get this—deception off the ground?' It was an agreement, and they both knew it. 'And don't suggest the party at the Prestons' again,' she warned, adding sourly, 'I'm not into public reconciliations any more…I was put off them after a bad experience once.'

'A low hit, Madeline,' he admonished, then stood up straight, flexing his broad shoulders in a way that made her suddenly aware of just how tense he had been. 'You're having lunch with Vicky tomorrow, aren't you?' he enquired, and at her nod went on, 'I'll gatecrash, if you don't mind. And we'll take things from there, I think.'

'Fine,' she agreed, and turned suddenly to walk towards the door.

'Where are you going?' he shot at her, genuine consternation in his voice.

'Home,' she informed him coolly. 'We've discussed all we intended to discuss, and now it's time for me to go.'

In truth, she was more than ready to escape from his proximity.

Too much of Dominic Stanton is bad for your health! she warned herself drily.

'Still infuriating when you want to be, I see,' he muttered, reaching her in three long strides. 'I like it, by the way,' he added.

'Like what?' she asked blankly.

'The new you,' he explained. His gaze ran slowly over her, lighting warning signals as it went. 'A sophisticated witch,' he mused. 'The mind boggles at the concept.'

'Dominic...' she warned, not in the mood for his brand of back-handed compliments.

'I've just thought of something,' he said, setting her nerves really jumping as he moved closer to her so that she was trapped between him and the closed door behind her. 'We'd better get in some quick practice while we have the privacy to do it.'

'W-what are you talking about?' she demanded warily, watching that old roguish glint enter his lazy dark eyes.

'Touching,' he said with a casual shrug. 'Kissing, that kind of thing.'

Latching on stupidly late, Madeline tried to push by him, only to find herself folded tightly against him.

'Don't!' she cried, but he ignored her, the smile on his lips half playful, half passionate. And it was the passion that set her struggling to get away. He simply waited for her to stop, eyes mocking her puny strength.

'You have the most delicious figure it has ever been my pleasure to hold,' he told her softly. 'This dress should carry a danger warning with it, it's so damned provocative.' His hands did a sensual slide down the side of her body from soft breast to firm hips, and Madeline couldn't hold back a small gasp of pleasure at his touch. 'And that mouth,' he murmured, 'that gorgeous raspberry mouth…'

'No—!'

Too late. He lowered his head and caught her lips, and everything alive in her went haywire and she fought not to respond to him. Clouds gathered across her mind, then cleared once they'd taken her back four years to when this was all she lived for. His body felt the same as it had then, still hard, strong and sensually assertive. His mouth was the mouth which came to her in her dreams and wrung her senses out with a frustrated longing. He even smelt the same, his skin, warm and satiny to the touch, evoking a hunger in her that she'd known all along had never been quenched. And the hot, sweet, melting sensation trickled insidiously through her body so that she had to hold herself stiff and unbreathing to maintain her resistance.

Dominic lifted his head, his eyes black where the pupils had engulfed the silver-grey iris. A dark flush stained his lean cheeks, and his mouth was parted, the air softly rasping her face as he breathed unsteadily upon her.

'Take another deep breath, Madeline,' he softly advised, his mouth so close to her own that the words vibrated against her trembling lips. 'You're going to need it, because that wasn't good enough. Not by a long way.'

This time everything that had been missing from the first kiss was there in strength in the second. Heat—a heat that burned her lips apart. Hunger—which sent his tongue snaking into her mouth to tangle greedily with her own. And passion—passion so intense that it forced a groan from her as her body caught fire, the flames dancing in applause for something her senses had been starved of for years.

Dominic muttered something, impatient because she was still putting up a token resistance. His arms tightened around her, one forcing her into an arch so that she had to cling to him to maintain her balance, the other burying itself in her hair, tugging her head back so that she was completely vulnerable to his demanding kiss. And she felt the heated press of his own response begin to throb against her.

It was her downfall. On a final distraught groan, she melted, and gave him what he was demanding of her, the hot sensual response of her own desire.

The kiss changed then, drawing a hunger from both of them that had them straining against each other as wave after wave of hot drugging passion swept over them.

When at last he dragged his mouth from hers, Madeline was so disorientated that she swayed dizzily, her limbs weak and trembling, heart throbbing loudly against her panting breasts.

Appalled with herself, she pushed him away, anger—thankfully—coming to her aid alongside the self-disgust which helped feed her voice with contempt as she bit out huskily, 'That was a mistake. You shouldn't have done that.'

'Why not?' He sounded husky and warm, his hand stroking her hair as though he were soothing a frightened fawn instead of a sexually furious female.

'Because you've just spoiled all our plans,' she informed him coldly, by quick degrees grabbing back her composure. 'I'll look for another way to heal the family breach,' she told him. 'But it won't be with any help from you!'

'Because I kissed you?' He sounded horribly mocking. Madeline felt her cheeks grow so hot that they burned her with humiliation. 'I had to do something to get through that wall of ice you've surrounded yourself in. God knows,' he derided, 'we'd convince nobody of anything with you freezing me off every time I so much as look at you!'

The derision brought her head up, her mouth beginning to tingle when she found her eyes drawn to the throbbing fullness of his still savouring the recent kiss. 'Well, now you won't have to worry about my reaction,' she said, turning stiffly away from him and placing a trembling hand on the door-handle. 'I want nothing more to do with you, Dominic. Please let me leave,' she added when he stopped her opening the door with the simple pressure of his palm on the wood.

'Don't be stupid!' he rasped, getting serious at last. 'You can't seriously be running away because of a couple of inconsequential kisses!'

Inconsequential! If she didn't get out of here quickly, she would hit him for that! On a strength born of anger, she managed to tug the door open despite his pressing hand.

'Is it Linburgh?' He followed her into the hall, his hand coming out to grasp her arm and pulling her to a protesting halt. 'Because, if it is, why not just say so instead of pretending all this—virginal outrage over a damned kiss?'

Madeline spun around on him then, her eyes alight with anger. 'No,' she said tightly. 'It is not Perry, nor any other man, come to that!' His face was no longer passion-softened but hard and watchful. As she glared at him, she saw him frown and begin mentally backing off, recognising the signs that the old and unpredictable Madeline had broken through her sadly slipped composure. But she didn't care any more; she just wanted to get out of his flat, out of his life by the quickest means possible. 'If you want to know the full unvarnished truth of it,' she bit out stingingly, 'then I'll give it to you. I came back here because I hoped four years was long enough to make my point.

But it seems it wasn't. So I'll state it clearly so there should be no mistake. I am not available, for a dalliance, a flirtation, or a romance feigned or otherwise with you. And not because my feelings are involved with another man! But because I just don't want you!'

'Finished?' he clipped out coldly.

Madeline nodded.

'Then I'll take you home.'

He drove her to the apartment in a stony silence which was reflected in the granite hardness of his features, and Madeline sat beside him in a state of panicked near hysteria, wishing she had never come back, wishing she had just stayed in Boston where nothing nor anybody had the power to hurt her like this man did.

He escorted her all the way to her door before he delivered his own bitter reply to what she'd thrown at him.

'You're a liar, Madeline,' he said. 'Whether you're lying to me or, worse, to yourself as well I don't know. But you are—a liar. You responded to me in the exact way I responded to you—with a fire and a hunger built up over four long bloody frustrating years! Think on that while you lie in your bed tonight in lonely splendour. And think on this too.' He pushed his face up close to hers, his anger so strong he pulsed with it. 'If this—thing between our two families isn't resolved soon, not only will Vicky be more hurt than she is already, but your father will find himself in dire financial difficulties! He needs my support, and the only way he will get it is by you co-operating with me!'

His mouth landed a final stinging kiss to hers, then he was striding angrily away while she watched him go without a single word, too shaken by the unpalatable truth in what he'd said.

Tears filled her aching eyes as she watched him step

into the lift and stab the 'down' button, felt a desperate need to go after him and even took a jerky step forward with that intention, before forcing herself to remain exactly where she was, and watching the lift doors slide across his hard, angry face.

The old Madeline was the one who had gone chasing after her angry man. This one held on to her pride at all costs.

CHAPTER EIGHT

HE HADN'T come. Why she had expected him to turn up at all, Madeline didn't know. But the wayward hope had lingered with her all through their first course and was just beginning to shrivel as they waited for their second course to be served. She had only picked at her food, too tense to eat. And Vicky was too engrossed in an involved story about a potential client she was trying to capture to notice Madeline's complete lack of appetite.

'I tell you, Maddie,' Vicky was saying excitedly to her inattentive audience, 'if I could land this one, I'd make my father eat every single one of all those deriding remarks he's made about women in a man's world! And he's so delicious to look at. He…'

Madeline glanced despondently around the crowded restaurant, wondering what all these people busily enjoying their lunches had to talk about. She couldn't think of a single thing to say herself. She wasn't hungry. She wasn't up to conversing with anyone. And she was tired from lack of sleep, and fed up.

Last night had been a disaster, so much of a disaster that she had spent the rest of the night pacing her bedroom floor, berating herself for thinking she and Dominic could spend time together in constructive discussion when even a fool should have expected it to degenerate into a slanging match! And not just a slanging match, she reminded herself heavily; the seduction scene had been pretty despicable too.

She despised him for that, if only because it had shown

her how little he'd really cared about mending the family feud if he had been ready to risk it by grabbing her like that. And the new Madeline told her to forget him and look in another direction for a solution to the problem— while the old Madeline wanted to weep, because last night had proved to her that, far from getting over Dominic, she was still as vulnerable to him as she had always been.

Vulnerable. Perry had warned her but she'd taken no notice. Her own common sense had warned her but she'd taken no notice of that either! 'He led you around by the nose,' Perry had taunted, and last night she had come perilously close to being led by it again.

God, she couldn't believe she was still that gullible, that big a fool! Dominic Stanton was just not—

It was then that she saw him, framed against the oak and warm brass fixtures forming the restaurant entrance— and her heart stopped dead, then began to bump heavily against her ribcage.

He had come after all. Despite all the bitter words she'd thrown at him, despite the contemptuous ones he had thrown at her, he had come, and she had to press her teeth into her lower lip to stop it quivering on a sudden wave of wretched elation.

So much for your new Madeline contempt! she mocked herself as she watched the slate-grey eyes search the busy tables.

He saw them. Over the top of Vicky's bobbing head, she watched him fix her with a steady look, and had to squeeze her trembling hands together beneath the table as he began threading his way towards them, looking unspeakably good in a dark pin-striped suit and crisp white shirt, his lean face full of grim purpose.

'...American through and through...' Vicky was saying. 'You know what I mean. All hard muscle and sexy politeness. Has a face like Superman and the body to go with it.' She paused to allow herself a small quiver. But Madeline didn't see it; she was too busy watching Dominic come towards them, unable to break that helpless eye contact they'd achieved from the moment he walked in here.

He came to a stop behind his sister's chair. 'Hello, Madeline,' he greeted quietly, his hands going lightly to Vicky's shoulders as the poor girl almost jumped out of her skin at the sound of his voice, her eager chatter abruptly stemmed.

Madeline dragged her eyes from him to look at Vicky. She looked like someone who had been turned to stone, horror etched into her paste-white face. She looked back at Dominic. He was banking on her not making a scene in front of Vicky, but his expression was guarded—just in case.

'Hello, Dominic,' she answered quietly.

'Do you mind if I join you?' He requested smoothly.

'Dom...' Vicky's plea was huskily offered. She hated scenes of any kind, always had done. Vicky might give the impression of being a very liberated and independent creature, but she was also acutely sensitive to atmosphere. She just looked at Madeline through huge hunted eyes.

'Move your bag off the seat next to you so your brother can sit down,' Madeline told her gently, bland-eyed and bland-faced despite the turmoil going on inside her.

A waiter appeared at Dominic's elbow the moment he sat down, enquiring if the gentleman would like to order. Dominic shook his head. 'I'll just have coffee with the ladies when it comes,' he dismissed, and the waiter melted away, looking relieved that his table reservations were not going to be put out by the late arrival.

'How are the wedding plans going?' He swung his attention back to Madeline.

'Very well,' she replied. 'There's still a whole month to go before the big day, but you know Louise,' she smiled, 'she's well ahead with her planning.'

'Charles Waverley is a good man,' he said, no mockery. In fact, the mockery had been plainly missing since he arrived. 'I hope Nina will be happy with him.'

'I'm sure she will be,' Madeline glanced at Vicky. The tension the poor thing was giving off was awful, and she sat with her head bowed to the empty space between her cutlery, hands lost and probably clenched beneath the table. Madeline's eyes filled with tender pity as she shifted them back to Dominic. He gave a slight shrug, his mouth twisting ruefully. 'Do you know Charles well?' she asked, keeping her voice smooth and casual.

'Fairly well.' She saw his arm move, and guessed he had taken hold of his sister's hands. The suspicion was confirmed when Vicky glanced up jerkily to catch her brother's encouraging smile. 'Vicky fancied herself in love with him for a while, didn't you?' he teased her gently.

'I did not!' she denied, the tease effectively bringing her to life. 'He isn't my type! He's too—too…' Her voice trailed off on a fresh wave of discomfort, her head beginning to dip all over again when Madeline suggested,

'Bland?' And was rewarded with one of Vicky's rueful grins. 'I know what you mean,' she went on drily. 'He's so—so…'

'Bland?' Vicky murmured, and they both fell into soft laughter.

'Are women always so bitchy when they discuss a man?' Dominic drawled.

'Be glad you came along when you did,' Madeline murmured provokingly. 'You were next.'

'Really, though,' Vicky inserted quickly, fearing a row

brewing, 'Charles suits Nina perfectly. She needs a man who'll protect and cosset her.'

'And you don't?' her brother mocked. 'I thought all women liked to be cosseted.'

'God, no!' Vicky shuddered at the thought, her earlier mortification all but gone. 'My ideal man must be strong-willed and damned determined if he wants to take me on. I need challenge in a relationship. Not total dependency. He has to be—' Her eyes had been flicking restlessly around the restaurant when they skidded to a halt, bring her words to a sudden halt also. 'God,' she breathed, then reached urgently across the table to grab Madeline's hand. 'It's him!' she whispered excitedly. 'No—! Don't turn around! It's the one I was telling you about before Dom arrived—you know…' she whispered at Madeline's blank look. 'The one I— God,' she choked, 'he's coming this way!'

Dominic glanced curiously in the direction his sister was staring, and while Madeline watched both faces opposite her, unaware of whom they were looking at, she saw Vicky's face colour up, and Dominic's harden. He flicked his gaze back to her, and she almost blanched at the look of cold accusation he lanced her with.

'I had no idea you were expecting anyone,' he bit out frostily.

'I'm not,' she denied, frowning.

'Madeline!' the call went up, and she went very still for the moment it took her to understand what had changed Dominic from the genial companion into a cold and angry man.

Several things happened at once then. The waiter arrived with their main course. Vicky's eyes widened then hooded when she realised that the newcomer was not coming over to speak to her, but because of Madeline. And Perry arrived at her side, confusing the waiter who was trying to serve them by bending down to kiss her cheek.

'What are you doing here?' she greeted him in surprise, thinking, Perry—Superman? Had Vicky gone blind?

'Same as you, I should image,' he grinned. 'Having lunch with Forman.'

Forman, Madeline repeated ruefully to herself. Superman. So Forman was Vicky's bigshot American client.

She got up, turning to smile in welcome to the other man. 'Forman, how nice to see you again.'

'Hello, Madeline,' he smiled back, reaching out to take her hand, then laughed when the waiter almost lost his serving dish. 'I think we're causing something of a traffic jam,' he drily observed.

The waiter finished serving as best as he could then got quickly out of the way, so that Madeline could then complete the introductions. Dominic was already on his feet. But it was Vicky she made known to the two men first, smiling as she informed Perry who her friend was.

'This is the girl you've been dying to meet,' she told him. 'My friend Vicky—Victoria Stanton—Perry Linburgh, Vicky,' she explained.

'The same Vicky Madeline tied to a tree during a game of cowboys and Indians, then proceeded to forget all about?' he asked, his hazelnut eyes alight with amusement.

Vicky laughed, 'She told you about that?' Her hand was taken and shaken warmly, brown eyes dancing to Madeline then back to Perry again. 'Did she also tell you about the time she cut me adrift in a leaky old rowing boat on the river then just stood by to watch me sink?'

Perry looked suitably horrified, 'You mean that god-awful river she had me walk along last weekend? I bet you were glad to see the back of her when she left!'

'Oh, no,' Vicky's denial was movingly sincere. 'I missed her dreadfully.'

'We all did,' Dominic put in, causing a small silence that only Forman Goulding did not understand. Dominic turned a brief smile on Perry. 'We've met before, Linburgh,' he said with a cool nod of his arrogant black head.

'I remember,' Perry was equally cool.

'Forman...' Madeline quickly brought the other man into their group. 'Vicky I think you've already met,' she murmured drily, 'but her brother I don't think you know. Dominic,' she turned glacial eyes on Dominic Stanton, 'this is Forman Goulding. He runs the European end of Linburgh's.'

Introductions completed, Perry glanced at his watch. 'I'm glad I've caught you, Madeline,' he said quickly. 'I was going to ring you later to find out what time you want me for this Preston thing on Saturday.' Madeline saw Dominic stiffen up from the corner of her eye. 'Only I have a meeting arranged for Saturday afternoon, which may mean me cutting it a bit fine if this party is an early starter.'

'No problem,' Madeline assured, an idea hitting her suddenly as she looked from Vicky to Forman Goulding who were talking quietly to each other. 'It's a ''come when you arrive'' kind of thing, so don't worry about messing up someone's dinner settings. And,' she went on casually. 'If Forman would like to join us this weekend, I'm sure Vicky wouldn't mind making up a foursome for the evening.'

Dominic was furious; she could almost feel him seething beneath the cool surface he was projecting. But there was more to her plan than just a little bit of matchmaking, and she was not going to allow him to spoil it.

'You did that deliberately to annoy me!' Dominic accused the moment the other two men had left, arrangements firmly made. He seemed to have forgotten his sister's presence at the table. But Madeline hadn't.

'Come to dinner on Saturday,' she invited her friend, 'then we can all leave from the same house.'

'Oh, Madeline!' Vicky groaned, the old problems reasserting themselves to make Vicky feel cornered. 'You know I can't come to your house! I wasn't even going to the Preston party because...' Not bothering to finish, she chewed anxiously instead at her bottom lip.

'See what you've done?' Dominic muttered. 'Now what the hell is Vicky supposed to do? Casually inform our parents that she's dining at the Gilburns' on Saturday, and expect them to just accept that without feeling hurt?'

'You come too,' she said, knocking the wind right out of his sails, then made a sound of impatience. 'Think about it!' she sighed. 'It's the ideal solution! Your father can't afford to offend people of Perry's and Forman's standing! He must know that Vicky is chasing Forman's account. The fact that both men are spending the weekend at my home shouldn't prejudice Vicky's chances. Isn't it a man's motto not to allow the personal to intrude on business?' she challenged.

'Hey—you're right!' Vicky put in excitedly. 'Daddy can't possibly protest!'

'But Madeline's father can,' Dominic inserted dampeningly, 'and he has no qualms at all about mixing personal with business.' His slate gaze derided Madeline with a look before he turned back to his sister. 'Have you forgotten, sister, dear,' he drawled, 'that the Stantons are no more welcome in the Gilburn home than they are in ours?'

'So, what do you propose we do?' Madeline said. 'Keep avoiding each other like the plague just because of a silly rift that should not have been allowed to develop in the first place?'

'I told you my solution last night,' he snapped.

'Yes, and I told you what I thought of it!'

'Last night?' Vicky put in sharply. 'You two saw each other last night?'

'Swine,' Madeline muttered at Dominic, going red.

'Then this isn't the first time you've met since that time at the bank last week?'

'You asked for it,' Dom said, unrepentant.

'How many other times have you met?' Vicky demanded suspiciously.

'Once was enough!' Madeline said bitterly.

'Twice,' Dominic corrected silkily. 'Remember the time down by the river?'

'My God, you sneaky pair of devils!' Vicky gasped.

'This food is cold,' Madeline sighed, sitting back in her seat.

'Does anyone else know you've been meeting in secret?' Vicky was like a dog gnawing at a bone, asking questions, forming her own answers while the other two fought a battle of their own. 'What about Perry Linburgh?' she wanted to know. 'Or Diane Felton, come to that?'

Madeline's attention was suddenly caught, and she lanced Dominic with a look. 'And who,' she demanded silkily, 'is Diane Felton?'

'You'll be able to meet her on Saturday night.' Dominic smiled an acid smile. 'I shall personally introduce you both—when I bring her to dinner at your home!'

'Oh, you won't like her, Maddie,' Vicky put in absently, still trying to grappling with her new-found knowledge. 'She's one of those really sophisticated bitches he favours these days. She—'

'Watch it, half-pint,' her brother warned, then added deridingly to Madeline, 'You know the type, darling. Not very different from the new you.'

'I won't have it.' Edward Gilburn huffed. 'I won't have that Stanton man in my house!' Madeline sighed impatiently, and he glowered at her for it. 'And quite honestly, Madeline,' he went on haughtily, 'I am amazed at you for inviting him after what he did!' He shook his silvered head in disgust. 'I thought you'd learned your lesson about him the first time around.'

'Edward!' Louise snapped, and it was so unusual for her to shout at her husband that he almost sat down in surprise. 'Perhaps you should try considering Madeline's difficult position in all of this! She didn't ask you to fall out with the Stantons.'

'Us, Louise, us!' he corrected forcefully.

'You, Edward,' Louise insisted. 'It was you and James Stanton who had the fall-out; Beth Stanton and I just got carried along on the tide, while poor Vicky and Nina got trapped right in the middle! How do you think it feels to Madeline to know her childhood friend is not welcome in her own home?'

'Did I make a single protest about Vicky?' he countered. 'Vicky is welcome here any time she wishes!' he exclaimed. 'But her brother is another kettle of fish entirely. He hurt my baby, and...'

'They hurt each other, Edward. Please remember that. And Madeline is right. It's time it was all forgotten.'

Madeline was beginning to rue the moment she'd had her brainwave this lunchtime, when a soft, gentle voice from across the room piped in, 'I have an idea.' And all faces turned in surprise in Nina's direction, and she smiled uncertainly. 'The way I see it,' she said tentatively, 'is that Madeline has as much right as any of us to invite whom she pleases into her own home. But, on the other hand, I don't think she should expect Daddy to calmly sit down to dinner with a man he hasn't spoken to in four years—'

'Thank you, angel,' Edward Gilburn said stiffly, puffing up because Nina was giving him her support.

'So,' Nina took a deep breath. 'I think we should let Madeline have her dinner party—in private,' she suggested. 'And, so no offence is taken on the Stanton side, we'll let everyone believe that we have another engagement—to dine with Charles at his home. That way nobody is made uncomfortable, are they?'

Madeline dressed with a deliberate intention of making an impact in an exquisite gown of dark red velvet with off-the-shoulder little sleeves and a plunging neckline. The skirt was short and tight, with a simple slit at the back which gave glimpses of her silken thighs when she moved.

She swept her hair up high on her head and secured it with two gold combs. At her ears she wore large gold loops which swung as she moved and a thick gold chain circled the base of her slender throat.

Perry pronounced her ravishing when he saw her, but she felt herself fade away into nothing when Dominic walked in with Diane Felton on his arm. She wore white, a frosted, shimmering white that skimmed her svelte slim figure as she moved. Flaxen-haired and milky-skinned, she made Madeline feel dark and heavy by comparison.

'He certainly has taste, I'll give him that,' Perry murmured at her side, watching Madeline's too-revealing face as she studied the other woman. 'Would you like me to lure the Snow Queen away so you can move in?' he suggested tauntingly.

'Snow Queen just about says it,' she gritted bitchily through stiffly smiling lips as she watched, with unwanted

resentment, Dominic lower his dark head to murmur something in her shell-like ear, leaving Perry laughing softly
behind her as she walked forward to greet her guests, aim-
ing her attention at Vicky first.

'You came.' She smiled warmly at her friend and kissed
her on both cheeks. 'I did wonder if you would.'

'It was touch and go for a time,' Vicky admitted. 'I'm
afraid I turned coward and left Dom to do the arguing with
Daddy.'

'And why not?' Madeline sent the listening Dominic a
mocking glance. 'He has to come in useful sometimes, I
suppose. Hello, Dominic.' She held out a hand to him.
'How nice of you to come.'

His mouth twisted at the polite little greeting. 'I just
couldn't resist,' he drawled, taking her hand and holding
on to it when she would have pulled away from his burning touch. 'It's been such a long time…'

'Darling?' Diane Felton's voice was as light and as col-
ourless as the rest of her. She turned superbly anxious eyes
on her man. 'Are you two going to be rude to each other?'
she enquired pensively.

She knew about their past relationship, Madeline made
a dry note, then wondered acidly if there was anyone living
in Lambourn who didn't know.

'We are never rude,' she assured the other woman, smiling her best social smile. 'You must be Diane.' She wrig-
gled her hand out of Dominic's to offer it to the blonde,
who took it with a perfectly cold smile.

'Diane, this is Madeline,' Dominic made the introductions. 'Just back from Boston and ready to take
Lambourn by storm.'

'Already taken it,' Perry appeared beside her, his arm
going comfortably around Madeline's waist. He turned a
charmer's smile on Diane Felton. 'I've had to fight off

more than one potential beau since we arrived,' he explained.

'You're my beau,' Madeline softly assured him. 'Perry Linburgh,' she informed Diane.

The wide-spaced eyes the colour of a summer storm suddenly came to life, and revealed a surprising intelligence. 'I've heard of you, Mr Linburgh,' she said. 'I sit surrounded by your name every single day!'

'You do?' Perry drawled. 'Tell me more!' And true to his word, Perry deftly drew the Snow Queen away.

'Diane is a computer expert,' Dominic explained. 'Her office is a minefield of electronic gadgetry, all with the Linburgh logo emblazoned on it.'

'She's—lovely,' Madeline said as she watched them go, relieved that the little truth hadn't stuck in her throat.

'Just my type,' Dominic agreed, then bent to murmur in her ear. 'She really is very nice, you know. You might even find yourself liking her if you give her a chance.'

'I never said I wouldn't,' she protested.

He was laughing at her. 'Your expression gave you away, green eyes.'

'I haven't got green eyes.' She frowned at him.

'No?' he mocked. 'They certainly looked green to me a moment ago. But then,' he added whimsically, 'perhaps it was a trick of the light.'

'Don't play games with me, Dom,' she said impatiently, angry because he was right and she was seething with jealousy. 'I thought I made it clear to you the other night that I don't like it!'

Suddenly he was grim-faced. 'And I don't like the way Linburgh touches you all the time,' he threw back.

'If you two don't get your act together,' Vicky put in tightly, 'you'll be putting our families through another scandal—I can see it coming!' With that she stalked away to join Forman, who had taken on the task of mixing cocktails.

'She's of the unshakeable belief that you and I have been meeting secretly every day since you arrived back,' Dominic told Madeline, adding ruefully, 'I'm not sure if she's miffed because neither of us have confided in her, or worried for us both in case we make as big a mess of it this time around as we did the first.'

'But that's rubbish,' Madeline dismissed. 'Didn't you tell her so?'

His eyes mocked her naïveté. 'Do you honestly think she would believe a denial after the performance we put on the other day?'

'That was all your fault,' Madeline accused.

'Fifty-fifty,' he corrected admonishingly. 'We have to take the blame for our sins both past and present on a fifty-fifty share-out, Madeline.'

'And the future?' she asked. 'What will the share-out on that be?'

'Oh, that all depends on how you behave,' he murmured, unmoved by her sarcasm.

Madeline turned fully to face him, glorious, with her blue eyes sparking. 'I warned you, Dominic,' she said tightly. 'I won't play games!'

'Too late, darling.' He touched a finger to the tip of her small straight nose. 'The game began at the restaurant the other day. You could have put a stop to it then if you'd really wanted to.'

'God,' she choked, spinning away from his disturbing touch. 'You're insufferable!'

'I know,' he sighed just behind her. 'One of my worst failings, so I'm told.'

'Why are you doing this?' She was busily watching the brilliant way Perry was holding everyone's attention away from them, but her own attention was stingingly locked on the man standing directly behind her.

'Why? To set the record straight of course,' he drawled. 'Blame it on the accountant in me. I can't stand long-outstanding debts.'

'I owe you nothing!' she spat at him furiously. 'And just remember,' she warned, 'we're all here tonight for Vicky's sake. Not so you can—'

'Strange,' he cut in smoothly. 'I thought we were here so Madeline Gilburn could show us all how wonderfully grown-up and sensible she has become.'

She moved angrily away from him, his soft laughter gnawing at her nerves. For the rest of the evening she played the gracious hostess to the hilt, and no one, not even Dominic, could have faulted her performance.

CHAPTER NINE

'OK, I'M not too big to admit it. I'm impressed,' Dominic said, hours later, when Madeline had at last paused for breath and allowed herself to stand back and view her triumphs with a well deserved metaphorical pat on the back.

Only one potentially explosive incident had taken place since her altercation with Dominic before dinner, and ironically it had happened as they were preparing to leave her home, and Madeline realised she'd left her wrap in her room.

'I'll get it,' Perry offered, already striding for the stairs when he added questioningly, 'The black velvet thing I saw draped over your chair, is it?'

'Yes,' she called, smiling warmly after him before turning back to face the hallway to find Dominic's gaze narrowed on her. He stared coldly at her for a moment, then flicked his gaze up to where Perry was disappearing along the upper landing. Madeline felt the air lock tight in her throat, a dark blush running angrily up her cheeks when she realised what was going through his suspicious mind. Her chin came up, eyes defying him to question Perry's right to be familiar with her bedroom. He said nothing but his contempt was obvious.

Perry came back with her wrap, and lightly caressed her nape with his lips before settling it over her shoulders. Dominic spun his back to them and, sharp as always, Perry noticed the movement and sent Madeline a smugly amused look which told her he had done it all quite deliberately.

'You're a devil,' she murmured drily to him.

'He's seething,' he remarked unrepentantly.

'And I repeat, you're a devil.'

Perry just laughed and placed his arm warmly about her shoulders as they walked outside. Dominic watched them appear, then deliberately turned Diane to face him and kissed her on her mouth.

Madeline froze, taking his form of punishment like a punch in the solar plexus. Perry's arm tightened consolingly. 'Sorry,' he murmured. 'My fault.'

'Let's go,' was all she said, but inside she was a seething mass of the kind of emotions only the old Madeline had used to experience. And she was glad to climb into the back of Perry's bright red Lotus so that she could hide her face in the dim interior of the car while she brought herself firmly back under control.

They drove to the Prestons' in two cars, Dominic driving Diane while the rest of them travelled with Perry. By the time they all arrived at the Prestons' home, it was getting late. Dominic and Diane were already waiting for them at the door, Diane huddling into her warm fur jacket against the cold April night air.

'You should have gone in,' Perry quizzed their sense in waiting out in the cold.

'Solidarity is the order of the evening.' Dominic levelled his cool gaze on Madeline. 'Isn't that so, darling?' he drawled.

'Yes,' she said firmly, taking in a deep breath for courage.

'Have I missed something important to do with this evening?' Forman drawled sardonically.

'Not a single thing,' Vicky murmured very drily as all six of them walked into the Prestons' home.

For impact value, their arrival was perfect. No one, but no one, could misunderstand the statement being made when Madeline Gilburn and Dominic Stanton arrived so obviously together—but with different partners each. Forman glanced at the sea of astounded faces turned their way, then down at Vicky, who was trying hard to look nonchalant—but her fingernails were almost cutting into his flesh where they gripped the crook of his arm.

'I did miss something,' he murmured softly. 'I have to assume that all this tension is caused by two certain opposing factions in our group?' he suggested curiously.

'You mean you don't know?' Vicky looked up at him in surprise. 'I thought Perry would have explained it all to you.'

'Not a single thing,' he mocked her own dry answer of earlier.

'It's a long story,' she whispered as their host and hostess, looking a trifle harassed, approached. 'I'll explain it to you later.'

'You certainly stage-managed it all beautifully,' Dominic was saying ruefully to her now.

Her cheeks were glowing, eyes sparkling with the success of her efforts. Over to one side of the crowded room, her parents were talking to Dominic's parents. There was restraint there, but at least they had seen the folly of carrying on a feud their children had so obviously discarded.

Madeline had led her party around the room with the grace and charm of the true socialite, introducing, chatting, laughing lightly, always in control and knowing exactly what her next move would be.

With a diplomacy learned from the highly experienced Dee, she'd sent Perry off to dance with her mother, Dominic to dance with his, and Vicky had found herself inviting her own father on to the dance-floor while Forman took care of Diane so that Madeline could grab her own father. As if it had been well rehearsed, they all came together at the end of the dance beside a wide-eyed Nina who had witnessed the whole thing from the sidelines, her fiancé standing sentry behind her.

'So I don't have to prostrate myself after all. Shame,' Dominic sighed. 'I was almost looking forward to it.'

'As you see,' Madeline turned her glowing face up to him, 'such dire actions are not necessary. And I did it without—'

'Without needing to mount even the lightest hint of romance with me,' he completed for her, sounding mockingly saddened about it. 'And,' he went on, 'without giving all these—lovely people the nice juicy scene they've been so looking forward to since Madeline Gilburn arrived back home.'

'Vicky's glowing,' she pointed out, forcing him to remember the main objective of the evening.

Dominic swung his glance over to where his sister was talking animatedly to Forman. 'The poor man,' he murmured. 'I wonder if she's drowning him in FT index points and the Japanese stockmarket.'

'Dominic!' Madeline rebuked. He just laughed; he had meant no malice towards his sister. 'Where's your Snow Queen?' she asked, wishing he would just go away. People were beginning to look.

'I've deserted her, for a black-hearted pagan,' he said. 'Where's your faithful beau?'

'Dancing with your Snow Queen,' she noticed then, the amused glint in Dominic's eyes telling her that he had seen them too.

'Come on.' He reached for her hand. 'Let's you and I do the same thing.'

'But I don't want to dance with you!' She tugged protestingly as he began to draw her towards the dance-floor, her heart already beginning to hammer at the prospect.

'Of course you do,' he insisted. 'You don't want to spoil everything now, do you? They'll have noticed, you know,' he added succinctly, 'that you've danced with everyone else in our party except for me.'

Beaten, she went silently into his arms. Dominic drew her close, the flat of his hand pressing against the base of her spine. Their bodies fitted together as perfectly as they had done four years ago, and he swung her away to the haunting sound of a Gershwin melody.

'Do you know you are the most beautiful creature in this room tonight?' he said suddenly, surprising her into glancing up at him. He caught her gaze and held on to it. 'Four years ago you were beautiful, excitingly so. But now...' His silken sigh disturbed the thick fall of her lashes, making them flutter. 'Perhaps you needed those years with Dee to learn how to deal with it all...' he added soberly. 'There's certainly more danger in the new self-controlled Madeline than there was in the younger, more easily read one.'

'Danger?' She picked up on the word because she wasn't sure she liked it.

'Danger,' he repeated huskily, looking grim all of a sudden. 'All beautiful women are dangerous, but you, Madeline, have the power to be lethal.'

'Don't be silly,' she admonished, giving a soft dismissive laugh, her heart beginning to race. 'You make me sound like some deadly weapon!'

'And there is the danger,' he said grimly. 'When you decide to ''go off'', as they put it, it promises to be one hell of a show. And I intend to be the only one around to watch it happen.'

'Stop it, Dom,' she whispered, glancing anxiously around her in case people were watching them.

'What's the matter,' he taunted, 'afraid this may become an action replay of the last time we danced?'

She shuddered, the mere idea of it making her feel sick inside. 'I've told you, I don't make scenes any more.'

'Good,' he said, 'then just shut up and dance.' He pulled her closer to the warmth of his body, and they danced on in silence for a while, Madeline too aware of all the curious eyes on them to relax.

But eventually, as one tune drifted into another, and they lost their interest value when it became obvious that she and Dominic were not going to treat them all to a scene, she began to relax, let her body lean more reliantly on Dom's, and surrendered to the weak pleasure of being in his arms.

The continual brush of his thighs against her own and the slow caressing movement of his hand against her back eventually sent her eyelids flickering shut, soothing her into a state of near euphoric pleasure until the dance, the music, the people all began to fade into the background of her consciousness as the awareness always buzzing between them swamped out everything else until her head was full of it, her senses homed on to the alluring smell of him, the touch, the sweet sensual taste where her lips kept brushing against the silken warmth of his throat. She sighed softly, her breath moistening his flesh where it brushed, and Dominic touched his mouth to her cheek, his hands drawing her even closer. They danced on and on, the world around them melting further and further away as they moved.

The Prestons' home was old and rambling, old enough to possess its own ballroom built in a time when the rich had played more than they worked. And Dominic danced her around and around the floor until she felt dizzy, disorientated, too weak to even want to fight the feelings busily resurrecting themselves between them. This, she decided, was what she had been born for. And her four years away had done nothing—nothing to erase this need in her for this one man.

'This isn't what I want to be doing, Madeline.' His mouth was a trembling whisper against her ear. 'I want to be alone with you.'

'Please don't, Dom,' she pleaded, groaning at her own weakness as his words sent her swaying closer to him.

'Too late,' he murmured in husky triumph, and swung her away from him so suddenly that she stood blinking up at him, the amused gleam in his eyes only half concealing the passion burning beneath.

Madeline gazed bewilderedly around them, stunned to find the music gone, the hum of light chatter; and that Dominic was quietly closing the door of the Preston's beautiful book-lined study.

He had danced her out of the ballroom and across the hall into this room without her even being aware of it! Appalled that, while she had believed him as absorbed in their dance as she had been, he had actually been coolly planning to get her alone like this, she flung herself away from him, and stood trembling with angry humiliation.

'I am not going to fight you for supremacy over that door, Dominic,' she informed him coldly. 'I would prefer if if you would just move away and kindly let me pass.'

His eyes were lazy on her angry face, the proud lift of her chin, the faint quiver of her mouth which said she hadn't quite managed to grasp back her self-control. A fire burning in the Prestons' grate surrounded her in a warm rousing glow, highlighting the pagan blackness of her hair, the perfect symmetry of her slender figure, the agitated rise and fall of her breasts beneath the passionate red velvet. Her skin, pale and smooth, and her eyes, dark and luminous, like sapphires on fire themselves.

'You don't want to go anywhere, and you know it,' he said, suddenly no longer sleepily amused, but angry—angry enough to make her back warily as he began moving towards her. 'Like me, you want this so badly that you're actually trembling with it, so damned hungry it's eating you up inside!'

He reached her, and her heart leapt as his hands came firm and determined to her hips, pulling her against him. She put up her hands to his shoulders to hold him off, but they were shaking so badly that they held no strength. And his tight smile said he knew it.

'Four damned years trying to fight something that has no intention of going away!' he muttered. 'What a waste, Madeline. What a damned stupid waste!'

She made a small sound of denial, but it came out as nothing more than a strained little whimper, and on a husky growl that sent her senses leaping his mouth claimed hers with a burning demand and they were kissing with a frenzy which left neither of them with any barriers to hide behind.

The fire was hot on her back, the front of her burning from the heat of his body pressed hard against her, alive and throbbing with a need that sent a thick insidious heat drenching through her.

'Meet me later,' he pleaded huskily.

'Where?' It never occurred to her to refuse. The old excitement was running like fire through her veins, the old compunction to go where her instincts took her—where Dominic led. She felt suffused with the power of it, alight and alive.

'At the boathouse,' he said, reviving memories which

had her groaning painfully, and, on a soft growl, his mouth came back to hers to deliver a kiss hard with angry frustration. 'As soon as you can get there.'

He put her away from him then, holding her with his arms locked so that she couldn't sway closer to him. And on a surge of that old Madeline desire to pierce his control, she ran the flat of her palms along his shirt-front where the skin burned beneath—then on down his groin, fingertips tantalising the taut sensitive muscles so that they contracted violently to her touch. Her eyes lifted, catching his with a look so utterly salacious that he had to shut his eyes to it.

'Witch,' he whispered tightly. 'Do you want me to take you here where anyone could walk in and catch us!'

Her hands jerked away from him; she was horrified because she was suddenly aware of how easily she had slipped back into the old Madeline ways, driving him further than any decent woman had the right to do. 'No,' she whispered, and wrapped her arms around herself as a shudder of self-contempt rocked through her.

As if he sensed what she was feeling, Dominic was suddenly behind her, his own arms coming to cover her own, hugging her back against him. 'I want you, Madeline Gilburn, ex-love of mine,' he murmured huskily against her hot silk cheek. 'Any way I can get you. I've never stopped wanting you. The new Madeline, the old Madeline—any Madeline I can have will do, so long as she is *my* Madeline!'

She quivered, too, too susceptible to the passionate possession in his words to refuse. 'You and I, this time,' he promised. 'You do know what I'm saying, don't you? I'm talking about us trying again. Being whatever we want to be to each other, no family intervention, no arm-twisting, no outside collusion—understand?' She nodded, and was rewarded with his mouth feathering heatedly across her cheek. 'You won't let me down?'

She shook her head. No, she thought bleakly, she wouldn't let him down. It was, after all, only what she wanted herself. Dominic was right, and the four-year-long separation had made not an ounce of difference to this— this madness which was their passion for each other.

'I'll be there,' she promised. And he let out a long breath, his body relaxing behind her.

It was gone three in the morning by the time Madeline led her saddled horse from the stall and took the frisky mare over to the hard-packed soil before mounting her and turning her in the direction of the river.

The rest of the house was asleep at last. The grey stone walls looking cold and bleak against the murky April darkness. They had not returned from the Prestons' until an hour ago, and, exhausted, everyone had drifted immediately to bed—except for Madeline.

She had paced her bedroom, trying to analyse her feelings for Dominic, worrying if she was doing the right thing meeting him, telling herself it was pure folly to make herself vulnerable to him again, and battling to subdue the delicious clamour of anticipation she had not allowed herself to feel in years.

They had stayed away from each other for the rest of the evening, she sticking closely to Perry and Dominic to the lovely Diane. But that didn't mean they weren't excruciatingly aware of each other every second. Wherever she looked she seemed to find the fierce glitter of his eyes on her, keeping her senses heightened, and reminding her of her promise.

The turf was hard beneath the horse's hoofs, pounding out an even beat as they galloped across the open countryside. A low ground mist enveloped everything in a soft skirt of billowing white. She was making for the river, and the closer she got the thicker the mist became, until by the time she entered the wood it swirled in and out of the tall trees, leaving its silvery cobweb patterns on the low growing shrubs. She let Minty pick her own way through the dry undergrowth, unable to see the way herself through the mist, taking it slowly, trusting the horse to take her where she wanted to go.

She saw Dominic's black mount as she came to the edge of the clearing and urged Minty carefully forwards. A hand came out from nowhere, grasping the reins and making Madeline gasp in fright. 'It's OK,' Dominic's deep quiet voice soothed her. 'Let me lead you,' he said from somewhere inside the swirling mist.

He tethered the horse next to his own, then reached up to help her dismount, his hands firm about her waist, pulling her against him before lowering her booted feet slowly to the ground.

'I wondered if you would come,' he murmured huskily. 'I worried that you might change your mind.'

'I said I would,' was all she said, and he nodded, accepting what added up to a small rebuke. For all her faults, Madeline had never gone back on her word once given.

Dominic stepped back from her, and the mist closed in between them. Startled by how quickly it had blotted him from her view, she put out a hand in search of him.

'Not the ideal morning for this.' She heard him laugh softly. 'Still...' Her hand was taken and she felt herself being drawn towards him until she could see his face again. He was smiling, mouth crooked. 'One can't be too choosy in this country,' he mocked.

'A typical April,' she smiled, tensely joining him in the small joke.

'Thick mists and heavy ground frost,' he sighed as he pulled her gently beneath the warm crook of his arm. 'Not Boston, hmm?'

'No,' Madeline agreed. 'Not Boston.'

'Come on.' He hugged her closer, leading her to the big black bulk which was the old boathouse, having to lean his full weight against the creaky old door to get it to open.

His smile when he turned it on her was full of rueful whimsy. 'Welcome to my humble abode,' he drawled, offering her a mocking bow. 'Please step this way, ma'am.'

'Oh!' She gasped in surprise as she stepped inside and saw the light from a flickering oil lamp hanging from the old oak rafters, lighting the thick red blanket spread out on the boarded floor. On top stood a bottle and two fluted wine glasses. 'Charming,' she complimented, pulling off her warm woollen gloves and shoving them into the pockets of her thick sheepskin coat. 'Champagne?' she quizzed, wrinkling her nose at him enquiringly.

'Breakfast,' he improvised. 'Here…' Taking her arm again, he led her over to the blanket and invited her to sit down using the boathouse wall to lean against, then joined her, groaning ruefully as his sparse behind made contact with the hard floor. 'I think I'm getting too old for this!' he complained.

'But not for drinking champagne on a cold and frosty morning?'

'Oh, never too old for that, I hope.' He reached for the bottle.

The cork popped, and Madeline made a mad grab for the glasses, laughing as she held them quickly beneath the frothing wine. In minutes they were sitting huddled into their warm coats with the boathouse wall against their backs and their shoulders rubbing against each other as they drank.

'Like old times,' Dominic murmured after a while.

Madeline turned wide eyes on him; they looked larger than life because she had a black woollen hat pulled closely around her ears. 'We never actually did this before,' she said.

'Well...' He gave a small shrug, his smile warm and teasing. 'Almost like old times, then,' he amended. 'Remember the time we punted up the river and got ourselves tangled in a salmon poacher's net?'

'My,' Madeline recalled, 'but you were angry that day.' She remembered the way he had almost overturned the boat as he yanked the poacher's net out of the river.

'My, but I was,' he mocked the loose accent.

She glanced quickly at him to see if he was deriding her, then dissolved into soft laughter at his teasing expression. 'Don't be cheeky!' she scolded, then gasped when she found herself pulled across his lap, their faces very close, the teasing gone, to be replaced by something far more disturbing.

Her soft sigh fanned his face, and his did the same to hers. Without taking his eyes from hers, he lifted his glass to her lips, and Madeline drank, the bubbles fizzing on her tongue. Without having to be prompted, she offered him her glass and watched, with breathless fascination, him sip and slowly swallow.

Their eyes remained locked on one another as silently they fed each other wine, nerves beginning to tingle while they told each other things they dared not put into words. Overhead, the flickering flame from the oil lamp played across his lean features, his satin-black hair, his eyes, not hooded but lazily engrossed, his lips, wet with wine and wearing the sensual softness of a man anticipating what was to come. She smiled gently at him, and struggled to pull her hand out from where it was trapped between their warm bodies so that she could dip her finger in the champagne then stroke it across his mouth, the finger trembling as his lips trembled. Then he caught the finger in his mouth, and sucked it delicately. Her stomach turned over and secreted a warm, stinging heat to her loins. Solemnly, Dominic returned the gesture, slowly circling her parted lips with champagne before allowing her to take it into her mouth.

Her eyelids lowered, the sensation of that smooth-textured pad against her tongue holding her languid with pleasure. Then he was taking the glass from her hand, and placing them both aside, and still they remained like that, Dominic leaning against the boathouse wall, Madeline cradled on his lap, their faces close enough to read every expression on the other.

Tension began to build between them, a deliciously warm kind of tension that centred itself low down in her stomach and slowly inched its way outwards. Her pulses quickened, her breathing with it, and she felt the muscles in his thighs begin to tighten, heat fanning out from both of them.

'Madeline...' he murmured, then reached up to pull the hat from her head. Her hair tumbled down, wild and free, just how he liked it, and his hand was burrowing into the thick silken mass, cupping her head and slowly—painfully slowly bringing her mouth up against his own.

He tasted of champagne, his breath warm, face cold and clean-smelling. She found the parting in his coat and ran her hands inside it, exploring his rock-hard ribcage beneath the fleecy check he was wearing. A shaky sigh broke from him, sheer pleasure at her touch, and she sighed too, against his mouth, this kiss threatening none of the angry passion of the night before, yet just as poignant, making its own special kind of statement like a pledge.

Her head was resting in the thickly padded hollow of his shoulder by the time he drew his mouth from hers. 'I'm not going to seduce you here,' he said quietly, reaching inside his coat to capture one of her hands so that he could tangle his own fingers with hers, bringing it up to kiss her knuckles one by one. 'And it would be a seduction if I were crude enough to make love to you here, on a cold bed of wood and coarse blanket.' His eyes ran intently over her face, for once completely free of the sophisticated masks it usually wore these days. 'It will be a soft bed and silk sheets for you, Madeline, my love,' he promised huskily. 'But I'm going to touch you,' he added darkly, 'touch you and caress you until you can't think of any other man but me. And not because of any barbaric desire to inflict my own will on you, but because I just can't help myself.'

He covered her mouth with his own again, slowly, luxuriously almost, deepening the kiss, and Madeline let him move at his own pace, too aware of the times before when she had inflicted her needs on to him. His hands drifted inside her coat, fingers lightly feathering along her blouse until they found her breasts, and she let out a soft sigh of satisfaction as he began stroking lightly.

Their coats formed a warm cocoon around them, their mouths drinking deeply of each other. Outside the birds were just beginning to waken, their spasmodic bursts of song barely impinging on the cosy little world inside the boathouse. A horse whinnied, its bridle jingling as it tossed its head, and the kiss broke reluctantly apart.

'More,' she demanded, not even bothering to open her eyes, her kiss-moistened lips parted and ready.

'Patience,' he admonished, and shifted their position, gently laying her down on the blanket so that he could lean over her, and he began parting the buttons of her shirt. She shivered as the cold air hit her exposed skin, bringing her lashes flickering upwards to find him gazing at her with black burning eyes.

'No bra,' he said.

'Not for you,' she answered, bringing his gaze up to clash with hers.

It was such a telling admission, one which sent a light tremor rippling across his resting body. Unbreathing, they gazed at each other for a long beautiful moment, feeling and allowing the tension to build between them until it played like static on the surface of their skin.

Then his eyes were back on her breasts, those thick curling lashes of his fanning his cheeks as he studied her lazily, the full firm mounds with their darkened circles and hard, tight, inviting nubs trembling a little as they moved in rhythm with her quickened breathing.

His own shirt parted quicker than hers had, his fingers fumbling with the buttons and dragging the two pieces of fleecy cloth apart to expose his own deeply tanned and muscle-packed chest covered in a thick covering of crisp black hair.

Features taut now with the control he was forcing on himself, he came over her and lowered his naked chest on to hers. Tiny darts of pleasure shot out in all directions, making her gasp and him groan.

'Wonderful,' he sighed, and she watched with an inner thrill his lashes close over his eyes in pleasurable response. 'You have no idea how much I've wanted to do this,' he murmured thickly, burying his face in her warm throat, 'feel your skin against my own.'

'You said no seduction,' she reminded him.

'Trust me,' he urged. 'I know what I'm doing.'

His eyes closed again. Madeline watched the taut sensual line of his mouth soften, part and turn slightly to cover hers, and allowed her own eyes to close. Dominic knows what he's doing, her brain chanted soothingly to her, and curled her hands inside his shirt. As the kiss deepened, her hand had already found the tight male nipples nestling in their bed of crisp black hair...

Her head was resting on his arm, cushioned from the hardness of the wooden floor. Their breathing becoming more laboured as the minutes ticked by. They could have been all alone in the world for all it mattered. Just the two of them, with Dominic caressing her breasts with the light pleasing touch of his hands, one jeans-clad thigh pressed between her own and moving in a slow tormenting rhythm along her inner thigh.

Several times they stopped kissing just to gaze at each other. No words; they didn't seem necessary. As Dominic had said, he was in control of things. This was no seduction, just a beautiful loving they had shared many times in the past. Often here, by the river, sometimes in his apartment above the bank. Soon he would stop, as he always had, before things got really out of hand. Soon he would begin to withdraw, gently soothe her back to earth with his hands and his mouth, murmuring the same words she still recalled from years ago. 'We have to stop now, we have to stop.' The chant played languorously in her mind. 'We have to stop....'

But he didn't stop. Quite when Dominic had lost control of the situation she wasn't sure, but it was the zip sliding down on her jeans that alerted her to the fact that he was taking this further than he had ever done four years ago.

'Dominic?' she whispered uncertainly.

'It's all right,' he assured her tightly. 'I just want to touch you, Madeline. I need to...' The words trailed away on a broken sigh as he eased the jeans away from her hips and slid his hand between her thighs.

Lightning struck the throbbing core of her being, sending her into a convulsion of gasps. And suddenly he wasn't so slow and languid, but tight with urgency, his mouth hard on her own, his skin burning hot where he pressed down upon her, his fingers drawing a cry from her as she felt her body quicken, become engulfed in wild liquid heat, and she was thrown into a spiralling world she had never visited before, tumbling down and down with no control over herself or the feelings rocketing through her.

She cried out his name in sheer fright, her fingers clinging to him, nails digging into the sweat-sheened skin at his shoulders. She heard him mutter something, then those tormenting fingers sent her flying over the edge while he leaned over her, watching the rapturous torture convulse her body, his eyes bright and black with impassioned triumph.

When it was over, he pulled her to him, cradling her against the warmth of his body, rocking her to and fro as if she were a baby in dire need of comfort.

'My God,' she gasped when she found the air to do it. 'Why?' Bewilderment threaded her tone, her eyes wide and staring at the rickety old ceiling above their heads. He rolled away from her, covering his eyes with his arm, but Madeline could see the self-contempt in the tight line around his mouth.

'I'm sorry,' he muttered.

'Sorry!' She sat up, dizzy with the drunken aftermath of what he had just done to her, and confused as to why he had done it. 'Dominic—what was the difference between what you've just done and making love to me properly?' she demanded in a strangled tone.

'You're still a virgin.'

'I'm—what?' Anger surged up from nowhere, brought on, she suspected, by the sheer shock of what had just taken place. 'Y-you mean you've just put me through—that—because you think I'm still a virgin?'

That brought his arm away from his eyes, the guarded look in them overlaid by a sharp question. His face was pale, the tension in him clenching his lean frame.

Madeline climbed to her feet, her body trembling as she angrily straightened her clothing. Humiliation and embarrassment stung along her body; she had never felt so ill-used in all her life!

'You used to hate it when I stopped too soon before,' he explained. 'I didn't want to disappoint you this time.'

'And what you did just now was supposed to make me feel better, was it?' She sent him a bitter glance, 'Well, let me tell you how I really feel,' she muttered on a burst of fury which had been building over four long frustrating years. 'I feel used! Used and manipulated! As I always did when I was with you!'

'Madeline, I—'

'I want to be loved, not relieved!' she choked. Tears were burning at the back of the throat and her eyes and she looked away from him. 'Loved, and wanted so desperately that you wouldn't be able to stop no matter how hard you tried!'

'I didn't want to stop,' he put in gruffly.

'But managed it anyway.' The short laugh was more a cry of scorn as she fumbled to do up her shirt buttons with fingers that trembled badly. 'As always,' she went on self-condemningly, 'it's Dominic who plays the tune and Madeline who dances to it!' she scoffed at herself, then shuddered in sickening self-disgust. 'You always did only have to touch me to have me panting for more, didn't you?' she accused him and viciously mocked herself.

'It wasn't like that,' he sighed out wearily, sitting up to run an angry hand through his hair. 'It was never like that.

You were so young then, Madeline! Just eighteen, dammit!'

'And now?' she challenged shakily. 'What am I now, Dom—four years older and therefore eligible for the next stage in sexual titillation?'

'Don't be so damned crude,' he grunted, lurching grimly to his feet. 'You enjoyed what we just shared, Madeline, and you know it.'

'But we didn't "share" anything!' she cried, the tears spurting to her eyes again on a fresh burst of anger and ravished pride. 'We never did "share", and that's just my point! You manipulated me to suit your own ends four years ago and you're still trying to manipulate me now!'

Four years ago he had held her on a knife-edge of mind-blasting sexual frustration with his clever hot-and-cold tactics. Then, when she'd inevitably toppled over the edge, he'd had the absolute gall to be appalled by her! And this morning he had done the exact same thing, fooling her into that mad, crazy, beautiful experience only to blow cold on her yet again.

She couldn't stand it. Not again. She should not have come back. She should never have set foot inside England again until she'd worked Dominic Stanton right out of her system with however many lovers as it would have taken to do it! But instead she'd held them all off, and secretly dreamed of Dom, of his touch of her skin, of his kisses and caresses.

God, she felt sick. Sick with herself and with him. 'I don't wish to see you again,' she said as she pulled her thick coat around her. 'Not in this way, anyway.' Her gaze did a cynical run of the old boathouse. 'You aren't good for me, Dominic. You rob me of my self-respect. You always did.'

'And what do you think you did to me?' he threw back harshly.

'I made a fool of you,' she said. 'And do you know what?' she added. 'For the first time in four years of feeling guilty about it, I've just come the conclusion that you damned well deserved it!'

CHAPTER TEN

'EVERYONE has accepted,' Nina remarked from the elegant secretaire where she sat shuffling through the replies to her wedding invitations. 'Including all the Stantons,' she added with smiling satisfaction.

'And so they should,' Edward Gilburn gruffed, 'considering the way you went over there and flannelled around them all.'

'I did not flannel!' Nina protested. 'I just thought it was best to give them all their invitations personally since they had to know that everyone else received theirs weeks ago.'

'And very right it was, too,' Louise put in, soothing her daughter's ruffled feathers.

'Did you see Dom?' Madeline couldn't resist asking the question, but hated herself for doing it.

But she hadn't seen or heard from him since that awful scene at the boathouse over a week ago now. And the pained sense of loss she was experiencing felt as desperate as it had done four years ago.

'Dom said he would be delighted to come to my wedding,' Nina answered her.

Madeline waited, with bated breath, hoping that Nina was going to tell her that Dom asked after her, but she added nothing else, and on a sudden fit of restlessness she got up and walked over to stare out of the window. When she'd told Dom they were no good for each other, she had been right, she decided. These awful feelings at wretchedness were just not worth it.

'Did you know old Major Courtney passed away last year, Maddie?' her father said suddenly.

'No!' she gasped, turning around to stare at him. Major Courtney had been the local recluse, living in his tumble-down old house for as far back as Madeline could remember. The house and the man fitted together somehow. It didn't seem right that he would be there no longer.

'So who's living in the house now?' she asked, oddly resenting the idea of anyone else but the major being there.

Her father shrugged. 'Nobody in their right mind,' he scoffed. 'It was common knowledge that none of his relatives wanted to live there. After all, they didn't give a hoot about the old major or his house. But someone seems to have taken it over—although it never actually came on the open market,' he added thoughtfully. 'There have been builders in there for months now doing it up. You wouldn't know it, Maddie,' he said. 'It's had a new roof, and all the black and white wooden facers have been renovated. Whoever it is who's bought the place, they're spending a small fortune on it—fools. I wouldn't want to live there if you paid me to!'

I would, Madeline thought yearningly. I would have loved to buy the place and bring it back to its former glory—make it look just like that picture she'd seen hanging in Dominic's den. She let out a soft sigh, turning back to stare out of the window at the bleak cold day beyond. Years ago, when she and Dom had been a pair, she'd used to make him drive past just so she could gaze at the crumbling old place. Why she felt this affinity with it she'd never really understood.

'I bet ghosts go around it clanging rusty old chains with their heads tucked underneath their arms.' She heard her own voice, filled with relish, echo back at her through the years.

'While ladies in miserable grey robes go sailing mournfully by?' Dom had suggested mockingly.

'Why not?' she'd pouted, then quivered expressively. 'Mmm, what a lovely atmosphere to live in!'

'You gruesome creature,' Dom had exclaimed.

'I may take a walk over there this afternoon,' she pondered out loud.

It would give her something to do. This last week had seemed endless. Endless—endless...

'Missing Perry already?' her father remarked, completely misreading the wistful sound in her voice.

Perry had returned to Boston a couple of days ago, not even trying to hide his disappointment in her. 'You didn't even put up a fight against him,' he'd accused her. 'He just crooked his little finger and you went running.' He'd seen her ride out that misty morning, and heard her return telling hours later. 'What has the man got that makes you so easy for him?'

My heart, she answered now, though she'd given no excuse to Perry. There hadn't been one. He was right and she had made it easy for Dom.

'Perry and I are just friends, Daddy,' she answered a little irritably. 'Good, close friends, but that's all.'

'Then it must be Boston you're missing,' he decided, studying her from beneath thoughtfully lowered brows. 'Because we certainly don't seem to be providing whatever it is you need to make you happy here.'

Quietly, with a nod at her daughter and a sympathetic glance at her husband, Louise got up and left the room with Nina.

'I'm fine,' Madeline said, hearing the other two go with a rueful little smile playing about her lips because she knew just what their exit meant. They'd all had enough of her moping aimlessly about the place, and her father meant to get to the bottom of the reason for it. So she took in a deep breath and turned to smile at him. 'It isn't Boston, or Perry that's bothering me,' she assured him. 'It's just that I feel...' What did she feel? she wondered helplessly.

That was it, she realised with a grimace. She felt helpless. Helplessly in love and helplessly—helpless to do anything about it.

'You know what you need?' her father said, eyeing her sagely. 'You need something to fill up your time. In Boston you worked in that interior design place Dee spends all her money in—what was it called?'

'Shackles,' she provided with a small smile because he was looking disapproving, and not because his darling daughter had taken herself a job, but simply because poor Dee had got her that job instead of himself.

'Stupid name for a shop,' he muttered. 'But,' his eyes lit up with a sudden idea, 'there's no reason why you couldn't find a similar post here—or even better,' he added, leaning forwards in his chair with enthusiasm. 'We could set you up with an interior design shop of your own, right here in Lambourn—or Reading if you prefer!'

Her dark head shook apologetically. 'You need some formal training to set up a place like that, Daddy. I'm just not qualified to open up my own place.'

'Only because you pulled back from going to art college because of Dominic Stanton,' he said with gruff censure. 'But that doesn't mean you haven't got it in you to do the job! Or, if it comes to that, go to university and get your degree now!' Her expression brought the gleam of challenge to his eyes. 'Why not?' he demanded. 'You got good grades in your A levels, and you wouldn't be the only student to take on further education several years late! Why not, Maddie?' he insisted when she still looked reluctant. 'There is nothing to stop you after all!'

Nothing at all, she agreed, turning away again so that he wouldn't see the depression weighing heavily on her features as her thoughts went inevitably back to Dom. Finding herself still vulnerable to Dominic had put a stop to any idea she might have had of remaining here in England.

'I'll think about it,' she offered as a salve. 'After the wedding. I'll think about it then.'

'Maddie, dear...' It was only as he spoke that she realised her father had got up from his chair and come to stand beside her. 'Is it still Dominic Stanton?' he asked, oh, so gently.

Tears spurted into her eyes, and she blinked, unable to answer, even though she was desperate to offer a reassuring no.

'We were all so damned pleased when you two got together four years ago!' he sighed out heavily. 'And I know we all have our own bit of blame to carry around for the way we pushed you both at each other. Louise warned me—she warned all of us that we should leave you alone and give you time to explore your feelings for each other. But we—James Stanton and I—we were—'

'Daddy.' Madeline turned, placing her fingers over his lips to stop him, her eyes bright with unshed tears. 'Please don't,' she whispered. 'I love you very dearly, but please—please don't?'

His sigh was warm and shaky against her resting fingers, then he was gathering her into his arms and hugging her in the same way he had done all her life.

'Go for your walk,' he suggested gruffly after a moment. 'It will help clear your head.'

She was standing in the hall pulling on her sheepskin coat when the telephone in the study began to ring, she

heard her father's voice answer, and was just turning away
when his head popped around the study door.

'Oh,' he said, sounding faintly disconcerted, almost disappointed that she was actually there. 'I caught you, then.
It's—it's for you,' he informed her gruffly. 'Dominic,' he
added, cleared his throat, hesitated a moment longer than
walked off briskly down the hall toward Louise's private
sitting-room while Madeline stared blankly after him.

She found her feet dragging as she went into the study
and closed the door. The plain buff receiver lay off its rest
on her father's desk, his gold-rimmed spectacles lying at
right angles to it.

Dom was on the phone was all she could think, staring
down at it. Dom was on the phone and wanted to speak
to her.

Her hand was trembling as she picked up the receiver
and carried it to her ear. 'Hello?' she murmured, then
closed her eyes while she waited for the seductive beauty
of his voice to wash over her.

There was a pause, as though he was no longer certain
he wanted to speak to her, and her heart began to thump
heavily in her breast. 'Dominic?' she whispered prompt-
ingly, having to bite down hard on her bottom lip to stop
herself begging him not to ring off.

God, she thought wretchedly. This is awful! Much much
worse than it had been the first time around. She was shaking all over, even her knees were trembling, like her breath
as it left her agitated lungs.

'I want to see you,' he said, and the husky tone in his
voice told her he was finding this just as difficult as she
was. 'I've been away,' he added quickly. 'I only got back
an hour ago or I would have rung sooner. Will you meet
me somewhere this afternoon?'

'I...I was just on my way out, actually,' she said, saying

the first thing that came into her head because the relief at hearing his voice was so violent that she'd gone light-headed with it.

'Linburgh's gone back to Boston,' he stated curtly, as though he believed Perry was the only reason she would ever step out of the house.

'Did I say otherwise?' she asked, blinking in bewilderment.

'Will he be coming back?'

'I… Well…' She frowned, not seeing the relevance of the question. 'Not until Nina's wedding, no,' she answered honestly. 'But I don't see what Perry's movements have to do with—'

'I would say they have a lot to do with everything,' he cut in gruffly. 'I have something for you, something I promised you once. Will you meet me, Madeline?'

Something he'd promised her? Her frown deepened as she tried to think what in heaven's name it could be? 'Where?' she asked, and closed her eyes again in the hopes that doing so would shut out Perry's voice telling her how easy she made it for Dom. 'He just crooked his little finger', he'd said. And he was right.

'Were you about to go anywhere special?' he countered curiously.

'Just for a walk,' she admitted. 'I was on my way to take a look at the old Courtney place. My father has been telling me that someone is having the old place renovated, and I thought I would like to take a last look at it before it changes beyond all recognition.'

There was a short silence, then, 'It's a bit early in the year to go crab-appling, isn't it, Madeline?' Dominic murmured softly.

Despite the tension in her she had to smile at that. In her young day, she'd used to find nothing more exciting than making secret forays into the major's orchard to steal from his overgrown and neglected fruit tree. It wasn't the fruit that drew her there, but the sheer exhilaration in knowing that if the old man caught her he would think nothing of threatening her with his loaded shotgun. He had never actually fired it, of course, but in those days she had been impressionable enough to believe he might.

'You, of course, were never young,' she mocked him drily.

'Once,' he confessed wistfully. 'A long, long time ago before a black-haired witch with dangerously alluring eyes cast her wicked spells on me and turned me into a very old man.'

The growing smile began to ease some of the strain out of her face. 'Have you any idea who bought the house?'

'Haven't heard anything on the grapevine,' he answered. 'Are you riding, or driving?'

'Walking, actually,' she informed him a little defensively, knowing she was revealing more of her present mood than she would like. April was being its usual seasonal self and blowing up crisp cold winds from the north which were likely to bring rain with them, the dark clouds rolling in from nowhere to drop their icy load before rolling onwards again. And Dom would be well aware that she had decided to walk simply because she couldn't resist battling with the unpredictable elements.

'I'll meet you there in about an hour, then,' he said, and put down the phone.

Madeline stared at it, wondering pensively just what she was doing agreeing to meet him when she knew it would bring her nothing but pain. Then she happened to glance sideways at the mirror hanging above the old marble fireplace, and she knew why she had agreed. It was all there in her face, shining like a damned beacon for anyone to read if they wished to. Her eyes were glowing, her mouth had taken on an upward curl, and she felt happy, alive for the first time in over a week. And that was why she was going to meet him, because he was the only person on this earth who could make her feel like this.

Dominic's car wasn't anywhere to be seen when she arrived in the driveway to Courtney Manor, and she paused, gazing along the tree-lined driveway to where the old house stood, still looking charmingly rickety despite the amount of work which had obviously been done to it already. As her father had said, the roof had been completely replaced, and the black and white facer beams no longer wore the yellow-grey tinge of age and neglect. The rustic bricks, too, had been neatly repointed, and the tall chimney stacks had been straightened out. Madeline tipped her head to one side in an effort to put them back as she remembered them.

'There was a crooked man who bought a crooked house,' she murmured softly to herself, recalling the time she had chanted the rhyme at Dominic.

The wind gusted suddenly, blowing her long hair across her face, and she had to take a hand out of her coat pocket to push it away again, her gaze darting up to one of the upper diamond-leaded windows when she thought she'd caught a glimpse of a face there. But there was no one. Could it be haunted? Her eyes skimmed the upper windows once again but saw nothing, and her smile went awry. She always could think herself into a state of high drama for no other reason than because she enjoyed it.

No self-respecting ghost would even want to haunt this house in the state it was in now!

She began walking down the drive, eyeing with some deep inner pleasure she had never been able to explain the small-framed leaded windows with their thick black-painted wooden lintels above and below them. The front porch had a new shiny coat of black paint on it, its high-pitched slate-covered roof built at the same steep angle as the main roof to the house. It was supposed to be empty, and there were signs that major work was still in progress in the several types of heavy machinery standing idle in the drive, but she could just make out what appeared to be curtains hanging at some of the windows, and whoever had bought the place was obviously very close to moving in.

Hands dug deep into her coat pockets, she moved closer until she was standing in front of the deep porch, and let her curious gaze skim slowly over the downstairs windows before she decided that, since she had come this far, it couldn't hurt to take a tiny peek inside a few of them. Moving cautiously, tentatively almost, she stepped on to the newly turned flowerbed just below the closest window and peered inside.

It was impossible to tell what kind of room it was since the light today was not very good and the tiny windows had not been designed to let much light in, but there was just enough light to tell her that, far from being ready for habitation, the inside of Courtney Manor had a long way to go yet.

Stepping back, she began walking slowly around the house, pausing to peer into each window as she reached it. Around the back, the garden was still overgrown and wild. Once upon a time there would have been a well stocked kitchen garden here, then the orchard beyond it leading right down to the edge of the river, but it had all become so badly overgrown now that it was impossible to tell where garden finished and the orchard began.

The old coach house and stable block appeared barely touched as yet, and she guessed by the huge padlock chained to the doors that the builders must be using them as storerooms for now.

The back door was big and old, reached by several cracked and very worn steps, to one side of which were the moss-covered steps to the basement. The windows here were too high for her to see through, so after a wistful scan of the rear view of the house she made her way around the front again, feeling an odd heaviness of heart as she paused there for a final long look.

'Try the door if you like. It is unlocked.'

Madeline yelped, fright rippling along her spine as she spun around to stare in the direction the voice had come from.

Dom stood just a few yards away from her, his dark hair blowing in the strong wind.

'What a stupid thing to do!' she cried, anger flaring with the sudden rush of adrenalin to her system.

'Did you think I was the major's ghost?' he grinned, not in the least bit penitent.

'Where did you come from?' she asked, glancing around in search of his car.

'It isn't here,' he murmured, correctly guessing what she was looking for.

It was only as her eyes came back to him that she realised that he was not wearing a coat. In fact, he was standing there in just black trousers and a thin white shirt. It hit her then with a disturbing thud.

'It's your house, isn't it?' she said. 'You're the one who's bought this place.'

He sent her a mocking little smile then let his eyes drift away from hers to run over the improved frontage of his latest purchase. The wind was getting stronger, rippling the thin fabric of his shirt against his chest, disturbing the cluster of black hair at the open V where the buttons were left casually undone.

He looked oddly very alone standing there like that, with his shoulders hunched slightly against the cold and his hands pushed into the pockets of his trousers. The cold was etching out the strong bone-structure of his face, paling his skin a little, making his hair appear blacker, his eyes darker.

'It looks like rain,' he murmured suddenly, returning his gaze to her. Then slowly, uncertainly almost, he lifted a hand towards her. 'Let's go inside,' he suggested gruffly, 'and I'll show you around.'

A fleeting vision of how that outstretched hand had last touched her came shuddering into her mind and she had to close her eyes on the violent upsurge of feeling she experienced, her own hands clenching tightly in the pockets of her sheepskin coat, shame at her own wanton behaviour drawing in the corners of her downturned mouth.

'Come on.' Suddenly he was beside her, the hand gentle on her arm, and she opened her eyes to find him standing right in front of her, his taut expression telling her that he knew exactly where her thoughts had taken her off to. 'Come on,' he repeated, low and gruff, and the hand slid up to her shoulders, drawing her close into the side of his body as he turned them towards the front door of the house.

They entered together, Dom moving only slightly away from her so that he could close the door behind them, shutting the sharp cold wind outside—and closing them in.

Met by the sudden silence, Madeline stood very still with Dom's arm warm about her shoulders. She was barely breathing, her senses tuned exclusively in to him, and she had to force herself to take in her surroundings.

They were standing in a large square hallway on a very

old stone-flagged floor which would probably once have been the main room of the house where an Elizabethan family would have eaten off a huge refectory table, and sat in the evening by a blazing log fire set in the grate of an enormous stone and timber fireplace which almost completely dominated the central wall of the house.

It would have been cold and draughty, and, with the wind blowing from a certain direction, probably engulfed in smoke from the fire. But it was all here in this big almost ugly reception hall—the history, the sheer romantic excitement of wild and wicked Elizabethan living. And Madeline knew that if she closed her eyes she would be able to summon up the ghostly apparitions of swashbuckling men, and women draped in velvet and ermine laughing and joking, uncaring of the discomfort of their surroundings, their voices ringing against the solid stone walls and up the heavy wooden staircase which hugged another wall, curving up to the galleried landing above.

'There is a crystal chandelier to go back up there,' Dominic said beside her, noting the way she was staring up at the age-blackened beams of solid oak which spanned the crudely plastered ceiling. 'It was so filthy that we didn't know what a treasure we had until we got it down. Superb thing,' he murmured with quiet satisfaction. 'It's being professionally cleaned and restored at the moment— along with a whole lot of other old treasures we discovered beneath the centuries of dust once we began looking.'

'Poor major,' Madeline murmured sadly. 'If everything was in such a poor state—how did he live with it?'

'Sheer cussedness, I should imagine,' Dom said with a wry smile, then, 'Actually, the few rooms he seemed to use in the house were all kept in a surprisingly pristine condition. The library, for instance.' He moved away from Madeline to go and open a door to their left. 'He seemed to live, eat and sleep in here, poring over his old books and papers—most of them military. They, like everything else in the house, have been taken away to be restored and valued.'

Madeline was frowning as she went to join him at the open door, her footsteps echoed on the cold flagged floor as she went to join him at the entrance to a big, surprisingly well lit room literally lined with empty bookshelves. 'But surely the Courtney family would have emptied the place of anything valuable before you bought it from them? I mean,' she murmured in puzzlement, 'if some of the stuff in here is as old as you say, it must be worth a fortune!'

Dom just shrugged. 'I offered them a good price for the lot,' he informed her dismissively. 'And they—indifferent fools that they were—accepted it. Morons, the lot of them.' His derision was obvious. 'It's no wonder the major had nothing to do with them. They cared nothing for the old man or his belongings. And all they wanted was the best price they could get to have the whole thing taken off their hands. I gave it them and they accepted it. It was their loss and my gain.'

'Speaks the hardened banker,' Madeline mocked his dismissive shrug.

'Speaks a man who abhors neglect, whether it be of a human being or his possessions,' he corrected. 'By the time I've finished with this place, it will look exactly as it would have done if the old man and his house had not been left to rot alone.'

Looking up at him, Madeline saw that the mask of disgust was tinged with something else she couldn't quite recognise. 'And you'll enjoy filling it with all those weird and wonderful curiosities you've been gathering about you all your life.'

That brought a crooked smile to his face. 'Of course. This house is the ideal setting for them, don't you think? Come on.' He reached for her hand. 'I'll show you the rest of the place.

The house was much larger than it looked from the outside, with an interesting hotchpotch of oddly shaped rooms all with at least one outstanding feature to fire Madeline's artistic mind into action, and within minutes they were discussing how best to decorate and furnish without spoiling the period flavour of the house. The work still in progress on the ground floor was extensive, but as they moved up to the first floor Madeline could see that up here was almost ready for habitation.

'We've been working from the top down,' Dominic explained. 'And the workmen moved off this floor only last week—which is why we keep the doors up here all tightly closed.' He reached out to open one of them and stepped inside, drawing her with him. 'Though this is the only room that's completely finished. The master bedroom,' he announced with an oddly mocking little bow.

'Oh!' she gasped in surprise, moving away from him to go and stand in the centre of a thick-piled dusky-pink carpet. Her eyes were wide with surprise as she turned in a slow circle, so shocked that she didn't know what to say, his colour choice in here nothing like she would ever have expected a man like him to choose.

The room was dominated by a ceiling-canopied four-poster bed built of rich mahogany and draped with heavy silver and dusky pink brocade. It was huge, outrageously flamboyant in the way the brocade looped and twisted its way around the thick wood frame. The mattress itself was covered in a reverse match of the same fabric, its size alone enough to intimidate, and she glanced jerkily away

from it to stare at the incredibly ornate mahogany fireplace
that took up almost all of the wall opposite.

The room was big—big enough also to accommodate
two big and comfy-looking armchairs flanking the fireplace, again upholstered with a matching blend brocade,
like the windows and the several lamps dotted about.

'Well,' Dominic prompted when she had stood there for
a good long minute without uttering a single sound, 'what
do you think?'

Think? A hard lump formed in her throat. It was a beautiful room. But a room so obviously designed to share with
a woman he must love deeply that she felt the lump melt
into tears and had to turn away from the intense expression
on his face, so that he wouldn't see just how deeply she
was affected. This room was suggesting so much—so very
much that she was actually afraid of what would come
next.

A silence fell, throbbing tensely in the air between them,
and, unable to stand it, she made to turn away towards the
window, only then she saw it, the gold-framed painting
hanging above the fireplace, and her body shivered to a
breathless stop.

'I promised to give this to you once, remember?' He
came to stand close behind her. 'The painting recently, and
the house a long, long time ago, when your dreams
were…well, just dreams and I was happy to play along
with them. Well…' His hands came upon her shoulders,
fingers closing gently, warming her all the way through to
her very heart. 'The painting—the house. They're both
yours, Madeline. My gift to you.'

'Oh, Dom,' she whispered thickly. 'I can't take…'

Suddenly his arms were around her, stopping her words
and crushing her body as he hugged her tightly to him.
'Once, what seems a lifetime ago now,' he murmured, his

deep tone throbbing with an emotion she felt echoing inside herself, 'a beautiful and enchanting creature I loved very much offered herself to me with all the passion in her loving nature, and I, fool that I was, turned her down.'

A hand jerked to her mouth to muffle the sob which leapt to her throat, and Dominic sighed unsteadily. 'Wild, Madeline,' he remembered gruffly. 'My God, you were wild then. I hardly knew if I was standing on my head or my feet most of the time. And I wanted you so desperately that it took every bit of my control to keep things as light as I did. And even that was taking things dangerously close to the edge.' The sob escaped and he bent to brush his mouth across her cheek. 'You were very young, my darling. And everyone kept telling me how lucky I was, and teasing me about how I was going to handle the wild and wilful baggage you were then. No one bothered asking how I was going to handle myself!' His harsh sigh vibrated against her resting spine. 'Every time I so much as looked at you my heart flipped over!'

'Dom—' She tried to cut in on him, her own voice thick with tears, but he wouldn't let her.

'Let me say it all,' he insisted. 'I wanted you so badly, Madeline, I was tormented by the need. But there they all were, all those pleased and interested people, reminding me of how young you were, advising me to take care with you, remember your age, your sweet, sweet innocence, warning me not to break that wonderful spirit of yours with too much too soon!' Another sigh ripped from him. 'Then there were the others,' he went on. 'The ones who questioned the wisdom of marrying myself to someone so young and headstrong. The ones who questioned whether you were old enough actually to know your true feelings for me—and they made me question it myself, forced me into an agony of wondering whether I was being fair to you to trap you into marriage when you'd barely even tasted life to be really sure of what you wanted from it— or from me come to that.'

'I knew,' she whispered.

His smile was sensed rather than seen. 'I could have been just another new and exciting experience to you, Madeline,' he suggested grimly. 'You have to remember how your life then was full of the need to try out new things. I began to worry that once I'd let you learn all I could teach you about love and loving you would need to be off, finding something else to soothe that frighteningly restless spirit of yours... What I'm trying to say to you, Madeline, is that I didn't dare risk making love to you before we married because I was so afraid it would mean my losing you!'

'You didn't trust my love.'

'No,' he admitted.

'And so lost me anyway.'

'Yes,' he sighed, then turned her around to face him, his eyes dark and sombre as he studied her upturned face. 'Well, now the tables are turned, and it's for me to do the offering and your chance to refuse me. If I kiss you now, and pick you up and carry you over to that big bed over there with the deliberate intention of making love to you, will you have me, Madeline?'

The silence hummed between them, tension springing along her nerve ends to hold her mute and still. Dominic looked down at her with a dark intensity which told her how absolutely serious he was, yet still she hesitated. The old Madeline would have thrown her arm around him by now, giving him his answer with kisses and wild ecstatic cries. But this Madeline had learned the art of caution, and rarely stepped into anything without being absolutely sure of its outcome.

'You want me, you know you do,' he muttered huskily when she still said nothing, her blue eyes full of her uncertainty. 'We're both four years older, Madeline. And if those four years have taught me anything besides misery and loneliness and self-contempt, then they've taught me that love, true love, endures any span of time. I love you, Madeline,' he stated solemnly. 'I think I probably always have. I know I always will. Will you please let me show you just how much?'

His voice broke and Madeline trembled, her pale face crumbling with emotion as she fell into his arms. 'Oh, Dom!' she choked. 'I missed you so!'

'Thank God.' He caught her tightly to him.

Their mouths fused and within seconds they were lost in each other. No more words, no gentle patience, the fierceness of their hunger taking them towards the big waiting bed on steps punctuated with powerful kisses and mad flurries of activity as they took the clothes from each other's bodies.

By the time Dominic pushed her down on the bed and followed her, they were naked and trembling with eagerness. Only once did he moderate his desire to a more controllable level, when their bodies, hot and burning, drenched in the sweat of love, were ready to join, and he eased himself away a little and caught her restless face in his hands, demanding she look at him.

'Pain and pleasure, Madeline,' he said thickly, his eyes black with passion and nostrils flaring at the control he was placing on himself. 'It has to be.'

'You know I haven't—?'

'You couldn't. I couldn't. We belong to each other.' And as she trembled at the full meaning of his words, he lowered his mouth back to hers, and slowly began the ultimate thrust of his hips which would unite their bodies.

He caught her soft cry of pain with his mouth, savouring it, holding her still beneath him until he felt her tension begin to wane, then he was moving fiercely, the moment of temperance gone and the full violence of their shared passion driving them to the ultimate victory, a mutual shattering of everything earthly, leaving only the spirit, stripped and vulnerable to attack. It was a woman's right to yield to the superior strength of her man—and a man's karma to have his very soul laid bare to the woman he impregnated with his need.

CHAPTER ELEVEN

MADELINE was over by the window, watching the rain pour from a storm-blackened sky, the wind lashing it against the leaded glass almost obliterating the view beyond.

Dom lay watching her from the bed, the sheet drawn down low on his hips, his body still languid from the slumber he had just woken from. His eyes were lazily enjoying the picture she presented, dressed only in his discarded shirt, her long legs bare, and her hair, that wonderful glory of black silk he so loved to smother himself in, rippling down her back in a tangle of soft glistening waves.

'What's so interesting out there?' he questioned after a while.

'Rain, rain and more rain,' she sighed, still staring outwards. 'I do hope it improves before Nina's wedding.'

'It will,' he assured with all the optimism of a true Englishman. 'Come back here to me, Madeline,' he held out his hand to her. 'I'm missing you.'

She hesitated only a moment before going to curl herself up against the warmth of his muscled body. She tucked her head into the warmth of his throat and Dominic's arms closed comfortably around her.

'I love you,' he said softly.

'I know.' She placed a kiss on his throat, but her mood was subdued, brooding, her arms folded tightly across her shirt-covered breasts.

'Hey!' Dom lifted his head from the pillow to frown at her, her strange tone making his heart miss a beat beneath her resting cheek. 'What's the matter? What's wrong, Madeline?' he demanded brusquely.

'I wish—I wish... Oh, Dom,' she sighed, suddenly stretching up to wind her arms tightly around his neck. 'I don't want to ever leave you again! I don't want to leave this house, this room—I don't want all those people out there spoiling things for us a second time!'

'They won't,' he assured, holding her tightly to him. 'We won't let them come near us if you don't want them to!' He was frowning in angry confusion at her sudden and unexpected flight into anxiety. She was actually trembling with it, her tears damp against his throat. It hadn't occurred to him that the old Madeline was back with a vengeance, wild passions and fears alike.

'But they'll know,' she choked. 'They'll have to know, and then it will all start up again. The teasing, the interfering advice. They'll be questioning your sanity in taking me on again, and warning me not to make the same mistakes a second time! And—and then all the taunts will start, the reminiscences of how it was between us the first time around, and what fools we made of ourselves, and—and before we know it we'll be fighting instead of loving, and it will all turn sour!'

'No, it won't,' he stated grimly. 'Because we won't let it. Listen to me!' he commanded. 'We'll get married. Now, tomorrow, as soon as I can arrange it. We'll get married and lock ourselves away in this house where none of them can get at us if that's what you want!'

'Marry? You mean you actually want to marry me?' She sounded so sincerely shocked that Dominic shook her.

'Of course I want to marry you, you bloody fool!' he growled.

'You don't have to, you know,' she told him softly, beginning to smile because she was suddenly feeling warm and safe and very loved, and the old Madeline way of flipping from one emotion to another had happened again. 'I'm quite happy to be your mistress. In fact it sounds a rather exciting thing to be, a man's secret mistress.'

With a jerk, he rolled her on to her back so that he could loom angrily over her. 'And if you think I'll accept anything less than marriage from you, then you can damned well think again! And stop smiling at me like that!' he growled, his blue eyes fierce.

'Like what?' she asked, her fingers coming up to stroke sensuously at his taut cheeks.

'Like the cat who's just pinched all the cream!'

'I love you, Dominic,' she murmured huskily.

'God,' he groaned, closing his eyes against the devilment gleaming in hers. 'I must be mad, getting myself involved with a teasing little witch like you.'

'I love you,' she repeated, and drew his head down so that she could shower his angry face with kisses. 'Love you—love you—love you.'

'Witch,' he muttered. 'I thought the new Madeline didn't go in for acts of sensationalism.'

'She doesn't,' she stopped kissing him to protest.

'Then what was that little scene you've just staged if it wasn't pure old Madeline sensationalism?' he grunted.

'Who is the new Madeline?' she grinned.

'Oh, God.' Dominic threw himself back against the pillows. 'Don't tell me,' he groaned. 'The new Madeline has scuttled back into oblivion.'

'Who has?'

'The—' He groaned again. 'I almost fell for that,' he smiled ruefully.

'Here,' she soothed, coming to lean over him, 'fall for me instead,' she offered and kissed his answer away.

It was growing dark when they eventually emerged again. 'God, what time is it?' Madeline sat up with a jerk.

'Time?' Dominic mumbled lazily. 'What do you want to know the time for? We aren't going anywhere.' He reached out to pull her back down to him.

'I have to get home!' she protested. 'They'll be worrying about me. God!' she added with dramatic horror. 'I told my father I would only be out a couple of hours! Let me go, Dom!' she pleaded when his arms only tightened around her squirming body. 'He'll have a search party organised if I—'

'No, he won't.' The words were muffled against the silken warmth of her throat, and his hands were already making sensual forays which had her senses quickening. 'I rang your home just after you left and spoke to your father. I told him I would be taking you out to dinner, so they won't expect you back for ages yet.'

'And what did he say?' she asked curiously, remembering her own conversation with her father only minutes before she left the house.

'He told me not to bother if I was intending to hurt his daughter a second time. And I told him that, far from hurting her, I hoped to convince her that I only wanted to love her—then I invited him to lunch next week to discuss the financial backing he was after and he—'

'Hey,' she interrupted. 'Back up a little will you?' she commanded, managing to break free from him so that she could sit up, looking like a wanton gypsy with her hair wild about her face and shoulders and her naked breasts standing pearly white against the darkening room. 'You informed my father that you intended to start courting me again?'

His eyes, which were lazily exploring her body now lifted grimly to her face. 'I tried the courting bit four years ago, Madeline. I have no intention whatsoever of going through that torment a second time.'

'So, what did you say to him? Did you tell him you owned this house?' It was odd, but she found she didn't want anyone knowing about this place. She felt safe here, sure of herself, of Dominic, but if the outside world began encroaching again she…

'No,' he said gently, reading her mind. 'No one but you and I and the builders who are working on it know who owns it.'

She was still looking anxious, and Dominic frowned as she quietly disentangled herself from his arms and climbed out of the bed. After a moment he followed her, a formidable sight with nothing to hide the sleek-muscled lines of his beautiful body. He took her in his arm and held her close. 'Madeline,' he said slowly, 'I told your father that I still loved you, and that I thought you still loved me. I told him I wanted to pursue that hope until we were both sure of each other, and I also told him that I didn't want any interference from anyone. He understood, I think,' he grimaced. 'Because, other than the one warning, he didn't try to put me off. Then I asked him if he had found anyone willing to back his latest ideas as yet, and when he said he hadn't I invited him to lunch next week so we could discuss it. The call finished quite amicably if a little restrainedly. But I think he already had a suspicion of how things were between you and me.'

'He asked me,' she admitted, 'just before I left today if it was still you.'

'And what did you say?'

'I said nothing. I couldn't lie, and I didn't really know the truth. I was still feeling hurt you see—over what happened at the boathouse.'

'I'm sorry about that.' His arms tightened around her.

'I set out with honest intentions, but before I knew where I was at the whole thing had got out of hand and I found myself with a wildly beautiful, utterly desirable and very aroused woman in my arms. Old memories stopped me from making love to you properly, but I knew it would have been nothing short of torment to leave you suspended on that kind of sexual high.'

'And what about your own sexual high?'

He just shrugged that away as if it didn't count. 'It wasn't new to me and I could handle it. And anyway,' he took hold of her chin and lifted it so he could look ruefully into her eyes, 'I wanted to spin you out of control. At that moment, it meant more to me than my own satisfaction. It felt a bit like stamping ownership, watching you, feeling you reach a full climax at my touch.'

'And you don't think I wanted—needed to see and feel the same response from you?'

He shook his head, his expression grim. 'I didn't so much as give that thought consideration until you pointed it out, and then I just felt ashamed, because while I was still playing sexual games with you as if you were still eighteen years old you showed me with your contempt how utterly inadequate I had been in response to the real emotion between us. The love.'

'And now what?' she buried her face in his shoulder, the uncertainties of the future still there to worry them. They had come a long way since they had arrived here this afternoon, so far in fact that she didn't know how she was going to breathe if it wasn't the same air he breathed also.

As if she'd spoken the words out loud, Dominic hugged her closer to him and murmured, 'I know, darling, I know.'

And she sensed a grim resolve about him, a determination to do what was right for them this time, no matter what that meant to anyone else. 'Just trust me, hmm?'

Nina's wedding day dawned bright and clear. True to its fickle nature, April had gone out on a clash of thunder and let May arrive on a blaze of fire.

Madeline climbed out of bed and stretched lazily. The last few weeks had placed an almost intolerable strain on her, what with the wedding arrangements heating up to today's boiling point, and her trying to keep her relationship with Dominic completely secret.

'I don't want to steal any of the limelight from Nina,' she'd told him. 'It's her day, and having all those gossips tittering about you and me would spoil things for her.'

'I can accept that,' he'd agreed. 'Anyway, I rather like having a clandestine affair with you,' he murmured, his eyes glinting wickedly down at her. 'You were born to do shocking things, Madeline, and I only wish we could do the shocking things going on in my imagination right now, but I suppose we can't.'

'You suppose right,' she'd said sternly. They were, after all, dancing as circumspect friends should do among a full complement of eager gossips.

That had been last night at the big dinner Louise and her father had thrown for close friends and relatives. The Stantons had come *en masse*, visiting the Gilburns' home for the first time as friends again in four years. Madeline had seen Dominic and her father slope off into his study halfway through the evening, and they had both returned smiling.

'He signed,' Dom had murmured to her as soon as he could speak to her later. 'We're equal partners on this one...I hope that damned nose of his hasn't let him down this time, Madeline,' he added drily, 'or I just may sink with him!'

'Is it that big a risk?' She had stared at him anxiously.

'Darling,' he had drawled, 'everything your father does is a big risk—having you for a daughter being the biggest one of all,' he'd added teasingly.

'I'll get you for that one later,' she'd warned him.

'I'll look forward to it.' His eyes had gleamed in a way that brought the colour pouring into her cheeks, so she'd stalked away, and half the room had looked from her to Dominic's smiling face and speculated on what he must have said to Madeline Gilburn to make her so angry. And Madeline had smiled to herself because only she and Dominic knew that it wasn't anger burning in her cheeks but excitement, pure anticipatory excitement.

Perry had arrived back last night just before the guests started arriving, driving down with Forman, who was playing a very wary kind of love game with Vicky.

Perry had taken one look at Madeline when she met him at the door and said, 'My God, I'll kill him!'

Blushing, her blue eyes alive with happiness, she'd gone into his arms for a hug. 'It's wonderful,' she'd whispered. 'But it's a secret, so don't tell a soul!'

'Are they all blind here?' He'd scoffed at her claim of secrecy.

'And what about you and Christina?' she had enquired gently, searching his hazel eyes for a glimpse of the same glow she knew she was displaying. It hadn't been there.

'It's funny really,' he had said musingly. 'I went to see her, determined to sort things out between us no matter what it took, then found it took nothing at all because one look at her and I saw her for the shallow, selfish, spoiled if beautiful little brat she actually is and thought to myself, Hell, Linburgh, you've had a damned lucky escape!'

Madeline had laughed in delight. 'What did you do?' she'd demanded with bright-eyed curiosity.

'I got the hell out of there as fast as I could—what do you think I did?' he had scoffed. 'God, it was a close-run thing, that,' he'd shuddered.

'Come on,' she'd linked her arm through his and given it a comforting squeeze, 'what you need is a glass of good Scotch whisky and some pleasant company to revive your jaded spirit.' And she had led him into the drawing-room where all her family waited.

'I'll vote for that!' he had exclaimed heartily. 'So long as there are no scheming females in there waiting to grab me. I'm off women at the moment.'

Not that this aversion had showed during the evening. Every time Madeline had looked at him he was charming some poor female or other, and neither age nor beauty came into it!

Her smile was wry now as she moved over to the window to check the weather. It was going to be a hectic day, she predicted, but at least when it was over she could relax. She and Dominic could relax.

Dom...just his name was enough to set her sense quivering.

These last few weeks had been the most wonderful passionate—nerve-racking weeks of her whole life!

By eleven o'clock you could have cut the tension in the Gilburn house with a knife. Vicky had arrived in her usual flurry of energy, turning a glowering look on Forman Goulding who, with Perry, was trying his best to merge with the wallpaper in the drawing-room.

'Had a fall-out?' Madeline asked as the two girls went upstairs together.

'The horrible man accused me of flirting with Perry the other night!' her friend scowled.

'Oh,' Madeline murmured. 'And I suppose you weren't doing any such thing?'

'Of course I—was,' she confessed. 'But since Perry was flirting with just about anyone wearing a skirt, I don't see what right Forman had to deny me my turn!'

'Go to it, baby!' Madeline mockingly enthused. Vicky was so obviously head over heels in love with the big American that she had to let off steam with someone or explode. Forman Goulding was a very cool and self-contained man.

'You've no room to mock,' Vicky threw back churlishly. 'I've seen the way you drool over my brother when you think no one is watching you!'

'And how does your brother look at me?' Madeline could not resist asking.

'The same way,' Vicky shrugged. She still suspected them both of having a secret affair, and hadn't forgiven either of them for not telling her about it. 'I hope you're both very pleased with yourselves,' she added huffily.

'Oh, we are,' Madeline murmured on a soft smile.

'What's that supposed to mean?' Vicky pounced like a hungry cat.

'Madeline, can you come and help me with this damned cravat?' To her undying relief, her father appeared at the door to his room, red-faced with impatience. 'What's the use of having a wife if she's never around when a man needs her?' he muttered. 'Hello, Vicky, dear.' He stopped grumbling to smile when he saw Vicky standing next to Madeline. 'Did your father get that magazine I sent over for him?'

'Yes, thank you, Uncle Edward.' The old endearment was coming easier each time Vicky said it. She had confessed to Madeline that no matter how she tried she could not call him Mr Gilburn; the formal title just simply stuck in her throat. She had been calling him Uncle for as far back in her life as she could remember. 'He said to tell you the article was just the one he wanted to read.'

'Huh, good, yes, well…Madeline, this damned cravat tie!' he growled to hide his embarrassment.

Adults, Madeline decided as she followed him back into his room while Vicky carried on down the landing to Nina's room, adults found it much harder to heal rifts than children did!

Louise's usual calm fell apart at the seams exactly ten minutes before the car was due to take her off to the church with Perry and Forman to accompany her.

It was seeing Nina dressed in all her wedding finery that did it, and when she began sobbing into her handkerchief Madeline ushered her quickly out of the room in case she upset Nina, who had been amazingly calm until now.

'She looks like an angel!' Louise sobbed. 'A sweet little angel!'

'Which she is,' said Madeline calmingly. Then to herself—Thank God I shan't be put through all of this!

'What if Charles has changed his mind?' Louise jerked out half hysterically. 'What if he doesn't turn up at the church and leaves my baby—'

'No, Louise!' Madeline cut in sharply. 'You know that won't happen. Why, knowing Charles, he's been camping outside the church since nine this morning just to make sure he gets his prize!'

In her raw silk suit of hyacinth-blue, Louise managed a thick laugh, and, relieved to see her regaining her control, Madeline quickly led her down the stairs and handed her over to her father with an expressive glance heavenwards for deliverance when she caught Perry's amused eye.

'OK,' she said bracingly as she entered Nina's room. 'Panic over…how are you feeling, poppet?'

Not long now, she thought wearily. The strain of it all was beginning to make her head ache.

The church organ struck up a traditional bridal march and Nina stepped forward on Edward Gilburn's proud arm, her gown of softly flowing pure white silk whispering on the carpeted aisle as she went. Madeline walked behind with Vicky, their matching gowns of rich cream silk doing different things for their contrasting colouring. She spotted Dominic immediately, standing in a pew next to the aisle. He turned to smile at her just as Charles turned to smile at Nina, and as she passed slowly by him their hands brushed, fingers briefly tangling and untangling in a single smooth movement, but it was all she needed to make her glow inside, her heart swelling with happiness and contentment as she stepped forward to relieve Nina of her pretty bouquet.

'Dearly beloved, we are gathered in the sight of God...'

The wedding service began, and Madeline closed her eyes, listening to the words, silently repeating the vows, pretending to herself that this was her wedding-day, and that it were she and Dominic standing there in front of the altar having their union blessed by God.

Long, tiring hours later, Dominic came up behind her and slid his hands around her waist, drawing her gently back against him. 'How much longer before we can get out of here?'

Her hands went up to cover his where they lay against the flatness of her stomach. 'Not long now,' she assured him. 'Nina is due to go and get changed. When they've left, we'll slip off quietly. I do so want to be alone with you, Dominic,' she sighed out wistfully.

He pressed her closer to him until she could feel that hard imprint of his body against her back. 'Me too,' he murmured huskily. 'I've had enough of all this secrecy, darling. You looked so beautiful today, I wanted to shout out in church that you belong to me. I love you, Madeline.'

'Don't, Dominic,' she pleaded with him, glancing quickly around the room to see if they were being observed. But everyone's attention was on the bride and groom who were dancing their final dance before leaving the celebrations.

'Do you remember that last time we were all together in this room?' Dominic murmured suddenly. 'You came in through those doors, Madeline, wearing that exquisite lime gown, with your hair billowing about your shoulders and your eyes huge and frightened in your too pale face— and my heart stopped dead as I looked at you—you looked so hauntingly, tragically beautiful!'

Louise and her father had decided to hold the wedding reception at the country club because it was far better equipped to deal with the hundreds of guests they'd invited. Madeline's gaze took the journey she remembered taking that fateful night four years ago, and she sighed quietly.

'You were very angry with me, as I recall it.' She smiled a little sadly at the memory and leaned closer into the comforting frame behind her.

'I was a lot of things that night, Madeline,' Dom stated a little grimly. 'I was angry, yes, but I was also seething with the jealousy that seeing you in that young swine's arms filled me with, frightened by what was happening to us both—and so damned enchanted by you that I couldn't even control myself enough to leave you alone. Perhaps if I had, things wouldn't have got so out of hand as they did. By the time I took you on to the dance-floor, I felt so battered by my emotions that I just let rip with them.'

'We made a terrible scene that night,' she recalled.

'We certainly did,' he agreed. 'I don't think I've ever felt so ashamed of myself as I did afterwards,' he added grimly. 'But there you were, a tragic vision at my feet in billowing silk, your beautiful head bowed in abject remorse and—dammit, Madeline, but I could have sworn you were mocking me!'

A smile touched her beautiful mouth. 'I was,' she said, as she went to pull away from him. 'Look, Nina is ready to go and change. I'd better—'

'What do you mean, you were?' he demanded, grabbing her wrist to stop her running away.

Madeline turned, her dark hair twisted elegantly on the top of her head, the Edwardian style of her cream silk gown giving her that air of majesty the people here in Lambourn had been forced to acknowledge as part of the new and dauntingly sophisticated Madeline over the last six weeks.

But the smile she laid on Dominic was old Madeline to the core. 'You didn't think I would let you get away with all those insults you'd thrown at me without giving you something back by return, did you? Trust your instincts where I'm concerned, my darling,' she wisely advised. 'They're invariably right.'

'You were mocking me!' he growled.

'Of course,' she drawled, blue eyes mocking him even now. 'I'll see you later, hmm?'

'Then why did you run away afterwards?' He wasn't about to let her go until she'd told him everything.

Madeline levelled thoughtful eyes on him for a moment. He was angry with her, and she hadn't wanted that, not tonight. Tonight was supposed to be special. Their night—their secret night. 'Because,' she said quietly, very quietly, 'I knew you would never forgive me for that last trick. It was just too public—even for a bad Madeline trick.' Her mouth twisted in a moment of self-contempt then straightened again. 'You told me to grow up, remember? So I went away to do just that, and grow up I did.'

'But I'd forgiven you by the next morning, dammit!' he rasped. 'It was myself I had difficulty forgiving, not you!'

Without either of them being aware of it, Dominic's voice had risen, and already several people were glancing curiously their way, seeing another Stanton-Gilburn scene was in the making.

Then Madeline heard someone groan out an, 'Oh, no,' and recognised Vicky's pained voice.

Her eyes lifted pleadingly to Dominic's. 'Dom...?' she sighed in tired warning.

His gaze flicked impatiently around the suddenly quietened room, seeing what Madeline could not see since she had her back to the groups of people all watching them, and he let out a short sigh as he brought his wry gaze back to hers. 'Tell me,' he murmured quite casually, 'are you the new Madeline tonight, or the old one—only sometimes I find it impossible to tell the difference.'

Madeline pretended to consider the question before answering. 'A bit of both, I think,' she decided. 'I have been for several days now.' Her blue eyes teased him gently. 'It's almost as if the one sort of blended in with the other, one dark and stormy afternoon about two weeks ago, and since then I have difficulty myself trying to separate them.'

He laughed, not loudly but in a soft, indulgent kind of way, 'Well, whoever you are, I think I should warn you that there is a small convention of Stantons and Gilburns making their hurried way over here.' Once again his eyes flicked to a point just beyond her right shoulder then came back to her. 'I'm afraid it's truth or consequence time, darling,' he warned her drily.

'Oh.' Her lovely face lost its teasing smile. 'I didn't want this, Dom.'

'Then come here to me, and let me deal with it.' The hand still clasping her wrist drew her back against him and twisted into a strong hand-clasp, and by the time their two families arrived in varying stages of concern and irritation Madeline was being held securely at Dominic's side, his arm bent possessively around her waist so that their clasped hands rested on the flat of her stomach.

Edward Gilburn glanced from one studiedly expressionless face to the other, then muttered angrily, 'What the hell do you two think you're doing?'

Madeline turned a brilliant smile on the apprehensive Nina. 'Hello, darling! Shouldn't you be thinking of getting changed quite soon?' Her smile shifted to Charles. 'You'll miss your flight if you don't hurry.' There was still a small chance she could divert this, she thought hopefully.

But Perry joined the group, his hazel eyes enjoying the fun. 'Problems, anyone?' he innocently enquired.

'Not if these two are kept at separate ends of the room, no,' muttered Vicky, glowering at them.

'You have to be kidding,' Perry laughed, glancing down at their clasped hands then up at Madeline with a faint enquiry. She glanced at Dominic, also in enquiry, and he smiled down at her in rueful defeat. She looked back at Perry, also in rueful defeat, and everyone else looked at them in growing bewilderment. 'You may as well get it over with, you know,' he advised softly.

'Get what over with?' snapped Vicky impatiently.

'But this is Nina's day,' Madeline reminded Perry.

'And Nina has had a wonderful day, haven't you, dear?' Perry enquired of that sweetly bewildered bride. She nodded mutely, afraid to say a single word and instead stepping back into the sure comfort of her bridegroom's arms.

Perry's eyes mocked the whole group. 'Look at their clasped hands, for God's sake!' he sighed out impatiently, but while everyone dutifully stared at their hands where the rich glow of gold mingled with the brilliant glitter of diamonds and sapphires, Perry was laughing into Madeline's and Dominic's rueful faces.

'We have an announcement to make,' Dominic said, and with the minimum of effort gained the full attention of the whole room. Madeline moved even closer to him, cheeks warming with a new and alluring shyness, and Dominic lifted their clasped hands to his lips, drawing her gaze up with them so that his eyes as he kissed her fingers showed her the burning depth of his love.

'Madeline and I...' he began, only to pause a second time, his smile taking her breath away before he gave his attention to their captive audience. 'Madeline and I....' he began all over again, his deep voice ringing out clear and proud across the silent room. '...married each other quietly a week ago...'

The low black Ferrari pulled up at the front of the old Courtney place, and Dominic withdrew the keys from the ignition and turned in his seat to look at the woman beside him. She was yawning, her head resting tiredly against the leather seat, eyes closed.

'Home,' he said with unbidden satisfaction.

'Mmm.' Her lips stretched into a sleepy smile. 'At least we didn't have to sneak off in the end.'

The news of their marriage had been supposed to be delivered by Perry after the celebrations were over and Dominic and Madeline had managed to make their escape. Things hadn't turned out quite like that.

A hand came to touch her cheek, gently caressing the satin-smooth skin so that her smile deepened into pleasure.

'Perhaps it was better that it turned out the way it did,' he pondered reflectively, 'even if we did succeed in causing yet another scene!'

'I suppose they'll blame it all on me,' Madeline complained. 'When this time, Dom, it was all your fault!' At last she managed to open her eyes so that she could glare at him.

He just smiled lazily. 'Sorry, darling.' The caressing fingers moved to her lips. 'I promise to make it up to you later.'

'We couldn't even manage to keep this place a secret,' she sighed.

'The house, you mean?' Dominic glanced into the darkness where the black and white painted house stood sheened by a silver moon. It still looked a rickety old place, even after all the work already done to it.

It had been Madeline's father who'd made the connection, turning to Dom with eyes turned as wicked as his daughter's as he murmured sardonically, 'Well, you must love her, Dominic, if you were willing to buy the Courtney place for her. Madeline always did love that funny old house.' And while the two men smiled ruefully at each other everyone else was gasping in horror, murmuring, 'The Courtney place? They're going to live in the old Courtney place?' as if they couldn't believe anyone with any taste could want to live there.

'It was only a matter of time before they eventually found out,' he pointed out, then, 'Come on.' He tapped her on the cheek. 'Let's go in.'

They met at the side of the car, Dom's arm going to rest across her shoulders as they stood staring up at the house. 'I'm sorry we don't have a resident ghost. It really does seem to need one,' he opined.

'And still could have,' Madeline declared with her usual

optimism. 'After all, what self-respecting ghost would want to live among the tip we've made of it?' She waved a deprecating hand meant to encompass the whole inside where the dust lay thick and heavy over virtually everything but their bedroom. 'They've probably taken a vacation until all the work is finished, but they'll be back.' She turned in her husband's arm to gaze up at him, her blue eyes shining with wicked humour. 'You mark my words, the moment the last workman leaves here, our ghosts will return—and they'll haunt you, Dominic Stanton, for seducing a poor innocent maiden like me!'

He laughed, pulled her fully into his arms and leaning back against the car so that he could study her mischievous face. 'You're the one who haunts me, Madeline,' he confessed ruefully, 'and have been haunting me since the day you cast one of your wicked spells on me in my own swimming-pool!'

'That long?' She blinked up at him, black lashes flickering over her bright, teasing eyes. 'My poor darling.' Reaching up on tiptoe, she placed a consoling kiss on his smiling lips. 'How ever did you survive it?'

'Oh, I didn't mind,' he drawled. 'I used to let her phantom make mad passionate love to me every night— I rather enjoyed it, as a matter of fact,' he added lightly. 'I think I may even miss her now I've got the real thing to make love to me.'

'You prefer fantasy to the real thing?' she cried.

'I suppose it all depends on how the real thing measures up to her phantom,' he drawled provokingly, moulding her soft body into the hardness of his own. 'I've barely had a chance to compare them as yet.'

'Your fault,' she instantly laid the blame. 'You wanted us to marry in the crazily unconventional way. In fact, you insisted on it.'

'I wanted you!' he corrected gruffly, and suddenly humour had left him and in its place was a man full of grim-faced passion. 'And this time I wasn't taking any chances. Time and people and our own stubborn natures were our worst enemies four years ago. This time I was determined to get you tied to me before anything or anyone could so much as whisper an opinion! But,' he added heavily, 'it was only as I watched Nina walk down the aisle in her lovely dress that I realised what I'd deprived you of. I had no right to rush you into that civil wedding; you deserved the same fuss and—'

Her fingers covering his mouth stopped him. 'We had a lovely ceremony,' she assured him softly, her eyes warm with her love for him. 'Just you and I making our vows to each other with no one to intrude on the beauty of it. I don't feel deprived of anything, Dom—except perhaps having you hold me in your arms for the seven lonely nights since we married.'

'Then we have a lot of making up to do,' he agreed as he bent and scooped her into his arms. 'So let's get to it!'

The big black door opened and closed behind them. No lights came on inside. They didn't need them; their love was all they needed to light their way.

Outside the moon shone down on the old Courtney place, bathing its black and white walls in a pale silver sheen—and suddenly it didn't look such a rickety old place any more, but more like the proud and elegant dwelling the artist had captured on canvas all those centuries ago.

And, as if it knew that with these two caring people it would one day look just as it had used to look, the house itself seemed to give a contented sigh and settle back into its foundations, happy in the knowledge that it was loved again at last.

Miranda Lee is Australian, living near Sydney. Born and raised in the bush, she was boarding-school educated and briefly pursued a classical music career before moving to Sydney and embracing the world of computers.

Happily married, with three daughters, she began writing when family commitments kept her at home. Miranda's first novel was published by Mills & Boon® in 1990 and since then, more than ten million copies of her books have been published worldwide.

Miranda likes to create stories that are believable, modern, fast-paced and sexy. Her interests include reading meaty sagas, doing word puzzles, gambling and going to the movies.

MISTRESS OF DECEPTION

by

MIRANDA LEE

CHAPTER ONE

'I PRESUME you'll be going to the wool fashion awards tonight?' Deirdre Carstairs asked her son over lunch.

'Unfortunately, yes,' was his cool reply.

'Why "unfortunately"? Fashion is your business, after all.' And your life, she added silently, and with some irritation. Alan had always been a workaholic, but lately he was worse than ever, sometimes working all night. One would have thought that establishing a chain of very popular off-the-peg menswear stores all over Australia, as well as personally running the manufacturing establishments to fill them, would have been enough. Now he was planning on branching out into designer clothes as well.

Deirdre suppressed a sigh. It was so difficult to tell Alan anything. He'd taken over as head of the family when he was only twenty, his father's unexpected death from a heart attack having left the family's clothes factory on the brink of receivership. Their home too had been found to be holding a second mortgage. Alan had had to work his fingers to the bone to pull them out of bankruptcy. But he'd succeeded, and succeeded very well. She was extremely proud of him.

The one unfortunate result of his success, however,

was that he'd become rather bossy. He expected people just to go along with whatever he wanted. It must have come as a considerable shock, Deirdre realised, when the one woman who'd managed to capture his heart had upped and married another man a few years back.

Her head lifted, eyes narrowing with suspicion as she watched her son forking his *fettuccine marinara* into his mouth. 'Is Adrianna going to be there?' she asked casually.

His shrug seemed non-committal, but he was a master at hiding his feelings. 'I doubt it. Her label hasn't been entered into the competitions. She rarely comes to Sydney any more.' He lifted his dark, glossy head, his very male but rather cruel mouth curving back into a wry smile. 'Stop fishing, Mother. The reason I don't want to attend tonight is because I'm tired.'

'Then don't go. Stay home here and watch it on television with your poor old mum.'

He laughed, and Deirdre wished he would laugh more often. Laughter lent some warmth to his coldly handsome face, and those hard blue eyes of his.

'Poor old Mum, my foot. You're not poor. *I've* made sure of that! And secondly, at fifty-five, you're not old either. Why don't you do me and yourself a favour and find some nice man to occupy your time? Then I won't have to put up with your trying to organise *my* leisure time for me.'

'Do you *have* any leisure time?' she remarked archly.

'Occasionally.'

'Heaven knows when. Or what you do with it.'

Alan's laugh was dry. 'Don't you worry about what I do with my time, Mother. I'm a big boy now.'

But Deirdre *did* worry about him. Since Adrianna's rejection, Alan had not brought one woman home. She didn't for one moment imagine her handsome son was celibate, but she shuddered to think he might be indulging in one-night stands rather than risk being hurt again. She did so want him to get married and have children, but she dared not broach the subject. He was very prickly about his private life.

'Will Ebony be one of the models tonight, do you know?' she asked instead.

'I dare say,' Alan returned in that same flat tone he always used when the subject of Ebony came up these days. Deirdre knew her son well enough to know that when he sounded his most calm he was, in fact, at his most annoyed.

It was a wicked shame, she thought, that their once close relationship had been ruined by money. Ebony was a sweet girl, but too proud in Deirdre's opinion. Fancy taking offence when she found out that her parents' estate had been negligible, and that Alan—as her appointed guardian—had generously, but quite rightly, paid for all her education and expenses. What had she expected him to do? She'd only been fifteen, after all.

Still, when the girl had discovered shortly after leaving boarding-school at eighteen that this was so, she'd apparently been most upset. She and Alan had

had some kind of altercation in the library over the situation, resulting in Ebony running to her room, crying. Deirdre had been unable to comfort her, the girl saying over and over that she had to leave.

At the time Ebony had been doing a grooming and modelling course that Deirdre herself had given her as a Christmas present that year. When the lady running the modelling course had recommended Ebony to a modelling agency, saying she had the potential to reach the top in that profession, the stubborn child had immediately dropped her idea of going to teacher-training college and had pursued a career that would start paying immediately.

She'd been an instant hit, on both the catwalk and behind the photographers' lenses, and it hadn't been long before she was giving Alan a cheque every week in repayment. Then, as soon as she'd been earning enough money, she had moved out of the house and into a flat of her own.

Alan had been furious, and had refused to speak of Ebony for a long long time. It wasn't till Deirdre had thrown her a twenty-first birthday party a little over a year ago that he had even deigned to be in the same room with her. Whenever she'd come to visit Deirdre on previous occasions, and Alan had been home, he would make some excuse to leave the house. This time, however, under threat from his mother, he had been civil to Ebony in front of the other guests, though far from pleased when he'd found out she was to stay the night. Forgiveness was not one of Alan's strong points.

The tension at the breakfast-table the following morning had been so acute that Deirdre had vowed never to ask Ebony to stay over again. It just wasn't worth it. But the ongoing feud was a thorn in her side. She loved the girl, thought of her as fondly as her own daughter, Vicki. Nothing would please her more than if her son and his ward made up.

'Don't you think it's time you and Ebony buried the hatchet?' she said with an unhappy sigh.

'I hardly think that's ever likely.'

'Why not? Maybe if you were *nicer* to her when you saw her, which you must do occasionally. You're in the same business.'

Alan's laugh was harsh. 'If I were *nice* to Ebony, she'd spit in my face.'

'Alan! She would not. Ebony's a lady.'

'Is she, now? Funny, I've never thought of her as such. A black-hearted witch, perhaps. But never a lady.'

Deirdre was truly shocked. 'Are we talking about the same girl here?'

'Oh, yes, Mother, we most certainly are. Your sweet Ebony has just never chosen to show you that side of herself.'

'I think you're biased.'

'Aye, that I am,' he agreed drily.

'What did you say to her that night in the library that upset her so much? I never could get the details of your argument out of her.'

Alan put down his serviette and rose. 'For pity's sake, Mother, that was nearly four years ago. How could I possibly remember? Probably told her she was an ungrateful little wretch, which she was. Now I must go. I have appointments lined up all afternoon with prospective designers dying to head my new Man-About-Town exclusive label.'

Walking round to peck her on the forehead, he strode from the patio into the living-room and towards the front door, an elegant figure in one of his own-brand business suits. Being six feet three and finely proportioned, Alan could have modelled his own products if he'd chosen to.

Deirdre watched him go with increasing unease. He was not happy, she decided, and, like all mothers, she wanted her son to be happy. She wanted both her children to be happy. Vicki seemed happy, living in a run-down house in Paddington with some artist whom she claimed to be mad about.

But he was the latest of a series of men she'd been 'mad about' during the past ten years. Anti-marriage and anti-establishment, Vicki had moved out of home when she was nineteen 'in search of her own identity', whatever that meant. Still, it was Vicki's life and she was supposed to be doing quite well, managing a record shop in Oxford Street, though she often dropped home to ask Alan for a 'loan', which he usually gave her along with a lecture.

Deirdre suspected, however, that Alan didn't mind giving his sister money—and advice—every now and then. He liked being needed. And he liked helping people.

'Mr Alan gone, has he?'

Deirdre sighed. 'Yes, Bob.'

He tut-tutted. 'That man works too hard. Have you finished too, Mrs Carstairs? Will I clear away?'

'Yes, do. It was lovely, Bob. You cook Italian like an Italian.'

The little man beamed, and began clearing the table, stacking up the plates with a very steady hand for a man pushing sixty. Deirdre watched him bustle off back into the kitchen, thinking to herself that he was another example of Alan's basic kindness.

Bob, and his twin brother, Bill, had up till two years ago lived on a chicken farm, with Bob tending to the household chores while Bill did the manual labour outside. Neither twin had ever married, both being very shy men. Their farm had been their life till the recession and high interest rates had sent them broke. Alan had spotted them being interviewed on a television programme on the day the bank was to repossess their property and evict them. Both men had broken down during the painful interview. It had torn Deirdre's heart out, making her cry.

When Alan had abruptly left the family room, she'd thought maybe he was upset too. And he probably had been. But, being a man of action, he'd left the room to telephone the station and start making arrangements to meet the elderly twin brothers. The upshot was Bob and Bill were brought to Sydney and installed in the Carstairses' home, Bob as cook and cleaner, Bill as gardener and handyman. Alan had even had the old servants' quarters fitted out as a self-contained flat for them. Both men thought him a

prince of the first order, and were devoted to his service. When Alan had casually mentioned one day that
he liked Italian food, Bob had raced out and bought
several Italian cookbooks with his own money.

Yes, Alan could do good deeds, but that didn't
mean he wasn't a difficult man. Deirdre hoped he'd
be polite to Ebony at the show tonight. Fancy his
calling her a black-hearted witch! Why, Ebony was
no such thing! She had always been such a sweet girl,
pleasant and polite to her elders. She was a little aloof
at times, but that was to be expected, given her background. Deirdre could not understand why Alan was
so hard on her…

Ebony came out on to the catwalk, tall and sophisticated in a black wool dress that was basically strap-
less but had a black lace overlay that went right up
to the neck and down her arms in tight sleeves. If the
intention of the lace was modesty, then it failed miserably.

Every male in the room snapped to attention as she
moved with a lithe, sensuous grace down that raised
pathway, her waist-length straight black hair draped
over one shoulder and her deeply set black eyes projecting a dark, mysterious allure from underneath
black, winged brows. Her wide, full mouth was
painted a deep scarlet in vivid contrast to her white,
white skin.

Alan shifted uncomfortably in his chair and looked
away. He needed no reminders of what she looked
like, or how easily she could bewitch.

'Geez, Alan,' the man seated next to him whispered. 'And to think you had *that* living under your roof all those years. How did you stand it, man?'

'Familiarity breeds contempt, my friend,' he returned smoothly. 'Besides, she doesn't look the same without her make-up on.'

'I'd like an opportunity to wake up in bed with her one morning and judge that for myself,' came the dry rejoinder. 'Still, from what I've heard, I'm not her type.'

Alan straightened in his chair. 'Oh? And what's her type?'

'Photographers, I gather.'

'Meaning?'

'God, Alan, don't you know anything about your own ward's life. Our supermodel is reported to have had a fling with all of her photographers so far. She and Gary Stevenson were a really hot item a couple of years ago before he took off for Paris. But he's back in Sydney now and has clearly taken up where he left off. I saw them myself only today, having lunch down at a café in Darling Harbour.'

'Is that so?'

'You don't sound concerned. Stevenson's a good deal older than her, you know.'

Alan tried not to bristle, but did, anyway. 'He's only in his thirties.'

'Closer to forty. And how old's your Ebony?'

'Twenty-two. And she's *not* my Ebony,' he bit out. 'She's a free agent. Now, can we watch the show?

We've paid two hundred dollars a seat for this ring-side table. Let's get our money's worth.'

Alan's colleague settled back in a disgruntled silence, leaving Alan forced to pretend to watch the rest of the parade. Ebony had been up and down a couple of times by now, and was sashaying back towards the group of models who were waiting their turn in front of the huge red velvet curtain. The highly sensual sway of her curvaceous buttocks and hips sent a cold fury into his veins.

Does she know what she's doing? he wondered savagely. Does she know I'm here?

Of course she does, came the bitter answer. She's a witch, a black-hearted witch!

God damn you to hell, Ebony Theroux.

He parked in the street opposite the three-storey square building that housed her flat, watching and waiting for her to come home. What he would do if she showed up with Stevenson, or any of her other numerous admirers, God only knew. Would he be able to meekly drive on? Or would he find some way to spoil her night, as she had already spoiled his?

He'd vowed after the last argument they'd had not to have anything further to do with her, *never* to come here to see her again. But he'd vowed that the time before as well.

His teeth clenched down hard in his jaw, his stomach muscles tightening. Would he never rid himself of this gut-wrenching desire? It had been four years now. Four painful, soul-destroying years. He really could not allow it to go on. He would have to do something about it.

But he'd said that before, as well.

A light snapped on in her flat, sending a wave of near-nausea churning through his innards. He hadn't seen her enter the building, anger at this crazy but uncontrollable desire having distracted him for a moment. Now, she'd slipped in without his knowing if she was alone or not.

He stared up at the square of light, his eyes darting left as he waited anxiously for her bedroom light to be switched on as well. That was a large window with gauzy curtains. If she had someone with her, he would soon know.

The light remained off.

After several tortuous minutes, he couldn't stand the waiting any longer. With an agitated, jerky movement, he extracted the keys from the ignition, not bothering to put the steering lock on, only just remembering to lock the door before swinging it shut. It was only when the bitter winter air cut through him that he remembered his overcoat draped over the passenger seat.

'Damn it!' he swore, and, ramming his keys and hands into the trouser pockets of his black dinner suit, strode angrily across the dimly lit street and up to the locked security door. For a moment he hesitated, self-disgust urging him to turn right round and go home. But other forces were at work, forces far stronger than pride. He jabbed the buzzer on flat eight with his finger.

His heart began to thud, disgusting him further. Why did he let her do this to him? Why?

'Yes?' came the low, husky query that sent a shiver down his hunched spine.

'It's Alan,' he said, despising himself.

'Alan…' she repeated as though trying to recall whom she might know called Alan.

He bit his tongue to stop himself from snapping at her. Male ego demanded he play her at her own game, keeping his cool, not allowing her any more triumph than was strictly necessary.

'What do you want, Alan?'

To strangle you, he thought viciously. God, but she liked turning the screw.

'For pity's sake, Ebony, it's bitter out here. Just let me in. Or aren't you alone?' he finished cuttingly.

There was a moment's tense silence from the intercom before a buzzing sound indicated she had opened the door. Alan hated himself for the rush of relief, not to mention the rush of something else that immediately stampeded through his body. But already he was on that treadmill of excitement that she could generate without any conscious effort. He couldn't look at her these days without wanting her so badly that it was a painful ache in his loins.

She met him at the door, still wearing that damned black dress. It was one of her contract conditions, that whenever she did a fashion parade she kept the clothes she modelled. The designers didn't mind. The fabulous Ebony wearing their clothes in public was great advertising, and cheaper than most.

'That dress looks even better up close,' he said in a desire-thickened voice.

She eyed him coolly over the rim of a glass of white wine, sipping while those black eyes stripped his soul naked. 'So you *were* there tonight,' she remarked casually, and, turning, began walking across the tiled foyer and into the living-room. Alan was left to come in alone and close the door behind him, following her as she wandered, glass in hand, into her strikingly furnished flat.

Alan glanced around the lounge-room and marvelled at the effect she had achieved with just a few pieces of furniture. Had she deliberately chosen white as a foil for her colouring, or in cold mockery of what white usually represented? He wouldn't put it past her. He wouldn't put anything past her.

She kicked off her shoes and curled herself into one of the squashy white leather sofas that flanked the mock-fireplace. A gas fire was softly burning, highlighting the blue-black sheen on that gorgeous hair as well as sending a warm honey glow to her complexion. She must have washed off some of that stark white make-up, he thought as his hot gaze travelled down her body and up again. Her mouth was still red, though. Red and softly pouting.

Alan swallowed.

Once settled, she threw an indifferent glance at him over her shoulder. 'Pour yourself some wine,' she suggested, and waved a scarlet-nailed hand towards the kitchen. 'The bottle's in the fridge.'

'No, thanks,' he said stiffly, hating her for the way she always made him feel so darned awkward.

She said not a word while she drank the rest of her wine, placing the empty glass down on the marble coffee-table with a small, shuddering sigh. 'Must you stand there like that with your hands in your pockets?' she said. 'You make me uncomfortable.'

His harsh laughter drew her eyes. 'Do I indeed? That's only fair, then.'

'Fair?' Those exquisitely shaped eyebrows lifted. 'What's that supposed to mean?'

'Nothing,' he muttered, and began walking slowly towards her. For a second he could have sworn he saw fear on her face. But just as swiftly, her expression changed to one of cool composure.

'I have my final cheque ready to give you. I'll get it.' She was up and past him before he could do more than breathe her perfume. Still, as the exotic scent teased his nostrils, he felt his loins prickle in instant response. It angered him.

'I did not come here for a cheque, Ebony. You know damned well I never wanted you to pay me back in the first place.'

Her smile was wry as she produced the cheque from a drawer. 'Ah, yes, Alan, but what *you* want does not always have priority in my life.'

'Meaning?'

Her eyes were like black coals, and just as hard. 'Meaning I want you to take this cheque and get the hell out of my life. I don't ever want to see you again. I'm going to be married.'

'Married!' Something exploded in Alan's head. She couldn't be getting married. He wouldn't let her. She was *his*!

'That's right,' she went on brusquely. 'To Gary Stevenson. He asked me today. He wants me to go back to Paris with him, and I'm going to.'

'I don't believe you.'

'Then I suggest you do, Alan. It's over between us. Over!'

'Is it, by God? I don't think so, Ebony. Not at all.' Snatching the cheque out of her hands, he ripped it into shreds before pulling her into his arms and kissing her till both of them were gasping for breath.

When she spun out of his grasp he caught her and yanked her back against him, one hand pressing her stomach so that her buttocks were hard against his arousal, the other wrapped around her heaving breasts. 'I won't let you go,' he rasped, his panting mouth against her ear. 'You're mine, Ebony. *Mine*!'

In a wild desperation, he started kissing her neck and stroking her braless breasts through the dress, the blood roaring through his veins as he felt the nipples harden beneath his hands. When he finally heard her groan, elation swept through him, steeling his sense of purpose, and his determination to win her total surrender one more time. Tomorrow did not figure largely in his mind. Nor the future. Not even her threatened marriage.

All he knew was that he had to have her naked beneath him, have her tremble as only she could tremble, have her take him to those places no other woman had ever taken him before.

'Alan, no,' she groaned again.

But it sounded like a yes to his impassioned ears. He had no mercy for her protests or her tears. He kept up the kissing and the touching till she gave one last shudder and whirled in his arms. Only then could he perhaps have seen the despair in her eyes, if he'd been capable of seeing *anything* beyond his own excruciating need. As it was, all he saw was that ripe red mouth, soft and swollen and seductive. He wanted to lose himself in that mouth, to have those pouting lips kiss him all over, to have them tease and torment his flesh till he could stand it no longer.

So that when she swept her arms up around his neck and pulled his mouth down to hers in a kiss far more brutal than any she'd ever sought before, his only thoughts were of what awaited him behind her bedroom door.

'I hate you,' she choked out when he scooped her up into his arms and carried her into that bedroom.

His blue eyes glittered in the semi-darkness. 'I love the way you hate, Ebony. Keep it up.' And with that, he dropped her on the bed and started stripping off her clothes.

CHAPTER TWO

EBONY woke the next morning knowing that she finally hated Alan Carstairs.

It had been a long time coming.

At fifteen, she had hero-worshipped him. At sixteen, she'd developed a full-blown schoolgirl crush. By seventeen, she was constantly fantasising about him, till finally, at eighteen, she'd made an utter fool of herself over the man.

She cringed at the still sharp memory of her throwing herself at him in the library that night four years ago, gushing with adolescent stupidity that he must love her if he'd paid for her out of his own pocket all these years. He hadn't known what had hit him when she'd upped and kissed him. How ironic that it had probably been his momentary but stunning response to that foolish kiss that had been responsible for what had happened three years later.

Oh, he'd stopped the kiss soon enough, well before he could have been accused of tampering with her morals. But the memory of his tongue thrusting deep into her mouth, of his arms tightening like steel bands around her even for a split-second, had been enough to keep fuelling her fantasy that underneath his bluster he loved her and wanted her.

And she'd naïvely told him so.

Of course, he'd torn strips off her at the time, telling her she was acting like a silly little fool, that his paying for her had been his way of showing gratitude to her father who'd once lent him money when no one else would, that he considered her guardianship a sacred trust that could not and would not be sullied by him, that his briefly kissing her back had been meant as a savage lesson on what could happen if a hormone-filled teenager like herself fell into the wrong hands.

She'd finally believed him that night, shame and embarrassment making her flee his presence. How she had cried and cried! Nothing Mrs Carstairs said—and the dear woman had tried everything—could make her stop. All Ebony had been able to think of was that she couldn't stay in that house, seeing Alan every day, reliving her moment of humiliation, living off his charity. She had seized on this last reason as an excuse to flee him, and his house, as soon as she could.

But she hadn't been able to forget him, no matter what she'd done. Hard work and a busy and varied social life had filled her hours, but not her heart.

Gary Stevenson had come into her life when she'd been a very vulnerable twenty. Still a virgin, despite her physical beauty attracting many admirers, Gary had become first her photographer, then her friend, and finally her lover.

Why had she given in to him and not the others?

He'd been good to her. Sweet. Kind. And one night he had caught her at a very weak moment.

Afterwards, there had seemed to be no going back. And in truth, she'd found much comfort in the human closeness of their affair, in having Gary hold her and tell her that he adored the ground she walked on. Oh, he hadn't pretended to really love her, which had been a relief in a way. His being in love with her might have made her feel guilty. But he'd liked her and desired her and, in the end, had even asked her to marry him. They would go to Paris together, he'd said, and become a raging success.

She had had to refuse, of course, and, though disappointed, Gary had not been heart-broken, taking himself off to Paris anyway while she had gone on with her modelling here in Sydney. For a while, she'd been very depressed and lonely, thinking she'd done the wrong thing. But then the unexpected had happened. Alan had become her lover, and she'd quickly found that what she'd experienced in bed with Gary had not prepared her for the intoxicating excitement and wickedly irresistible rapture of being in Alan's arms.

Which is why I'm here now, she groaned silently, and threw a pained look across at Alan's sleeping form.

God, why do I let him do this to me—take my self-respect and pride and grind it into the dust, make me say and do things when I know he doesn't love me? He told me the morning after the first night I slept with him. He loves Adrianna. What he feels for me is nothing but lust, an uncontrollably mad lust.

Ebony could still recall the horror she'd felt when

he'd told her that, and then added that he wanted to keep their relationship a secret from the world, and especially his mother. Their passion for each other would pass, he'd claimed. No need to hurt anybody with the knowledge of their liaison when it was only a fleeting thing.

Yet all the while he'd been saying this, *she* had been hurting. More than hurting—breaking into little pieces. She'd argued with him on this last score, wanting him at least to recognise in public that she was his woman. But no... People would not understand, he'd said. They'd talk.

So he'd kept her as a hole-and-corner mistress, to be visited in the dead of night, to be used for his pleasure in private while the world at large saw them as almost enemies.

And she had gone along with it, despising herself while counting the days till he came to her again, then vainly trying to salvage some pride by never showing any affection or special consideration towards him, by reducing his visits to nothing more than raw sexual encounters, with no love or warmth involved. There was a perverse pleasure in taunting him with her cold indifference to whether he came or not, in letting him think that there were plenty of other fish in the sea to fill her empty bed if he wasn't in it, in feeding his crazed jealousies that she might actually do some of the things she did with him with other lovers.

As if she would. Not even Gary had been able to coax such intimacies from her, or such abandonment. Only Alan...

Tears filled Ebony's eyes, but she dashed them away with the backs of her hands. The time for tears was long gone. Now it was time for action.

Last night had proved beyond the shadow of a doubt that she had no strength against Alan's sexual power over her. No matter how angry with him she was, he only had to touch her and she was lost.

And it would always be that way, she agonised. Love him or hate him, she was his for the taking whenever he wanted her. It was this mortifying realisation that propelled her not to change her mind from what she had already decided she must do—go to Paris with Gary.

Shivering a little, she slipped out of the warmth of the bed and dragged on her white bathrobe over her naked and vaguely aching body. She flushed guiltily to think it had been herself—and not Alan—who had been the insatiable one last night. Was it because she had known this would be the last time?

Probably. Even now, the temptation to return to that bed, to rouse him from sleep with her hands and lips, to…

A bitter taste filled her mouth. Maybe it was just that she needed to clean her teeth, or maybe it was the self-hate rising from within. Whatever, she suddenly felt unclean, wicked, rotten to the core. She had to get away from him, from Sydney, from Australia. That was the only answer.

Slipping quietly out into the lounge-room, she picked up her telephone and dialled the number she'd written on the notebook resting beside it.

'The Ramada,' the hotel receptionist answered.

'Could you put me through to Gary Stevenson's room, please?'

'Certainly, madam.'

Ebony's eyes flicked anxiously over at the bedroom door while waiting for Gary to answer. She hoped Alan wouldn't wake up. Instinct warned her she must keep her plans a secret. Alan must never find out, not till she was safely on that plane.

A bleary-voiced Gary finally came on the line. 'Hello.'

'It's Ebony,' she said quickly, huskily. 'I need to see you. This morning. Will you be in around nine?'

'Sure thing, love. What's the urgency? You've already turned me down. Again.'

'I've had second thoughts. Sort of.'

'Only "sort of"?'

'We need to talk.'

'I'm all ears.'

'Not on the phone.'

'Why not?'

She hesitated, then said softly, 'I'm not alone.'

Gary's chuckle was dark. 'So that's the way it is, eh? What's the problem? Won't he take the hint he's no longer wanted?'

'Something like that.'

'I see...' His sigh was weary. 'Well, get rid of him temporarily, love, and get over here pronto. If you feel as bad as you sound, then methinks you need a shoulder to cry on.'

A lump filled her throat. 'You're so good to me, Gary.'

'Yeah, yeah, all my exes say that. I'm a good bloke. But tell me one thing. How come in the movies—and I suspect in life—it's always the bad guy who ends up with the girl? Oh, never mind. I'll be here when you get here, love. See you.' And he hung up.

Ebony lowered the receiver silently back into its cradle, but, when she turned, there was Alan, standing in the open doorway, thunder on his face.

'You *can't* marry Stevenson,' he ground out. 'You don't love him.'

She glared at him, standing there in the nude, as arrogant as you please. And as lethally attractive. Not an ounce of fat graced his tall, lean body, a light covering of dark hair giving him a primitive appeal. Put a spear in his hand and he would make a good savage, she thought bitterly.

'How do you know?' she said, using her fingers to comb her tangled hair back from her face till it fell into a sleek black curtain down her back.

'Because you're incapable of loving any man,' he stated harshly.

Her short bark of laughter was half disbelief, half mocking. 'Certainly not a man like you!'

His blue eyes blazed for a second before adopting an expression of cold contempt. 'Then why keep going to bed with me?'

She shrugged. 'Perhaps I'm a masochist.'

'A hedonist, perhaps, not a masochist. You enjoy

pleasure, Ebony, not pain. And you can't deny I give you pleasure.'

'I wouldn't dream of denying it.'

When she moved to brush past him on the way to the bathroom, his hand shot out to enclose her upper arm in a vice-like grip. 'You can't go from me to Stevenson,' he rasped.

She locked eyes with him, aware of nothing but the emotional quaver in his voice. Could that be love talking? she puzzled briefly before dismissing such a stupid notion. No. Not love. Possessiveness. Jealousy. Male ego. But not love. Alan's heart already belonged elsewhere. If he had a heart, that was. She was beginning to doubt it.

'I have to talk to him,' she admitted, then added, 'I have to tell him personally that I'm not going to marry him.'

There was no way she could have mistaken the relief in Alan's eyes. But that didn't prove anything, except he wasn't ready yet to give up his private supply of free sex. Free in every way. Emotionally, financially and physically. What man would want to give up such a cushy arrangement?

When he went to draw her back into his arms, she yanked out of his grasp and took a step backwards. 'No,' she said coldly. 'I have to shower and dress. Then I'm leaving.'

'What happened to breakfast?'

'I'm not having any. If you want some, get it yourself.'

His smile was sardonic. 'So kind of you.'

'Oh, but I'm not kind, Alan. There again, you don't want me for my kindness, do you?'

'Hardly.'

'Then don't complain. You've got your way. I'm not marrying Gary. What more do you want from me?'

'Not a thing,' he bit out.

'Then if you'll excuse me?'

He watched her sweep into the bathroom, black anger in his heart. What more did he want of her? He wanted her to grovel at his feet, to beg him to visit her more often, to suffer from the same type of blind, obsessive need that was even now sending the blood pounding through his veins, making his flesh expand into a tight, painful instrument of torture.

Only an instinct that seducing Ebony this morning might rebound on him in some way made him put that solution to his frustration aside. All he could do was wait for her to leave and then he would plunge his pained body beneath the coldest of showers till he could comfortably face the day ahead.

Meanwhile he would dive back under the bedcovers and pass the time contemplating the many and varied ways he could exact vengeance on this creature who had been tying him in knots for years.

Yes, years!

Four, to be exact. He couldn't count the first three. She'd spent most of them in boarding-school. And while at fifteen she'd been a budding beauty, her shy, almost introverted nature at that time had protected her from male admiration, his own included.

Not that he would have dreamt of seeing Pierre's daughter in that light, especially at such a tender age. No, he was not guilty of that, thank God. Still, he remembered having enjoyed her company when he'd taken her on the occasional outing back then, finding her opinions surprisingly mature and her gestures of gratitude towards him quite touching. He actually still kept a pair of gold cuff-links she'd given him for his twenty-eighth birthday, after saving the money herself from delivering pamphlets during the school holidays.

Where had that sweet child gone to? he wondered. When had she turned from virgin to vamp?

A type of guilt twisted his heart. Surely it couldn't have been *his* fault, could it? That night, in the library... She'd caught him unawares, kissing him like that. For a few seconds he'd completely lost control. Hell, he could still recall how it had felt as her soft, breathless mouth had flowered eagerly open to accept the thrust of his tongue, as well as the way her heart had beat madly against his.

For a split-second, he'd wanted to forget his conscience and just drown in her delicious young body. He'd been tempted to take it for his pleasure and his pleasure alone, knowing he could seduce her virginal flesh quite easily, knowing he could mould and form her, body and soul, to his wants and needs.

She wouldn't have stopped him. He knew it. So in the end he had had to stop himself. He'd thought himself so right, so noble, so...good. He'd been made her guardian, for God's sake, not her corrupter. Not even her teenage declaration of undying love had swayed his determination to put aside such a wicked temptation. Not then, nor during the subsequent years as she'd gone from child to woman, from a shy and somewhat awkward teenager to a sophisticated and successful model, had he wavered in his resolve.

The crunch had come, predictably enough, at her twenty-first birthday party. He should have known seeing her on that occasion would be his undoing. It had been three years before, on her eighteenth birthday, that his lust had first raised its ugly head. Till then, he'd only ever seen Ebony in either her school uniform or shapeless jeans and tops. Teenage girls never seemed to wear anything else.

But that fateful night, his mother had bought her a white lace dress that might have been virginal on the peg. On eighteen-year-old Ebony, complete with make-up and high heels, it looked so seductive that it was criminal. When Alan had spotted her coming down the stairs, his heart had stopped beating. Not so the rest of his body. It had leapt with a desire so fierce and so instant that he'd been thunderstruck.

He'd stared at Ebony and she had stared right back, those deep black eyes of hers showing not a hint of understanding of what was happening to him. *Had* she understood? Was that why she'd been so shocked that evening in the library a few months later when he'd knocked her back, scorned her offer of love?

Maybe. Maybe not.

Ebony's thoughts and motives were a mystery to

him. *She* was a mystery. Sometimes he wondered if those three years of sacrifice had all been a wicked waste. Maybe at eighteen she'd already started on her sexual journey; maybe she hadn't been a virgin at all.

She certainly hadn't been a virgin three years later. And how!

There was no peace for his flesh as he recalled what Ebony had done to him the night of her twenty-first birthday. No peace at all.

She'd been a bit tipsy, of course, and the guests had left. But that was no excuse for stripping off all her clothes and blatantly going swimming in the pool in the nude in full view of him. She'd claimed afterwards she hadn't known he was there, but he didn't believe her. She'd been watching out for him all night, baiting him, tempting him.

Besides, there'd been no resistance whatsoever when she'd climbed out of the water and he'd come forward to draw her dripping nakedness against him, nor when he'd claimed her supposedly startled mouth in a hungry kiss. She'd been more than willing to let him touch her all over, to take her right there by the pool, to carry her back to his room where he'd worked his will upon her body all night.

Naturally, he *had* heard the rumours about her, but rumours about models were rife and not always true. For some inexplicable reason, he'd been reluctant to believe she could be as promiscuous as people said she was. He had found out that night that she was all that and more. Never had he known a woman so wild and wanton and willing. She was sex mad, he decided. Totally sex mad. Just like her father.

His first thought the next morning had been that he had to keep what had happened from his mother, as he'd kept from her the rumours about Ebony's private life. His mother thought Ebony a sweet, old-fashioned girl and he didn't want to destroy that illusion, or the close relationship the two women enjoyed.

Maybe he had explained it badly to the naked girl in his arms. He hadn't meant to hurt her, though he suspected he had. But what was to be gained by dressing up reality with false words of love? It wasn't as though she were an innocent, whose sensitive feelings had to be treated with kid gloves.

They lusted after each other. That was the plain and unvarnished truth. In a way, it was fortuitous that Ebony was of such a highly sexed nature, since not many women would have endured the kind of unrestrained lovemaking he'd insisted upon in an effort to rid himself of his own insatiable need. With a bit of luck, he might not need any repeat performance.

Or so he had deluded himself at the time.

Alan made a scoffing sound just as Ebony came out of the bathroom, made-up but not dressed. She was breathtakingly nude, the exquisiteness of her beauty stabbing at his heart. And elsewhere.

God, but Mother Nature had been cruel, sending a creature like her to torment him. Or was it the devil himself who had fashioned that incredible face and body? Yes, that sounded right. Who but Satan would be wicked enough to combine all those assets, to give

one woman everything that a man could possibly
want? Long, silken black hair that screamed out to be
stroked; exotic, thickly lashed ebony eyes that flashed
fire and promised pleasure at the same time; a full-
lipped smouldering mouth which would tempt a saint.
And that was only her face.

Her body was another dimension, another hell to
be endured. High, pointy breasts with large pink areolae and long, sensitive nipples, a delightfully tiny
waist, deliciously curvaceous hips and long, long legs
that wound their shapely way down to dainty ankles
and feet.

Then there was her skin…

What man wouldn't want to run his hands over her
skin, the pale magnolia-like skin whose texture was
like cool velvet, till it was heated by desire. Then it
would glow. It was glowing now. But not with passion. With the heat of the shower. Her eyes were cold
as they raked over him.

'You still here?' she said scathingly.

He gnashed his teeth as she went about dressing in
front of him, first drawing on a silk black teddy, then
sliding into a black woollen jumpsuit.

Black was Ebony's trademark. She wore nothing
else, modelled nothing else. So was her lack of smiling, her full lips looking far better fashioned into a
sullen, sulky or seductive pout.

Alan would have thought that such restrictions
would have been disastrous to her career, but, surprisingly, it had all worked in her favour, creating an

individual and highly sensual image that kept her and her agency busy.

'I have to go, Alan,' she said briskly, popping on black pumps before picking up a black holdall and heading for the bedroom door. Only then did she stop for an indifferent look at him over her shoulder. 'Lock up when you leave, will you? And wash up any mess you make.'

One day, Alan thought as he lay there, fuming. One day he was going to wipe that cool composure from that beautiful face of hers. One day he was going to make her cry. And what would he do? Walk away. That was what he'd do.

Oh, sure, sure, came a dark, cynical voice.

Flinging back the sheet, Alan leapt from the bed and marched into the bathroom where he snapped on the cold water jets. Bracing himself, he stepped under the freezing cold spray, telling himself it was penance for his sins.

He must have had a lot of sins on his soul, for he had to stay in the shower for a long, long time.

CHAPTER THREE

EBONY slumped into the back seat of the taxi, strain telling on her face. The façade she always put on in a vain attempt to punish Alan was beginning to take its toll. How long before she actually became that person for real? Brittle and cynical and cruel.

It was the cruel part that bothered her the most.

There was no doubt about it. She had to get out from under the crippling effects of this appalling affair before she self-destructed.

Sighing, Ebony closed her eyes, her head tipping back against the seat. It wasn't far from her flat in Randwick to the Ramada Hotel, but at eight-thirty in the morning she was in for at least half an hour's run into the city. Might as well try to rest.

Rest was not on the agenda for her troubled soul that morning, however. She was too full of regrets and bitter recriminations, the main one being why she had allowed Alan to become her lover in the first place. There'd been no seduction, no courtship, no nothing. All he'd done was look at her a few times on the night of her twenty-first birthday party.

But that was all it had taken to start her heart beating madly for him, not to mention make her grasp at straws where his feelings were concerned, especially when once or twice she had surprised him staring at her with desire in his eyes. Had he too not forgotten that kiss in the library three years before? she'd begun wondering. Could he have been lying that night, saying he didn't really want her when all along he had?

It would be the sort of gallant thing Alan might do, she'd reasoned, considering his over-active sense of responsibility towards those under his care. He was very protective of all the females in his family, including his mother and that wayward sister of his. Maybe he'd believed that, at eighteen, Ebony was too young for him, far too young to embark on the kind of relationship he might want and need; certainly far too young for marriage.

That possibility had tormented her for the rest of the party, sparking a resolve to confront Alan later that night. She'd long given up any hope of getting the man out of her system, so, if there was a chance that some twisted scruple was keeping them apart, then she'd aimed to try to unravel it. Who knew? Maybe her turning twenty-one had already heralded a change in his attitude towards her. Maybe he was now beginning to think of her as a grown woman, an adult, not the child who'd come into his home as a young and innocent fifteen-year-old.

This train of thought had excited her. Why hadn't she reasoned this all out before? Of course that was it! His sexual response three years ago had made him feel guilty. But there was no longer any need for guilt. Couldn't he see that? She couldn't wait to talk to him alone, to tell him that time had not changed what *she* felt for *him*, but that time *had* changed the status quo between them. He was no longer her guardian in any way. He was simply a man, as she was a woman.

But when she had turned round from seeing the last guest leave shortly after one-thirty, it had been to find Alan saying an abrupt goodnight and striding off to bed. Frustrated at having her wishes thwarted, Ebony had wandered around the house for ages, helping clean up, afterwards sitting alone in the kitchen, finishing off one of the half-empty bottles of champagne, thinking it might help her sleep.

No such luck. It had fizzed through her veins, sparking further restlessness. Having swallowed the last drop of wine, she had walked out on to the back patio and down the steps to the next terrace where she had stood and stared, first out across the darkened harbour waters, then down at the heated pool.

A swim will tire me out, she'd decided, make me sleep…

Positive she was alone, Ebony had slipped the tiny straps of her black crêpe party dress off her shoulders, shimmying till it had slid down over her hips and pooled on to the pebble-effect concrete. Stepping out of the circle, she had kicked off her shoes then peeled off her panties and tights.

The night air might have felt cool on her naked flesh, if her blood hadn't been so heated by the wine. She had balanced for a few moments on the edge of the pool before flicking her long sweep of hair back over her shoulders and diving into the water.

If she had known for a second that Alan had been sitting in the shadows of the pool-house, she would never have dreamt of being so provocative as to go skinny-dipping in front of him. She certainly wouldn't have floated up and down the pool on her back, idly splashing water over her breasts and stomach.

She'd really believed herself alone when she had climbed out of the water, and stood there, wringing her hair dry. Her shock when he had materialised out of the darkness had been very real. But he hadn't allowed her any opportunity to speak, or explain. He had simply swept her hard against him, uncaring if his clothes were ruined, uncaring of anything but his ruthless intention to reduce her to a trembling mass of unconditional surrender.

It hadn't been difficult. She'd been half aroused already from the way he'd looked at her earlier in the night. That, combined with her long-suppressed love just dying for expression, had made her a ready victim for his lust.

The trouble was she hadn't interpreted his actions as lust at the time. She'd mistakenly believed that he had finally realised his own love for her, had at last given in to an extremely powerful and very natural need to make love to her.

Ebony groaned silently at the memory of her very rapid capitulation.

How could she have been so naïve not to have seen there was nothing loving in the way he had kissed her and touched her? His hands had been quite rough on her flesh, demanding no quarter. But by the time he'd pulled her over down on top of him on one of the deck-chairs, she'd been beside herself with passion and emotion. Alan loved her and desired her and needed her. There had been no question of not doing what he had clearly so desperately wanted.

Even now she could still recall the animal cry of satisfaction he had emitted when his body had finally fused with hers. Never mind that he hadn't waited to undress properly, or that someone could have come down from the house and caught them in the act. She had been making love to the man she loved and who loved her.

It was not till the morning after that she was forced to review her way of looking at their first coupling, then all their subsequent couplings during that long and tempestuous night. Not till Alan had made his appalling suggestion in his bed at dawn had Ebony seen that what she'd thought of as love on his part had been only lust, and that his 'making love' to her had been no more than 'having sex'.

She had hoped to become Alan's wife. Instead he'd offered her the role of his secret mistress. She hadn't been at all happy about it, but he'd secured her continued co-operation by turning up at her flat when least expected, then seducing her with a finesse that was as intoxicating as it was merciless.

For fourteen months, she'd endured his spasmodic visits, dying a little each time he came and left, hating herself for her weakness, yet unable to stop. More than once, she'd vowed to cut him dead, to send him away, unsatisfied. Whether he had sensed this or not, she couldn't be sure. But whenever she'd reached that point, he wouldn't come near her for weeks. Then he'd turn up out of the blue and, without saying a word, take her into his arms and start kissing her before she could utter a word of protest.

Those were the worst times—and the best—their lovemaking on the edge of violence, but so passionate and intense that she would despair afterwards of ever being able to give him up.

Could she now? Would she have the courage to take that step and walk away? No, *fly* away.

'Lady! We're here,' the taxi driver growled.

Ebony snapped to attention. Already the concierge at the Ramada was opening the car door for her. Checking the fare on the meter, she handed the driver a twenty-dollar note, told him to keep the change, then alighted with her usual style. Old habits died hard, and she was a model first, cool and composed and sophisticated. The shattered woman inside would remain hidden from everyone, even Gary. She was not about to tell him all the grim details of her relationship with Alan, only enough to make her plan feasible.

'Bob says you didn't come home last night.'

Alan took a sip of the black coffee his secretary had just brought in. 'Really, Mother,' he sighed into the phone, 'I'm not a child who has to answer for his actions. So I stayed out all night? So what? It's not the first time.'

'I realise that. That's what's bothering me. You're working too hard, Alan. Only yesterday you said how tired you were. Yet I'll guarantee you went from those awards to the office again. Or was it the factory this time?'

'Neither.'

'*Neither*? Then where, in heaven's name, did you get to?'

'Need I spell it out for you? I spent the night with a woman.' Something inside Alan twisted as he said that last word, yet he could not deny that Ebony would be a woman in everyone else's eyes. Though maybe not his mother's. God, but she'd be appalled if she knew whom he'd spent the night with.

'Oh,' was all she said, ever the tactful parent.

'No more questions?' Alan mocked.

'Would you tell me if I asked?'

'No.'

'So I won't. But I feel sorry for whoever she is.'

Alan bristled. 'What's that supposed to mean?'

'It means I hope she isn't in love with you, because you and I both know you're not in love with her. Or are you?'

Alan was startled, then annoyed. Ebony, in love with him? That was a laugh. As for himself…to even think about what he felt for her in terms of love was preposterous. Love was what his mother and father had shared, what Adrianna felt for Bryce McLean. Maybe even what Vicki felt for that excuse for a man she was living with. Love was not this black torture that wrung his soul every time he thought of Ebony, especially when he thought of what she might be getting up to when he wasn't around.

Had she lied to him about Stevenson this morning?

he began worrying. Was she, at this very moment, in bed with her ex-lover? If she was, and he found out, he wasn't sure what he'd do, but it wouldn't be pleasant.

'I hate to disillusion you, Mother,' he bit out. 'But these days, women are as capable of staying the night with a man *without* love as vice versa.'

'My, my, you *are* out of sorts this morning. Maybe you're not as capable of staying the night with a woman without love as you think. But as you say, that's your private business. You don't have to answer to me. The reason I rang is because I'm worried about Ebony.'

Everything inside Alan tightened. 'Ebony?'

'Truly, Alan, you are the limit! Are you trying to pretend now you don't know who Ebony is?'

'I wish I didn't,' he muttered under his breath.

Deirdre Carstairs sighed. 'You saw her last night, didn't you?'

A few ghastly seconds passed before Alan realised his mother was talking about the fashion show, not later. 'Not to talk to,' he hedged.

'Did you think she looked all right? She seemed very pale and thin on television.'

'Ebony has always been pale and thin.'

'Well, she looked extra pale and thin to me. You don't think she's getting that dieting disease, do you?'

'Anorexia? No, I'm sure she isn't. Black always makes women look slimmer, Mother, as you very well know. And the make-up she wore was that stark white look. Ebony's just fine.' More than fine, he added in vicious silence, thinking of those long slender thighs wrapped around him, and those firm white breasts with their long pink nipples arching towards his mouth.

He shuddered.

'I'm still worried,' his mother persisted. 'It's been ages since she came to see me and I know why. It's because of you, Alan. You and your rudeness. I won't stand for it any more, I tell you. I'm going to invite her over for dinner and you're going to be there. Not only are you going to be there, but you're going to be nice to her.'

'Mother, if Ebony knows I'm going to be there, she won't come.'

'Then we won't tell her, will we? We'll let her think you'll be away on business that night.'

Yes, Alan thought. There would be a certain sadistic pleasure in having her sitting at the table next to him, forced to be polite, unable to deliver any of those cutting little barbs of hers.

A malicious smile tugged at his lips. It would be an excellent revenge for that pathetic lie of hers that she was going to marry Gary Stevenson. For one ghastly moment, he'd thought she meant it, till he'd realised it was just another of those taunting, goading things she liked to say. It was another of her ploys to worry him, to make him jealous, to make him explode into the violent passion that turned her on so. Playing such games was part of her dark side, the side she kept hidden from everyone else.

Yes, he would enjoy making her squirm in front of his mother, enjoy it immensely.

'You're right, Mother,' he said expansively. 'Our feud has gone on long enough, but I do think we will have to surprise Ebony with my presence, otherwise she will find some excuse not to come.'

'I realise that, but I do so hate being deceitful…'

'Come, now,' he soothed. 'Your intentions are the best.' Even if mine aren't.

Deirdre brightened immediately. 'Yes, yes, they are. And if it means you two will become friends again, then it will be worth it. I'm so glad you're going to be co-operative, Alan. I'll call and ask her for tomorrow night. Friday.'

'Let's hope she's free.'

She was, as it turned out. But once the invitation had been accepted and the plan was in place, Alan was besieged with doubts. It was a dangerous thing to do, deceiving Ebony. The witch had a way of turning the tables on him.

Still, he could not deny that he was looking forward to seeing her again so soon, to feasting his eyes upon her cool exotic beauty, to finding some way, perhaps, of tricking her into staying over. And then…who knew? Maybe he would be able to exploit that incredible sexual appetite of hers to make her do what he knew her prickly pride would never want her to do again: spend the night with him, in his bed, in his own home.

Ebony had some misgivings in the taxi on the way to the Carstairses' home. She wasn't sure what it was about the invitation from Mrs Carstairs that worried her, unless it was the way the woman had repeatedly assured her that Alan would not be there. Ebony understood why she kept making the assurance. No way would Ebony have accepted otherwise. Now, more than ever, she was taking pains to avoid him.

In just under two weeks she would be on her way to Paris.

Perhaps her misgivings were due to the fact that she didn't want to be anywhere that even *reminded* her of Alan. Out of sight was out of mind, they said. And that was partially true. She would never forget Alan, but not seeing him was easier than encounters like the other night. They only served to enslave her senses with memories of what she could experience when in his arms. And while she fully understood that physical pleasure without love left a bitter taste in the mouth, one didn't seem to remember that till afterwards.

She wanted no more afterwardses. Not ever.

The taxi stopped outside the high security fence that guarded the Carstairses' home. She paid the fare and alighted, drawing her black woollen cape around her black woollen trousers. Her mohair jumper was black too, but with pearls sewn in a flower pattern around the neck and across the padded shoulders. Her hair was braided, falling down the centre of her back in one long thick plait. She was only wearing a smattering of make-up. Deirdre had said dinner would just be the two of them.

Using the keys still in her possession, she let herself in through the security gate and crunched up the gravel drive, glancing in fond memory at the fountain in the centre of the well-ordered gardens. She had used to like feeding the birds that flocked around that fountain in the spring. She used to like living in this house. It had seemed so warm compared to her growing-up years. Even the boarding-school Alan had sent her to was warm compared to those grim, lonely years. She'd actually felt loved for the first time in her life.

Loved…

Ebony ignored the contraction in her heart and stepped up on to the wide white-columned portico. The house itself was also white and looked relatively modest from street level, but actually had three levels which allowed it to hug the steeply sloped block as it dropped down to the shoreline of Double Bay. Besides the house itself, there was a terraced swimming-pool, a tennis court and a private jetty, Alan's small but luxury cruiser, *Man-About-Town*, moored not far off shore.

Ebony could have let herself in with her keys, but that would assume a casual intimacy with this house and its inhabitants which she'd lost four years before. She felt sorry that Alan's mother was slightly bewildered by her and Alan's public behaviour towards each other. Deirdre Carstairs had never been anything but kind to her since her son had brought her home as a shy, rather introverted girl of fifteen. Maybe Mrs Carstairs had been a little lonely at the time—Alan's

sister had just left home. Whatever, the woman had
welcomed Ebony with open arms and the two had
become as close as Ebony's reserved nature had allowed.

Ebony was very fond of her. Which was why she
could not refuse this invitation to dinner, despite having felt slightly uneasy about it from the start. Right
at this moment, that uneasiness seemed to be increasing, which was ridiculous. Alan's car was not parked
in front of the house where he always left it when he
was home. He was away in Melbourne on business.
Deirdre had told her as much only yesterday She was
safe.

Shrugging off her edginess, she moved forward to
press the front doorbell, sweeping her cape off in
readiness for stepping into air-conditioning.

Bob answered the door. 'Hello, Miss Ebony,'he
said, taking her cape as she stepped inside.

'Hello, Bob. What's on the menu for tonight?
Another of your fabulous Italian dishes?'

'I don't know about fabulous, but Mr Alan won't
eat anything else these days.'

Her panic was immediate. 'Mr Alan? But
Ithought—'

'Ebony, dear,' Deirdre Carstairs exclaimed as she
rushed across the foyer, looking flustered but stylish
in a pale blue shirtmaker dress that complemented her
silver-grey hair. 'You're a bit early.'

'Mrs Carstairs, did I misunderstand? Bob implied
just now that Alan would be here for dinner. You said
that he was going to Melbourne tonight.'

Guilt was written all over the woman's face. 'Yes, I know I did, dear, but you see, Alan said that…well, he was sure that… Oh, dear, I was afraid this wouldn't work.'

'It already has, Mother,' Alan drawled as he joined them, looking casually elegant in an extremely modern suit of the palest blue-grey wool, made all the more modern looking by his teaming it with a white turtle-neck sweater. 'Ebony's here,' he stated smugly.

'Yes, but she's not happy about it. You've only got to look at her…'

Ebony would have liked to slice the smile from Alan's face with a meat cleaver. Instead, she assembled every ounce of composure she had, squashing any panic and controlling her rush of adrenalin with a couple of steadying breaths. Then she did the very opposite of what Alan would have been expecting. She smiled back at him.

'Did you think you had to lie to me to have the pleasure of my company? Silly man. You only ever had to ask nicely, Alan, didn't you know that? All that old antagonism was quite unnecessary. I'm very amenable when men are nice to me. Just ask Gary.'

It seemed hidden barbs were far more effective than meat cleavers, Ebony decided when she saw Alan's smile fade. But the icy fury that slipped into his eyes was unnerving, till she remembered he couldn't do a single damned thing in front of his mother. All she had to do to protect herself was keep Mrs Carstairs in full view for the entire evening.

The woman herself was at that moment looking a

touch confused. Possibly she sensed the dark under-currents between her son and his ward and wasn't quite sure how to take them. 'I...I only wanted to try to get you two to make up,' she said unhappily. 'Life's too short to be on bad terms when it's not necessary. Both of you have far too much pride!'

'Pride, Mother? Ebony has no pride.'

'Alan!'

'I only meant that I've never met a more modest model,' he amended with mock-apology. 'She has no conception of her extraordinary beauty, of the effect she has on the opposite sex. Why, only the other night, the chap sitting next to me at the fashion awards could hardly contain his drooling. It's amaz-ing that she keeps such a cool head about her when so many men are willing to throw themselves at her feet.'

Her laughter was almost genuine. Alan throwing himself at her feet was a delightful image to contem-plate. Too bad it would never be true.

'Ebony has always been a very sensible girl,' his mother praised. 'Now why are we standing around out here when we could be comfortable in the living-room? Dinner will be ready shortly, dear,' she went on as she linked arms with Ebony. 'And don't take any notice of Alan's stirring. He's out of practice be-ing nice to you, I can see. Let's hope he finds his manners before the end of the evening.'

Now it was Alan who laughed, the sardonic sound drawing a frowning backwards glance from Ebony. Immediately, their eyes locked, Alan's narrowed gaze promising all sorts of punishments for her, if and when he got the chance. 'Don't be concerned, Mother,' he called after them. 'By the end of the evening, butter won't melt in my mouth.'

CHAPTER FOUR

BY THE end of the evening, Alan wished he had died
and gone to hell. Hell, he decided, was far preferable
to sitting a few feet away from that witch, watching
her eat, smelling that damned tantalising perfume she
always wore, and not being able to touch her.

Perhaps if his subterfuge of being here when she
hadn't expected it had *really* rattled her, he might
have found some satisfaction, despite his own discomfort. But there she sat, unaware—or maybe *very*
aware—of his torment, chatting away to his mother
while throwing him the odd crumb of a casual comment every now and then, as well as the occasional
glance.

Yes, he decided, hard blue eyes narrowing on that
perfect profile. She *was* aware. Why else would she
slide those seductive eyes his way with such sly reg-
ularity, if not to check that he was looking at her,
wanting her, *needing* her?

Bitch, he thought as his loins began to ache. What
I wouldn't give to wipe that cool composure from her
face, to ravage those lush red lips as they deserve to
be ravaged. He almost groaned aloud at the mental
image that flashed into his mind. For he'd never experienced a woman as wild in bed as Ebony could
be. Or as abandoned.

Which was her fascination, of course, he finally accepted. Why else was he compelled to keep coming back to her for more when there was no love lost between them, when she made no concessions to his male ego, when she didn't bother to hide her contempt for him?

Contempt?

He frowned darkly into his coffee, having never thought of Ebony's feelings for him in quite such derisive terms before. Oh, he knew she hated him. But he'd always imagined that was a reverse reaction to the schoolgirl crush she'd once harboured, a pride thing. No one liked being rejected as he'd once rejected her. Yet underlying that hate had remained the chemistry that had flared between them that night in the library, a chemistry that had survived their mutual antagonism.

It was a very explosive chemistry, Alan conceded ruefully. Explosive and volatile, sometimes bordering on violent. One day, he suspected it would totally self-destruct. In fact, it was probably heading for that moment right now...

'What do you think, Alan?'

Alan blinked once before focusing on the object of his mental rummaging. She was looking at him with wide, almost innocent eyes, her head tipped sideways as she had used to do as a young girl.

The blackest feeling of guilt swamped him. She's still little more than a girl, he agonised. God, what have I done to her? What do I keep doing to her?

But then he glimpsed the beginning of a very adult,

almost devilish glitter in those eyes, and every vestige of guilt vanished. He would have her in his bed tonight if it was the last thing he did!

'About what?' he returned silkily, secure in the knowledge that she would not have seen anything of his inner torture on his face. His earlier slip-up when she'd taunted him about Stevenson had put him on his guard. She had not coaxed any visible reaction from him over dinner, and she would not do so now. 'Sorry, but I wasn't listening.'

'It's not like you to daydream,' she said with a small, teasing smile.

His shrug was offhand. 'My concentration suffers when I'm tired.'

'Alan's been working too hard lately,' Deirdre put in. 'Sometimes he works all night.'

'Really?' Ebony arched her eyebrows. 'Well, he always was a one for all-nighters, Mrs Carstairs. Remember when I first came to live here with you? A couple of nights a week at least he didn't make it home.'

Alan tensed, knowing exactly what Ebony was referring to—not work, but his three-year affair with Adrianna. He had used to stay over at her apartment quite regularly, a fact which clearly had not escaped Ebony, despite her being in school most of the time. But all that had ended when Adrianna had fallen in love with another man and married him.

'He'll never change, Mrs Carstairs,' Ebony went on, a touch sharply. 'Old habits die hard.' Now she lanced him with a vicious look that only he could see.

'Unless someone takes a firm hand and makes them die. Perhaps it's time you found a woman to marry, Alan. You're not getting any younger.'

His smile was velvet around steel. 'I assure you, my dear Ebony, if and when I find a woman I *want* to marry, I will.'

'Huh!' his mother scoffed at him. 'You haven't even looked at another woman since Adrianna married that McLean fellow. If you think she'll ever get a divorce, then think again! The woman's besotted with the man.'

'I realise that,' Alan said tautly. 'Believe me when I say I am not waiting in the wings, hoping Adrianna will one day divorce her husband. Especially not with a baby and another on the way. What on earth do you think I am? A home-wrecker?'

'No, of course I don't,' his mother said impatiently. 'But I wish you'd give consideration to being a home-*maker*! Ebony's right. You're thirty-four years old. Time you were married and having babies of your own. I'd like to have grandchildren before I get too old to enjoy them.'

'I'm sure Vicki will give you some. Eventually.'

'Vicki! She hasn't a maternal bone in her body. As for that layabout she's living with… I doubt he's got it in him to father a child! But we're getting off the point here. The subject under discussion is *your* fathering a child. Or don't you want children?'

Did he or didn't he? He'd never thought he did. He'd always been too busy, too wrapped up in saving the family business, then in expanding it, making it into a success. One of the reasons he'd proposed marriage to Adrianna was because, at the time, she hadn't wanted children.

It was ironic that the moment she'd really fallen in love she hadn't been able to wait to have a baby. Her son, Christopher, had been born nine months to the day after she'd married Bryce McLean.

Now there was a lucky bastard, winning the heart of a woman like Adrianna. If only she'd fallen in love with *him* instead.

His mind turned inwards to the way Ebony treated him. No man would ever win that witch's heart, he thought savagely.

Alan looked up to find both women were watching him, expectant expressions on their faces.

'Will I be hung, drawn and quartered if I say I have no great yearning for children?'

Deirdre Carstairs sighed. 'I should have known. Well, it's up to you, Ebony. Your children will feel like grandchildren to me. I hope you haven't any objection to eventually having babies.'

'I'd love to have a dozen babies,' she said with such apparent sincerity that Alan was stunned. 'I hated being an only child. When I have a family, it will be a very large one.'

'And spoil that perfect figure of yours?' he asked, unable to eliminate the derision in his voice.

She turned cold black eyes upon him. 'Having a baby is worth a little figure-spoiling.'

'Not according to most of the models I've come

across. One hint of pregnancy and they're off for a termination before you can say Jack Robinson.'

'I do not believe in abortion,' she stated categorically.

'Not till it's you who's pregnant, you mean,' he jeered.

Again, her eyes speared icy daggers his way. 'I would never have an abortion. Not in normal circumstances. Other women can do as they please, but I wouldn't feel right about it. That is my belief and nothing and no one would ever sway me.'

Alan stared deep into her eyes and knew that what she said was true. He felt a grudging admiration for her. If there was one thing admirable about Ebony it was the implacable nature of her spirit. She had emotional strength. He would give her that. Too bad she often used that strength in battle against him. He would much rather she had a softer, more pliable nature.

Or would he?

A slow, sardonic smile creased his mouth. No... Much as her stubborn pride and outright defiance infuriated him at times, he would not trade her fighting ways for anything. There was nothing more pleasurable than his triumph after finally subduing her sexually, or the intense satisfaction he gained when his physically stronger body eventually gained the upper hand.

'You find something amusing in what I said?' she challenged icily.

'Oh, dear,' Deirdre broke in, her voice worried.

'Please don't you two get into an argument. You were both going along splendidly there for a while. Look, let's forget all about babies and talk about something else.'

'By all means,' Alan agreed curtly. 'I never brought them up in the first place.'

The loud banging of a door and noisily approaching footsteps brought all their attention to the archway that led from the dining-room back into the main living area.

Ebony, for one, was glad of the distraction. She'd been about to murder Alan, the insensitive swine. But she supposed he could never have guessed that the most treasured dream she'd ever had was to marry him and have his babies.

'Vicki!' Deirdre exclaimed when the unexpected visitor marched into the room. 'Whatever are you doing here at this hour?'

Vicki was an attractive but not beautiful woman. She was tall, with brown hair and blue eyes, like her brother; confident and assertive, like her brother; unconsciously selfish, like her brother.

'I've had it with Alistair!' she announced and, dragging out an empty chair, plopped herself down at the dining-table. 'He's the most stupid man it's ever been my misfortune to live with.'

'Then why keep living with him?' Alan remarked drily.

Vicki pouted, then laughed. 'Because he's good in bed?'

'Vicki!' her mother protested. 'We have company!'

'Ebony's not company,' Vicki retorted. 'She's family, aren't you, sweetie?'

Ebony could not help but notice that Alan looked momentarily uncomfortable at this remark. So he *did* feel some measure of guilt over her. Good!

She gave his sister a sickly smile. 'How nice of you to say so.'

'Nonsense. It's not nice at all. It's true. You've been a better daughter to Mum here than I've ever been. Too bad you had to get on your high horse and leave like you did. Not necessary, you know. My old money-bags of a brother didn't miss a few thousand dollars. He probably gives more to charity every year than he ever spent on you, honeybun. Still, I suppose a gal has to have her pride, which is why I walked out on Alistair tonight.'

'You mean you've come home to live?' her mother gasped.

Vicki suddenly looked crestfallen. Her chin began to quiver. They all stared at her. Alan's sister never ever cried.

'I...I guess so.' Gathering herself, she lifted her chin defiantly. 'Alistair needs to be taught a lesson!'

'In what?' her brother asked a touch warily.

'In understanding what a woman wants.'

'Which is?' Alan probed.

'Love. Romance. *Consideration!*' And she promptly burst into tears.

Her mother was up and mothering in one second flat, quite in her element as she made excuses and carted Vicki off to her old bedroom.

When Ebony had gone to stand up to see if she could help, Deirdre Carstairs had waved her back down again. 'You stay and keep Alan company,' she'd whispered across Vicki's bowed, weeping head.

'Poor thing,' Ebony murmured once the other two women were out of earshot.

'She made her bed,' Alan said. 'Now she'll have to lie in it.'

His ruthless lack of pity and understanding fired Ebony's temper. 'What a rotten thing to say about your own sister! Don't you care that she's hurting?'

'Vicki will be thirty next birthday,' Alan returned mercilessly. 'She's had more Alistairs in her life than I have fingers and toes, all of whom she's been madly in love with, and all of whom have used her shamelessly. One would have hoped that she'd have grown up a little by now, and that her judgement of men would have improved.'

'It's hard to be analytical and logical when one's emotions are involved. Or don't you know anything about emotions, Alan?'

His smile was vaguely smug as he surveyed her high colour. Ebony recognised that this was what he'd been trying to do all night—provoke her into having an open altercation with him. Why, she wasn't sure. Bloody-mindedness, she supposed. And he'd succeeded.

Yet somehow she didn't care. She was going to have her say; she was going to tell him what she thought of him. It would probably be her last chance and it would do her soul good to get it all off her chest.

'No, you wouldn't. Not you!' She threw down her serviette and stood up. 'Why, you're no better than Vicki's Alistair. When have you ever given a woman love, or romance, or consideration? Do you even know what any of those things mean? I wonder now if you were ever in love with Adrianna Winslow, if you're capable of loving any woman. I've certainly never seen any evidence of it. Because loving someone means giving a little. All you can do is take, Alan!'

His laughter stunned her, as did his applause. 'Wonderful! You should be an actress, not a model. If I didn't know you better, I would almost think you meant some of that.'

She simply stared at him, feeling sick to her stomach. Had she ever loved this cruel, heartless man?

Slowly, he too rose to his feet, taking his time as he moved round behind his chair and scooped it in to the table. He stood behind it, his long, elegant fingers curled over the curved wooden back, his hard blue eyes narrowing with the most appallingly explicit desire as they roved over her body. Immediately, she felt that curl of answering desire within her, and was disgusted by it.

'If you touch me,' she said shakily, 'I'll scream this house down.'

'Will you?'

'Try me.'

She meant it; Alan could see that. It surprised then

angered him. Who did she think she was, deciding when he could and could not touch her? She was his whenever he wanted her, damn it. Hadn't he proved that to her time and time again? God, but he was tired of her games, tired of the way she kept his desire dangling, just because it amused her perverse nature. Or was she still punishing him for having rejected her once?

Yes, that was probably it. No doubt he'd made a big mistake about her that night in the library. She hadn't been an innocent back then at all. She'd already been a little tramp, kissing him like that, using her Lolita talents to tempt him so severely that afterwards he hadn't been able to get her out of his mind. Even now, after having had her countless times, he hadn't tired of her. One would have thought he would have been able to rid himself of this obsessive need by now. But it was stronger than ever.

'Perhaps I will,' he said in a low, threatening voice, and began walking towards her.

'Everyone finished in here?' Bob asked, his sudden appearance bringing a frustrated scowl to Alan's face and a shudder of relief from Ebony.

He'd been going to kiss her, she realised shakily. And she wouldn't have been able to do a thing about it. Bob's arrival had come just in the nick of time.

'Yes, Bob,' she said. 'It was all lovely.'

'It certainly was,' Alan agreed, having gathered himself quickly. 'Come, Ebony, we'll go and see what's become of Vicki and Mother. Then I'll see you home.'

When Ebony hesitated, Alan came forward, all smiles, taking her elbow and steering her none too gently from the dining-room and across the living area.

'Let me go,' she hissed, her efforts to dislodge her arm from his grip unsuccessful.

'Stop acting like a cantankerous child,' he hissed back. 'Do you want Bob to see you for what you really are?'

'Which is?'

'Well, certainly not the sweet little thing you've convinced my whole family you are!'

'Is that so? Well, maybe Bob and your family could do with a bit of enlightenment of *your* character as well? You're hardly holier-than-thou. Maybe I should tell them what's been keeping you away all those nights this past year.'

'You won't do that,' he ground out as he urged her down the steps that led to the next level, and the bedrooms. But he didn't turn down the corridor to where his mother's and Vicki's bedrooms were, sweeping her instead round the other way and into his own bedroom. Her cry of protest was muffled when his hand closed over her mouth and he kicked the door shut behind him.

She bit him. Hard.

'You bitch!' he gasped, flicking his hand madly before trying to suck the pain away. His blue eyes blazed as he glared hate at her.

'You're lucky I didn't do you more damage. Keep

away from me, Alan,' she warned. 'I don't want you any more.'

Now he laughed.

'I mean it!'

'Might I remind you you've said all this before.'

'This time it's different.'

'How is it different?'

Ebony was about to throw Gary and Paris in his face again when she stopped. That would be a stupid thing to do. Alan in a jealous rage was both frightening and insidiously attractive to her. Desperately she searched around for something to say. Anything!

'You're beginning to bore me,' she bit out, not realising till the words were out that it was an even more stupid thing to say.

Alan's face darkened, then filled with scorn. 'Is that so? Well, you could have fooled me. Only the other night you couldn't get enough of me.'

She flushed fiercely, shame a bitter sword in her heart. 'That was then,' she went on, digging her own grave even further. 'This is now.'

'So it is,' he smiled. 'Shall we see how different now is, then? Shall I give you a little test?'

Ebony backed up against the door when he took a step towards her, her hand reaching blindly for the knob. She found it at the same time as his hands closed tightly around both her wrists, holding her in a grip of iron while he pressed his body up against hers, his head dipping to kiss not her mouth but her neck.

A shudder ran through her.

His mouth travelled slowly up the long white column of her throat, his sipping kisses soft and moist and seductive. They moved along her jawline, up over her ears, across her temples to press gently against her suddenly closed eyelids. By the time he worked his way down to the corner of her mouth, she was aching to part her lips to invite the sort of kiss that could only end one way.

'No,' she moaned, in protest against her own flaring passion.

'Stop being silly,' he rasped against her quivering lips. 'You still want me as much as I want you. There's no use denying it, Ebony. I can feel you trembling already.'

Sensing her inability to struggle at that moment, he let go of her wrists, his hands moving up under her jumper while his mouth continued to hover over hers.

'This is what you want, isn't it?' he tempted, stroking her braless breasts till she was really trembling.

But not entirely from desire. Despair was sending her crashing down a tortuous path she'd never been before. For the first time she could not totally block out the ugliness of it all, the sordidness behind the sensuality. A feeling of intense desolation flooded in, tears filling her eyes. She made a choking sound.

Alan's abrupt withdrawal bewildered her for a second. Her soggy lashes fluttered upwards, her blurred vision gradually taking in an Alan she had never seen before. He looked quite shattered.

'You're…you're crying,' he said, obviously shaken.

She blinked, gulped, and said nothing. She couldn't. The tears were still running down her face and the back of her throat. Yet now that he'd stopped touching her, she felt oddly desolate, which was a perverse reaction, given her devastation of a moment ago, not to mention her ongoing weeping.

'I...I don't *like* you crying,' he went on in a type of angry confusion. 'Stop it!'

Now she began to laugh as well as sob, bringing her rapidly to the edge of hysteria. His stinging slap across her face sent her mouth gasping and her eyes flinging wide.

'Stop it,' he groaned into the sudden electric silence, his face a tortured mask.

Her answer was a single strangled sob.

'God, Ebony,' he shuddered. 'I'm sorry. Sorry...'

And then he was cupping her stunned face, pressing impassioned lips to her eyelids, licking the tears away, tracing the red imprint of his hand on her cheek with trembling fingertips, whispering more wildly apologetic words that sent her heart soaring and her defences crashing. Her own hands lifted to his face, inviting him to take her mouth in a proper kiss.

His hesitation was only brief, and then he was crushing her to him, kissing her till their breathing had gone haywire. The love she had hopelessly tried to destroy came rushing back, firing her with the need to express that love in the only way he had ever let her.

'Make love to me, Alan,' she cried huskily. 'Make

love to me, Alan,' she cried huskily. 'Make love to me…'

With a raw groan of desire, he swept her up into his arms and carried her swiftly to his bed. Within no time they were both naked, both in the throes of a passion that knew nothing but each other. It was no wonder that they didn't hear Deirdre's first soft tap on the heavy door.

CHAPTER FIVE

DEIRDRE was worried. When she'd returned to the kitchen to make Vicki a drink of hot chocolate she'd noticed the dining- and living-rooms were empty. Bob had told her that he thought Ebony had gone home and Mr Alan to bed. But Ebony's black cape was still hanging on the coat stand in the foyer.

It wasn't till after Deirdre had taken the drink back to Vicki that the idea presented itself that Ebony and Alan might have had another row, with an upset Ebony forgetting to take her cape when she left. The more she thought about that possibility, the more she was convinced it was right. The atmosphere between them tonight had been as fraught with tension as ever before, and it was all Alan's fault. He'd tried to needle Ebony from the moment she'd arrived.

Annoyed with him, Deirdre went along to his room to confront him with what had happened. Already she'd knocked once, with no answer, yet she could swear she could hear noises coming from inside.

Exasperation joined her irritation. If Alan thought she would just go away if he ignored her knocking, then he had another think coming. She meant to give him a piece of her mind if he'd been fighting with Ebony again.

Her second knock was quite loud, as was her voice

asking if he was in there. But she waited no more than a couple of seconds before barging right in, intent on not letting her son brush her off so rudely.

Shock galvanised her to the spot in the open doorway, her fingers freezing on the knob. For there was no doubting what she had just interrupted her son doing. His state of undress, combined with his hurried rolling sideways and scooping a sheet upwards, was telling enough. But it was the sight of his open-mouthed bed-partner that caused Deirdre Carstairs's heart to stop beating.

'Ebony!' she gasped aloud, unable to believe what she was seeing.

The girl herself gave a choked cry and turned to bury her face in the pillow. Alan closed his eyes momentarily before throwing his mother a black look.

'Maybe that will teach you not to come into a man's bedroom unannounced,' he growled.

'But…but I *did* knock,' she wailed, appalled both with the situation and all the thoughts it sent tumbling through her mind. My God, how long had this been going on?

A long time, she realised with a mother's sudden intuition. Maybe even longer…

Nausea rose in her throat, and she swallowed convulsively. Dear God, not that long, she prayed.

Immediately, she turned on the person who, on age alone, had to be mostly to blame. 'Oh, Alan, how *could* you?'

His reaction staggered her.

'How could *I*? My God, that's rich, that is. How

could *I*?' he repeated, then laughed. 'Oh, get out, Mother, before I say things you won't want to hear. Get out and take all your presumptions with you because I'm not going to deny a thing. Yes, I heartlessly seduced your poor darling sweet little Ebony. Yes, I betrayed the sacred trust her father gave her. Yes, I'm a wicked depraved lecher. Will it make you happy to believe that?'

Ebony wanted to bury her face in the pillow forever when she heard Alan's indirect but scathing condemnation of her character, her despair so great it was beyond despair. It was death. He had finally sentenced her love to death. A little while before, when he'd apologised and started making love to her, she had thought he loved her. But no...she'd been wrong... again.

Her pride-filled spirit had not died, however. It was, if anything, made stronger by this ultimate of betrayals. Steeling herself, she rolled over and levered herself upright, tossing her long hair back as she swung her legs over the side of the bed and bent down to begin drawing on her scattered clothes.

Not a word was uttered by anyone as she pulled on her panties. Not a single word. She sensed that both Alan and his mother were watching her go about her coolly composed dressing in a state of stunned silence, but she refused to show any distress.

At last, with head held high, she started to walk from the room, stopping only briefly to bestow a sad little smile on the pale-faced woman standing with her back against the open door, her hand still on the doorknob. 'I'm sorry, Mrs Carstairs. Really, I am. Please don't see me out. Goodnight. Thank you for the lovely dinner.' And without giving Alan so much as a parting glance, she swept from the room.

Alan's mouth had dropped open with her blasé boldness, her total lack of shame. *He* was the one who was left with the shame, and the guilt, *and* the frustration. God, if only he'd thought to lock the damned door. Then he wouldn't be lying here with his mother looking at him as if he were the original Bluebeard, or worse!

'Should...shouldn't you go after her?' she managed to say.

'Not bloody likely. And before you start in on me,' he went on testily, 'Ebony was not dragged into this bed by the hair on her head. She came willingly enough. And it's not the first time, either.'

'So I gathered by your earlier comments.' His mother glanced daggers at him again. 'Yet you are the older party here, Alan, and I am not impressed by your trying to paint Ebony as some sort of scarlet woman. She is nothing of the kind! It would seem that you have—much to your discredit—taken advantage of the girl's one-time hero-worship of you.'

She dismissed his startled look with a scornful wave of her hand. 'Oh, yes, I knew about that. Do you think I go around here with my eyes shut? As for your both trying to hide this affair from me by pretending not to like one another...I find such deception most reprehensible. But once again, I heap most of the blame on you, Alan. I'm sure it was not

Ebony's idea. I can only conclude also that this intimacy began when society would have frowned on such a relationship.'

'It did not!' he defended fiercely. 'I didn't touch her till she turned twenty-one!'

His mother looked surprised, then relieved, then confused. 'Then why all the secrecy? Why not be open about your relationship? Good lord, Alan, I would like nothing better than for you and Ebony to marry.'

'Which is exactly why I didn't want you to find out about us,' he snapped. 'Ebony would never marry me for starters. And I damned well would never marry her!'

'Why not?'

'God...'

'Tell me, Alan. I think I have a right to know. The girl was placed in *my* care as well as yours. I worry about her. She's a very vulnerable type of girl.'

Vulnerable? Was his mother kidding? Hadn't she seen her swan out of here just now, unmoved at having been discovered *in flagrante delicto* with the man who was not only her legal guardian, but twelve years older than herself? Hell, Ebony was as hard as her name!

'You want the truth,' he challenged. 'The whole unvarnished truth?'

Deirdre squared her shoulders and her chin. 'I do.'

'So be it, then. So be it...'

Ebony did not cry till she reached the safety of her flat. Then it all poured out, all the hurt and the pain and the shame. She would never forget the look of horror on Alan's mother's face when she had walked into that bedroom. Never! Ebony had never felt so low in all her life. How she had got herself out of there with some shreds of dignity intact she had no idea. But she had, thank God.

As for Alan... She had never hated him as much as she had when he'd failed to defend her, when he'd destroyed his mother's good opinion of her. She'd never pretended to be a saint. But she wasn't a slut either. She was merely a woman, made weak by a love that had been doomed from the start. Now, there was no one left who thought well of her, who cared for her.

No one except Gary...

Ebony stood up and went to get her luggage. Time to start packing, she thought. Time to escape this torment for good.

The doorbell ringing sent her into a momentary panic till she remembered she was in control here. No one could get in unless she let them in.

Initially, she ignored it, till the insistent buzzing nearly drove her mad. Only Alan would be so persistent. Any normal person would have given up and gone away. In the end, she marched over and flicked the switch on the intercom. 'Yes, Alan?'

'I need to talk to you,' he ground out.

'Well, I don't want to talk to you.'

'So I gathered. Look, I regret what happened earlier. I should have locked that damned door. But I straightened Mother out about a few things, and she doesn't think badly of you. Quite the contrary. I'm the one she tore strips off. She's cast you in the role of the wronged woman. She actually thinks you're in love with me.'

Ebony sucked in a startled breath, then laughed. 'I hope you straightened her out about that as well,' she scorned.

'I tried. She wouldn't listen. In the end I decided to let her think whatever she liked if it made her feel better.'

'How gallant of you! And did you also let her believe *you're* in love with *me*?'

'Her mind did start going along those paths. Eventually,' he added drily.

'And you didn't want to disillusion her about her beloved son's morals, is that it?'

'Something like that.'

'You bastard,' she bit out. 'You stinking rotten bastard. Why didn't you tell her the truth? That the only thing you've ever wanted from me is sex. It's why you're here now. You think you can take up where you left off. But you're wrong, Alan. I'm finished with you,' she stated harshly. 'For good!'

'Stop being so melodramatic. It doesn't suit you. But I can understand you might be a little upset. And I'm sorry.'

'He's sorry! My God, can you repeat that? I'd like to tape it for posterity. An apology from Alan Carstairs to his slut of a mistress.'

'Don't call yourself that!'

'Why? It's how you think of me, isn't it?'

'God, Ebony, can't we discuss this in private? Let me come up. It's cold out here.'

'It'll be even colder in here, believe me. Just go home, Alan. And don't come back. I don't ever want to set eyes on you again.'

'You don't mean that.'

'Don't I? We'll see, Alan, we'll see.'

'Yes, we certainly will!' he snarled, and stormed off.

Alan sat in his car for quite some time afterwards, fuming. In love with him, was she? His mother was mad! That witch didn't know *how* to love. She was a vampire, a blood-sucking vampire, not content unless she drove a man to distraction.

And yet...

His gut twisted as he recalled her tears earlier on that night. God, but they'd affected him. Not with triumph as he'd once imagined, but with shock and real dismay. Ebony crying did not fit the image he had of her. Yet her tears represented some real evidence behind his mother's belief that Ebony was in love with him. Why should she cry unless her emotions were deeply involved?

And just now...

Was her bitter sarcasm another symptom of frustrated love? Had he finally driven her to the point where she couldn't bear to see him again because it hurt her too much?

His whole stomach turned over with the possibility. Goddamn it, maybe his mother *was* right!

Alan gripped the steering-wheel, his head spinning. He remembered that his first reaction to such an outrageous idea had been a mocking denial.

'You're crazy!' he had told his mother.

But once he'd revealed that incident four years before in the library, his mother had been adamant that she was right, steadfastly resisting any suggestion that Ebony was nothing better than a tramp and a tease, even shrugging off his telling her about Ebony's reputation with other men.

'You shouldn't believe everything you hear, Alan,' she'd rebuked. 'As for when Ebony kissed you in the library...you have no evidence she wasn't a virgin back then. I'm sure she was, just as I'm sure she was already in love with you. Can't you see that?'

He hadn't. 'A girl of eighteen? In love with a man of thirty? Oh, come, now, Mother. Next thing you'll be telling me I was in love with her.'

'No. I know better than that. You were in love with Adrianna.'

'Well, no, actually...I wasn't.'

'You *weren't*?'

'I was having an affair with her, but I wasn't in love with her, any more than she was in love with me. We were close friends as well as business associates, and we were both lonely. That's the total sum of our relationship.'

'But you asked her to marry you.'

'Yes...'

'Why?'

Alan had no option but to tell the truth. 'To protect Ebony.'

'To…protect…Ebony…'

'Don't look at me like that, Mother. It was as much your fault as mine.'

'How, for heaven's sake?'

'Remember that white lace dress you put her in for her eighteenth birthday party?'

'Yes, why? She looked lovely in it.'

'And incredibly sexy. I took one look at her that night and wanted her. It's as simple as that. Suddenly, she was no longer that schoolgirl who'd been flitting in and out of my life for nearly three years. She was, body-wise, a woman—a beautiful and highly desirable woman. And I wanted her.' He shuddered with the memory. 'God, I've never felt such desire, or such guilt, in my entire life.'

'Oh, Alan…'

'I thought if I had a wife in my bed every night, then I would be able to cure my lust. I think Adrianna was going to say yes, too. But as you know, she met Bryce McLean in the outback after her plane crashed, and there went my plans to be noble. Shortly after she got married, Ebony kissed me and all hell broke loose.'

'I see…'

'I hope so. Look, I did what I thought was right by forcing her to leave like that, but I never did get over wanting her. It got worse too as she grew in both her beauty and her sexuality. It killed me to hear about her multitude of affairs. So when she virtually offered

herself to me the night of her twenty-first birthday
party, I took her. And I've kept on taking her every
damned time I've felt like it. And you know what?
She's never said no, never wanted anything from me
but what I wanted from her. Pure unadulterated sex.
So don't go telling me she loves me, because I don't
buy it. The girl's sex mad. I'll warrant I'm not the
only man to grace her bed, though I'll kill the bastard
or bastards if I ever get my hands on them.'

His mother had looked at him then with shock and
pity on her face. 'Oh, Alan, you just can't see, can
you?'

'Can't see what?'

'You're in love with her too!'

He'd laughed at her at the time.

But now he wasn't so sure. Could this be love, this
gnawing at his insides, this ghastly regret that he
hadn't made Ebony stay earlier on, hadn't held her
close and told his mother that yes, she was his woman
and he was proud of that fact?

Adrianna had once told him what he felt for Ebony
was love, that he was blinded to his real feelings by
the intensity of his passion. Desire, she'd said, had a
way of tricking people, making fools of them.

Well, it certainly kept making a fool of him. Did
that mean he was really in love with the woman?
There! He had at last admitted it. Ebony was a
woman, not a girl. At least he didn't have to feel
guilty about that part any longer.

But what kind of woman?

Ah, yes…there lay the crux of the matter. What kind of woman was she?

Images tantalised his brain, and his body. Was it love that made her make love like that? Or sheer decadence? Did he really care?

Yes, came the astonishing answer. *God*, *yes*, *he did*!

A grimly determined expression thinned his mouth as he lent forward and fired the engine. He'd give her a couple of days to calm down, and then…then he'd set about finding out the answers to the many questions tonight had raised.

For he could not go on like this, he realised, his nerves stretched tight, his mind and body rarely at peace. If he didn't find some answer soon, something would have to give. He was a man, not a machine. And there was just so much a man could take.

CHAPTER SIX

EBONY rang Gary first thing the next morning, before he left the hotel.

'You haven't changed your mind again, have you?' he groaned, once he knew who was on the other end of the line.

'Far from it. I wanted to confirm our arrangements. We fly out Tuesday week, is that it?'

'Yes. I was only able to get you a holiday visa to start with, but once the fashion houses in Paris get a gander at you you'll have work offers coming out of your ears.'

'I'm not worried about working. I just have to get away from here.'

'You still having trouble with Carstairs?'

'Mmm.'

'One day, you'll have to tell me the whole gruesome story.'

'Maybe.'

Gary sighed. 'I'm your friend, love. I won't breathe a word of anything you tell me to anyone else. Are you worried the gossip rags might get a hold of it?'

'Hardly. They don't need real facts for a story. They make it up as they go along. I'm already supposed to have slept with every photographer I've ever met.'

'You should see some of the stuff they've printed about me!'

'All of which is probably true.'

'Of course,' Gary laughed. 'Doesn't hurt my career either. Amazing how many women want to be photographed by bad boy Stevenson. I wouldn't think a bit of reported spice has hurt your career, either.'

'Maybe my career hasn't suffered from the gossip, Gary, but my private life has.'

'You mean Carstairs *believes* all that rubbish they write about you?'

'Not only believes it but thrives on it, I think. He likes me bad.'

'Sounds like a bit of a rotten egg himself, Ebony. You're well rid of him. You *are* rid of him, aren't you?'

'I am now.'

'Good. Now what about your agency? What have you told them?'

'Just that I'm going on an extended working holiday overseas and won't be available for work for three months, starting next Monday. That way, I can leave my options open. Not that they were happy about it. They've had to cancel a couple of engagements I had, as well as turn down several new offers. Still, they'll survive. They have plenty of other good models on their books screaming out for work.'

'What about your flat?'

'I was going to put it in the hands of an agent to rent out, but I don't think I will now. I can't face the hassle. Besides, if I did that I'd have to store all my things, which would be time-consuming and expensive. I'm just going to shut it up and have the neighbours keep an eye on the place. If I decide to stay in Paris, I might have to fly back and sell up everything.'

'Yes, you could do that. As you say, no need to rush things. The main thing is to just get away for a while.'

'I can't wait,' she said with feeling.

'Good. Well, I'll ring you later in the week. We'll go to dinner somewhere.'

'I'd like that. Now I must away to the gym. I've a shoot on Monday for a fashion magazine. A swimwear layout, would you believe? In the dead of winter, of course. When else? Not that I mind, really. It's good to be busy. I've got a job every day this week.'

'I've a few appointments myself. Maybe we should leave the dinner till Friday night.'

'Yes, I think that might be wise.'

'How about dinner here in my room? We could have an intimate little candlelit meal and you could tell me all, without danger of being overheard.'

Ebony's laughter was softly rueful. 'You haven't given up on me yet, have you, Gary?'

'Oh, I think I have a realistic view when it comes to my favourite ex.'

'I hope so. One step out of line next Friday night and you might be having Security in your room, not Room Service.'

'You have my word of honour that I will honour your honour.'

'Gary,' she chuckled drily, 'you have no honour.'

'I realise that, love, but you have enough for both of us.'

'Do I?' Suddenly, her voice began to crack.

'You know you do. I can't think of another girl who looks like you, who was living alone and moving in circles you moved in, and who would still be a virgin at twenty. It took every bit of my worldly wiles to get you into bed that first time. And even then I remember you cried for a whole day afterwards. I'll bet my bottom dollar that other than that fool, Carstairs, there hasn't been another man in your life since then. Am I right?'

'Yes,' she choked out.

'Hell, but I feel like going over there and telling that bastard off. How dare he think wicked things about you? You're an angel. The man's a raving lunatic, or blind, or stupid, or all three!'

'No, Gary, I'm not an angel,' she denied unhappily. 'I'm not an angel at all. In fact, I sometimes wonder if I haven't created most of my problems myself...'

'What nonsense! Now don't you start blaming yourself, sweetie. You're a good girl and, if the man's not smart enough to see that, then there's no hope for him. Forget the fool! Believe me, once you're out of his life *he'll* forget *you*. I know his type. He'll have some other sexy little thing he thinks badly of in bed with him before you can say lickety-split. He doesn't want love, Ebony. He only wants sex. Take my word for it. Now, off to your gym and don't give the crumb another thought!'

*   *   *

Not giving Alan another thought was impossible. But Ebony kept herself busy enough over the weekend to stop herself from cracking up. She exercised, cleaned, gave her hair a special treatment, packed, forced some food down herself, listened to Jimmy Barnes, watched *Pretty Woman* for the third time, and tried not to cry too much. Puffy eyes did not look good on a model.

But always at the back of her mind was the fear that Alan would show up at any time, pressing her buzzer and pressuring her to see him again. And while she was determined not to—and quite confident that she would not give in—she knew such an encounter would upset her all over again.

Saturday and Sunday came and went, however, without any sign of him. Perversely, Ebony found this upsetting in itself. He'd implied he would not let her go, but it seemed he'd had second thoughts about that. Gary's assertion that Alan would quickly forget her seemed to be coming true. It underlined the shallow nature of his feelings for her, the lack of any real depth or caring. That should have been some comfort, some justification that what she was doing was right. Yet Ebony found little to feel happy about when she finally went to bed on Sunday night. All she felt was wretched and lonely.

Monday dawned blessedly dry, but there was not a skerrick of warmth in the sun. The photographs were to be taken on Bondi Beach and the company who'd contracted her had thankfully organised a caravan for her to dress and shelter in between takes. Since she had a dozen different suits to model, this was more a necessity than a luxury.

Actually, she hadn't done a swimwear shoot in ages, mainly because of her condition of only modelling black clothing these days. Most swimwear was colourful. But this particular sportswear company had created a new line to cash in on the idea that swimwear could double as sophisticated body-suits for evening wear. They were starting with an all black range, which featured daring necklines, a lot of stretch lace and net, and quite a bit of beading. Built into each crotch was a clever, velcro-type seam to facilitate the wearer's going to the bathroom without completely undressing.

Ebony could not imagine any right-thinking person actually wearing the costumes in the water, and fortunately the photographer seemed to agree. He kept her out of the surf, draping her across rocks, having her lie in the sand, even bringing a sleek silver Porsche down on to the beach so he could take shots of her beside it, in it, and on top of it.

It was while she was lying on the roof of the car, her face lifted to the watery sun, eyes shut, her long dark hair spread out in a circle on the thankfully warm silver metal, that Ebony felt the first prickling awareness of being watched.

She tried telling herself that of course she was being watched. Even in the middle of winter, Bondi Beach was never deserted. Surfboard riders in wetsuits still came to catch waves; joggers and power walkers strutted their stuff along the esplanade; overseas tourists came to see first-hand what they had only ever seen in a brochure or on a postcard. Bondi was, after all, Sydney's most famous beach.

But it wasn't the curious gazes of accidental passers-by and tourists that were making the hairs on the back of Ebony's neck stand on end. She was sure of that. Someone was watching her with an intensity that was being telegraphed to her through the air waves, someone with whom she had a close emotional and physical bond.

'Alan,' she breathed, and sat bolt upright, wide black eyes darting around.

'Oh, for Pete's sake!' the photographer exclaimed frustratedly from where he was standing on the hood of the car. 'I just had the greatest shot in my sights and you damned well moved. What gives, Ebony? It's not like you to be skittish.'

'I...I had this feeling,' she said shakily. 'I thought someone was watching...'

The photographer gave a dry, disbelieving laugh. 'Honey, in that rig-out, the eyes of every red-blooded male within five hundred yards are watching you. Now lie back down, like a good girl, and let's get this wrapped up. The light's beginning to go.'

It was too, despite being only three in the afternoon. But the sun set early on an eastern beach when the city behind it blocked out the sun's rays.

Ebony lay back down, extra-conscious now that the stretch-lace costume was semi-transparent where her curves stretched the material, her areolae and nipples partially visible through the thinnish lace. A blush of embarrassment coloured her cheeks, which surprised her. Over the years she'd become rather nonchalant about showing off her body. Familiarity did breed a certain contempt and she had ceased to be worried by the odd semi-nude shot, as long as it was tasteful.

Suddenly, however, she didn't like to think strange men were ogling her body. Even the photographer was making her uncomfortable, yet she had worked with him many times before and he was one of the best. A real professional. But he was also one of the men her name had been linked with at one time, simply because he had been able to coax a sensuality from her that previous photographers hadn't. One look at his photographs of her and people had jumped to conclusions. Their mutual denials had only made the story a hotter item for the gossip columns.

'Now arch your back, honey,' he was saying. 'And open your eyes, just a little. That's it. Perhaps a bit more pout. Yes, like that. Great! Mmm, yes, ve-ry sexy. Yes, hold that!'

The camera clicked away as she held the highly erotic look, and, while common sense told her she was only doing her job, all of a sudden she hated what she did for a living. It was a lie and a con. She didn't feel erotic at that moment. She felt cold and miserable and oddly ashamed.

The old dream she'd once had of becoming a kindergarten teacher came back with a rush. And so did the tears. It was just as well the shoot was over. She scrambled down from the car, wanting nothing more than to get away from here as quickly as possible.

'What's up, honey?' the photographer said kindly as he wrapped a blanket around her. 'Are you sick or something?'

She shook her head in abject misery, swallowing madly as she battled to keep the tears at bay.

'You're tired and cold.' He patted her hand. 'Tomorrow will be better. We're shooting the evening stuff inside the Opera House. Now you go and get changed, then go home and get a good night's sleep. Can't have our beautiful Ebony looking all wan and pasty, can we?'

Ebony was only too glad to escape and hide herself in the caravan. Or she would have been glad...if the caravan had been empty.

Alan was sitting on the built-in divan, underneath a window that overlooked the beach and would have given him a clear view of the Porsche.

'So it was *you* watching me!' she accused, her face flaming at the thought that what he'd seen would have only confirmed his opinion of her character. She was a Jezebel, happy to flaunt her body for other men's eyes, turning herself on for the camera as swiftly and easily as she'd always appeared to turn herself on for him.

'Shut the door, Ebony,' he said curtly.

'No. I want you to get out. I told you I don't want to have anything more to do with you, and I meant it. Clear out! Find some other cheap little tart to satisfy your needs, because it's not going to be me!' Too late she realised that sounded as if she categorised herself a cheap little tart as well.

'I don't want some other cheap little tart,' he said, and, unfolding himself, he stood up, striding over to remove her clenched hand from the knob, and shut the door himself. She glared up into his coldly handsome face with its hard blue eyes and thin, cruel lips, then did something she neither planned nor consciously decided to do.

She slapped him, the wild swing of her arm causing the blanket to slip from her shoulders and fall on to the floor. She stood there, half naked, shaking with emotion and trepidation, waiting for Alan to slap her back. Or worse.

But he didn't make a move to touch her, merely arched an eyebrow and absently rubbed the red mark on his cheek. 'I guess I deserved that,' he said, and bent to pick up the blanket.

'W...what?'

'I said I deserved to be slapped.' And he draped the blanket back around her shoulder.

Clutching it to her chest, she frowned up at this strangely meek and mild Alan. He didn't ring true.

'What's going on here?' she demanded agitatedly. 'Is this some new type of game, Alan?'

'Games were never my style, Ebony,' he said drily. 'I learnt them from you.'

A guilty heat zoomed into her face.

Ebony conceded there was a lot of truth in that statement. Not that she'd deliberately set out to turn their affair into a series of dark encounters. She'd reacted badly, however, to Alan's insistence that his relationship with her be a secret. Did he honestly think she hadn't noticed how much he hated himself for wanting her as he did? It had made her perversely determined to make him want her even more. So she'd fulfilled every sexual fantasy a man could ever have. And exulted in every moment of it.

Till afterwards...

Afterwards, she'd always been consumed with shame. It was consuming her now.

'No more, Alan,' she moaned softly. 'No more...' Her head drooped and her shoulders started to shake.

What happened then astounded her.

Alan actually drew her weeping self down on to the divan with him, cradling her gently against his chest and stroking her hair till the sobs subsided.

'There won't be any more,' he said at last. 'I can't take any more either. Let's start again, Ebony. Let's put the past behind us. No more hiding, no more secrets. We'll go out together in public like a normal couple, do things together, go for weekends away together. Would you like that?'

Would she like that? Oh, God...

'You...you want us to be open about our affair?'

'No, I want us to start a new one, a different one.'

'A different one...' She blinked several times. 'In what way will it be different?'

'In the ways I've just described. And others. Well, what do you say, Ebony?'

'I don't know *what* to say!'

'I was hoping you'd just say yes. Mother said you would if you loved me as much as she thinks you do.'

Ebony gasped into an upright position, facing Alan with rounded eyes. 'She said that?'

His gaze raked hers. 'Is it true? Do you love me?'

'I…I…'

He sighed. 'I can empathise with that. It's hard to be sure of one's feelings after the way we've been carrying on.'

'Are…are you saying you might be in love with me too?' she asked shakily.

His smile was wry. 'Do you want me to be?'

'Yes,' came her simple but intense reply. 'I've always wanted you to love me.'

He stared over at her, his expression pained. 'You shouldn't say such things when I'm alone with you like this. I promised myself I would be gentler with you this time. Gentler and more considerate and, yes, even romantic, if that would please you. But you make me want to rip that scrap of lace from your body and ravage you right here and now.'

Abruptly, he stood up, his mouth twisting into a cynical and quite sardonic grimace. 'I'm not sure this will work, Ebony. The patterns we've set are very strong. But I'd like to take you somewhere tonight for a long and leisurely dinner, then afterwards I'm going to drive you home where I'm going to try damned hard to keep my hands off you. I want to see if we've got anything going for us other than sex. I want to see if a marriage between us could possibly work.'

'Marriage!' She jumped to her feet.

'You don't want to marry me?' he said, blue eyes narrowing.

'Well, I…I guess I never allowed myself to think you would ever marry *me*. But yes, Alan, yes, I would marry you if you asked me.'

'So you *did* love me all along,' he muttered darkly, his frown an unhappy one.

'I told you I did, Alan. That night in the library…'

His eyes snapped wide. 'But you were little more than a child then, for God's sake. You couldn't have expected me to believe that was for real!'

'I don't think I've ever been a child where you were concerned. I've wanted you from the very first day I saw you.'

'That's ridiculous. You were only fifteen then!'

'Some fifteen-year-old girls are quite old in some regards, Alan.'

His stare showed shock.

A knock on the caravan door interrupted any further conversation. It was one of the crew giving her ten minutes to vacate the caravan. Alan said an abrupt goodbye, saying he had to get back to work and would pick her up at her apartment at eight.

'Wear something modest,' he threw over his shoulder at her as he strode off across the sand.

Ebony did not realise till much later that not once had Alan actually said he loved her.

CHAPTER SEVEN

ALAN parked his white Holden SV5000 outside Ebony's block of flats shortly before eight, but he didn't get out. He sat there for a while, thinking.

Why couldn't he accept that Ebony really truly loved him? His mother insisted she did. Adrianna had suggested the same years ago. Now Ebony herself had said she'd *always* loved him.

Was that the part that bothered him? The 'always' part? Or Ebony's implication that by fifteen she had already been sexually experienced?

If this was so—and her youthful experiences had been pleasurable—then it was possible her concept of love was so entwined with sex and sexual pleasure that she might not be able to separate the two. It troubled Alan, knowing what he knew about Ebony's father. Pierre had been notoriously unfaithful to his wife. Could his daughter be of the same ilk, a compulsive adventurer?

There were some women, Alan imagined, who, because of their make-up, made good mistresses, but awful wives. Their talent for intimacy lay in the bedroom and nowhere else. If they loved, it was not the sort of love that lasted, or could exist without constant physical release.

The image of Ebony spread out on that car this

93

afternoon flashed into his mind, his body remembering the way she'd responded to the intimate gaze of that camera, and the exhorted demands of the man holding it. It made it worse that the photographer was actually one of the endless stream of men she'd reputedly slept with.

How could he not believe the gossip after seeing her in action for himself? The girl was a vamp of the first order, a natural-born siren, unable to stop herself from bewitching every man she came across. His mother was wrong about that. She was not an ill-judged innocent. No way.

But all this rationale counted for nothing when he was with her. This afternoon, when she'd cried once again, he'd wanted nothing but to hold her and comfort her. And it was while he had done so that he had finally come to terms with his love for her.

Which was why he was here now, about to take her to dinner, desperately hoping that a marriage between them would work. Underneath, he doubted it. Ebony might think she wanted to marry him and have children, but he suspected the reality would not please her as much as the idea. He couldn't envisage her wanting that gloriously slender figure of hers swollen out of shape with a baby, or her having to put her own physical pleasure on hold for maybe weeks on end. Neither could he see her giving up her glamorous life as a cover-girl and internationally famous model, any more than he could see himself allowing her to continue her career.

Alan knew his own weaknesses. He was a jealous

and possessive man. At least he was where Ebony was concerned. Maybe she had deliberately fuelled his jealousies because of the nature of their relationship, but he knew he wouldn't be able to bear his wife working with all those men she'd already slept with. Neither did he want her flaunting herself in those skimpy outfits she modelled. My God, she might as well have been naked today. He'd been able to see right through that costume.

When his blood began to stir at the visual memory of those hard nipples poking at that black lace, Alan groaned and swiftly alighted from the car, slamming the door in anger at his own lack of control. He'd vowed not to touch her tonight, and just look at him! Damn it, he'd marry her soon, despite his doubts. He'd do anything to have her in his bed every night. He'd even let her go on modelling if he had to. But, by God, he'd get her pregnant as quickly as he could. And then he'd keep her pregnant. She had said she wanted a large family. Well, he'd give her one!

'I like your suit,' was the first thing she said to him on opening her door.

He glanced indifferently down at his clothes. It was just a plain grey suit. Nothing special. Then he looked at her and felt another surge of desire.

Her dress was a simple black wool sheath with long straight sleeves and a not too short skirt. But anything on Ebony looked sexy. His eyes drifted down her long, long legs encased in sheer black stockings till he came to her shiny black patent shoes, their thin ankle straps drawing his attention to her slender ankles and small feet. He recalled how she liked having the soles of those delicate feet massaged, and her toes tickled. And kissed. *And* sucked.

His inward breath was sharp and his eyes jerked upwards. 'Ready to go?' he asked tautly.

'I'll just get my coat and purse.'

The coat was a black and white hound's-tooth jacket, the purse a black clutch in the same patent leather as her shoes.

'You look beautiful,' he said on her return.

'And you look tense,' she returned with a small smile.

His glance was savage for a second, then he too smiled. 'You know me too well. Any chance of skipping dinner?'

'Certainly not!' she reproached. 'And I'm not on the menu for afters, either. I too want to find out if our relationship can survive without sex, Alan. Especially on *your* part.'

He was taken aback. 'Why especially mine?'

'You're the man, after all. Sex is more important to men than women.'

Alan just stopped himself from rolling his eyes at this. If Ebony was anything to go by, then he didn't agree with that statement. Even his own sister had walked out on her toy-boy lover because of sex. The poor devil had finally got off his butt and got himself a job, instead of sponging off Vicki, but unfortunately it was at night. Instead of being proud of him, Vicki was complaining that this would interfere with their love-life! The woman had to be certifiable, but it showed the importance that some females could put on their own satisfaction.

'And another thing I'd like to straighten out, Alan,' Ebony went on firmly. 'You haven't yet said that you love me. Do you or don't you?'

He eyed her closely. 'What answer will get me into your bed later tonight?'

'Neither.'

'OK. Neither.'

It amused him to see her exasperation. Hell, but he wanted to kiss that provocatively pouting mouth!

'Very funny.' She pouted some more.

He suppressed a groan. 'The way I'm feeling tonight isn't funny in the least, but, since you insist, then yes, I love you.'

'You...you do?'

There was something enchanting about the way she was looking up at him now, something soft and sweet and vulnerable. Ebony vulnerable he had little experience with, and he warmed to it. Like her tears, it made him want not so much to make love to her, but to simply take her in his arms and reassure her. But he dared not do so in his present state.

His hand reached out to tip her chin up further so that he was looking deep into those beautiful black eyes of hers. 'Yes, I love you. There's no longer any doubt in my mind. I can't say I loved you at fifteen, or even at eighteen, but by the time you were twenty-one I'd fallen in love with you. Is that what you wanted to hear?'

'Yes,' she said, her voice quavering but her eyes

glittering with what might have been tears, or triumph. Alan wasn't sure. The latter possibility bothered him for a second, but then she was snaking her long white fingers up around his neck and pulling his mouth to hers, and he didn't care any longer.

A curling sensation contracted his stomach when her tongue sought his, his desire leaping madly. Later, perhaps, he thought, desperately trying to control himself. Later…

His breathing was heavy by the time he pulled away. And so was hers. Her eyes were dilated, and her lips remained tantalisingly parted. I could take her now, he realised. She probably wouldn't stop me, despite her holier-than-thou assertion about not wanting sex for a while.

This realisation had an unnerving and dampening effect on him for once. Ebony as his secret mistress could be as wanton and willing as she liked. The Ebony he loved and wanted to marry was another matter. He would have preferred her to be a little less susceptible to a mere kiss.

'I think we'd better go,' he announced, and abruptly pulled the door shut behind her.

'Where…where are you taking me?' she asked as they made their way down the stairs.

Alan tried not to scowl at her, but, dear lord, even her voice sounded aroused. All breathless and husky and yes…seductive.

'To dinner, of course,' came his curt answer.

'Yes, but what restaurant?'

'Does it matter?'

'No, I suppose not.'

He ground to a halt. Damn it, but he'd see for himself what she was made of, if she had *any* control at all. 'Would you rather we go back upstairs and ring for a pizza?'

He watched her stiffen. 'No, Alan, I don't want to do that. I told you.'

'Just testing. Let's go, then.'

Ebony mulled over Alan's 'just testing' as they drove towards the city. He hadn't been kidding, she realised with some dismay. He *had* been testing her, seeing if a single kiss could change her mind about going back inside.

True, it had been hard to turn him down. She *loved* him. But her desire to forge a real relationship was much stronger than her desire for physical gratification.

Ebony knew, however, that the biggest hurdle to their having a happy life together was Alan's ambivalent feelings about her past behaviour. He had a conservative streak in him that had been seriously challenged by their clandestine and strictly sexual affair. It had troubled him in many ways, not the least of which was that she'd once been his ward, an innocent child whose moral welfare he had been supposed to protect.

Of course, he'd justified it in his mind by thinking of her as a tramp with no morals to speak of. That way, he'd lessened his guilt, but without entirely eliminating it. His opinion of her basic character didn't seem to have changed either, despite his feelings having changed. His lust might have deepened to love, but she was still, in his eyes, a loose woman.

The Alan Carstairs she knew would not marry a loose woman. Certainly not with an easy mind. Ebony believed she had to convince Alan she was nothing of the kind, otherwise any marriage between them was as doomed as their affair had been.

Thinking about marriage and Alan reminded Ebony of her one-time nemesis, Adrianna. Funny, not at any time today had she thought to question Alan over the woman he'd once wanted to marry. But, having thought of her, she could not remain silent.

'What about Adrianna?' she blurted out.

'What about her?'

'Do you still love her?'

Why did he hesitate? Why didn't he just say, No Ebony, how could I love her and love you at the same time?

'No,' he said slowly at long last. 'No, I do not still love Adrianna.'

Ebony frowned. Why didn't his answer satisfy her? Why did she get the feeling he was deceiving her in some way?

'Cross your heart and hope to die?' she challenged with the exuberance of a child.

His laughter was spontaneous and engaging. 'Cross my heart and hope to die.' And he crossed his heart, all the while smiling at her.

Now she felt better, settling back to glance around and see where Alan was heading. Clearly towards the city. 'You still haven't said where you're taking me?' she asked.

'To the Hyatt on the Rocks. Have you been there?'

'No, never. But I've seen it from the harbour. It doesn't look cheap.'

'Are any of the good hotels in Sydney cheap?'

'I don't know. I haven't stayed in any of them. I *live* in Sydney, remember?' Neither have you ever taken me to one of them before, she realised all of a sudden. Either for dinner or anything else. Why had he chosen a hotel? Why not simply a restaurant? Was it because a hotel had rooms for hire?

'I hope you don't think we're going to stay the night,' she said firmly.

'It's not like you to sound so prim and proper.'

'You'd better get used to it,' she countered, a touch sharply.

He slanted her a sceptical look. Ebony's earlier disquiet returned. She'd been right when she'd told Gary she'd created some of her problems herself. She hadn't realised that the day would come when she would desperately want Alan to believe she was a good girl, not a good-time girl.

'I...I'm not sure you have the correct idea about me, Alan,' she tried explaining. 'I'm not in the habit of leaping into bed with every Tom, Dick and Harry, no matter what the tabloids might have implied.'

'Oh?'

'Yes, for your information there's only been one other man beside you.'

'Is that so?'

God, he didn't believe her. She could tell. Should she go on, keep trying to convince him, or let the matter drop?

'Yes, that's so.' She decided to let the matter drop.

Several seconds of electric silence descended.

'Who *was* the other lucky fellow?' Alan finally asked, his voice curiously flat.

Ebony no longer wanted to pursue this conversation. It felt dangerous. She wished she'd never brought the matter up.

'It isn't important,' she mumbled.

'Was it Stevenson?' he demanded, his tone still deadly.

Oh, God…

'I want an answer, Ebony. Was it Stevenson?'

'Yes,' she sighed, and stared out of the passenger window.

'Did you sleep with him over the weekend?'

Her head snapped round. 'Of course not! What do you take me for?'

His eyes were hard as they lanced hers. 'A woman scorned. A woman who likes her sex. A woman who had no idea I loved her. Till today…'

'That's insulting!'

'It's the truth.'

'It's not. You…you don't know the real me.'

'Is that my fault?'

'No,' she sighed again. 'Maybe not…'

Ebony fell silent, her dismay growing. Alan's opinion of her was even darker than she feared. So she was intensely relieved when he said, 'I think it best if we try to forget the past, Ebony. It can't be changed, anyway. Let's concentrate on now, and the future. Surely that's all that matters.'

'I couldn't agree more, Alan,' she agreed eagerly. And flashed him a relieved smile.

His returning look was intense. 'I *do* love you. Too much, perhaps…'

The restaurant he took her to at the Hyatt was called Sevens. It was classy and quiet, with a cosmopolitan menu and an unpretentious but splendid service that would have pleased all but the most snobbish diner. But the most memorable aspect was the view, which would have to be unparalleled throughout the world.

Sydney harbour on a clear and still winter's night was a sight to behold. The inky black waters were a perfect mirror for the lights of the bridge and the surrounding city, the glittering reflections forming a diamond-studded carpet till a passing ferry disturbed the illusion, only to have it return a minute or two later.

'I could sit here and watch the water and the boats all night,' she commented while they waited for their starters to be served. Alan had ordered a white wine— *her* choice—and she was sipping the deliciously chilled liquid with pleasure. 'This is a fairly new hotel, isn't it?'

'Yes, it's only a couple of years old.'

'The site alone must have cost a fortune.' The hotel hugged a small headland that curved around underneath the city-side pylons of the Harbour Bridge. There weren't too many places in Sydney, Ebony appreciated, from which one had an unimpeded view of the harbour and most of its famous surrounds—the Bridge, the Quay, the Rocks, the waterfront and the Opera House.

'I dare say the prices here will reflect that,' Alan said ruefully, 'though the wine list surprises me. Quite reasonable, considering the quality.'

'You're not drinking any of it,' she pointed out.

The corner of his mouth lifted into a ironic half-smile. 'Drinking and going home to an empty bed are not compatible when I'm with you, my love.'

'Oh…' She flushed prettily, her cheeks going quite hot.

Alan frowned, but made no further comment. Silence befell the table. Ebony drank some more wine.

'What shall we talk about?' she asked once the starters had been served. Hers was smoked salmon, Alan's a hot-looking Thai curry.

His laugh carried a dry amusement. 'We're not used to talking much, are we?'

Her hurt look had him apologising.

'Right,' he went on, still with a wry expression on his face. 'Shall we discuss the economy, or the weather, or politics?'

'Tell me how your Man-About-Town stores are going,' she suggested. 'Have they been hit with the recession?'

He shrugged. 'To a degree. But all in all, the tough times have made us more productive and competitive. Once things pick up, we're going to do even better than before. Circumstances have forced me to find more efficient styles and suppliers, and more diverse markets. Would you believe I'm now exporting to Asian markets? That's like taking coals to Newcastle, I know, but there's a demand among wealthy Asians to wear imported garments rather than the locally made articles. Apparently, it's a matter of status. That's why I'm branching out into a designer label, to satisfy those who want to wear original and exclusive designs.'

'Alan, that's marvellous! But then you were always a clever businessman. I know a few womenswear labels who could do with some more progressive thinkers.'

'Do you now?' he smiled.

'I certainly do.'

'Tell me, Ebony, do you like modelling?'

Her disgruntled sigh reflected her recent feelings on the subject. 'I used to, or at least I used to do it without thinking about it too much. It seemed an easy way to make money. And it's always pleasant wearing beautiful clothes. But I'd give it up tomorrow if I could make a living at something else.'

'Or if your husband asked you to?' he said quietly.

She stared at him for a few seconds before realising he was deadly serious. 'Of course,' she said, and could have sworn his whole body shuddered, as though he'd been holding himself very tightly. 'I told you, Alan. I want a large family. When we're married I want to have a baby straight away. If that's all right with you…'

'It's perfectly all right with me.'

His smile was so broad that Ebony almost burst into tears; she'd never felt so happy.

The rest of the meal was eaten in a light, happy mood. They chatted away as they'd never chatted before, sharing amusing incidents in their work lives, teasing each other's tastes in clothes, exchanging opinions on movies they'd seen and places they'd been.

Ebony had never felt so relaxed in Alan's company, yet as the evening drew to a close the desire to have him make love to her was incredibly strong. Maybe because she knew that this time it would be different. This time it would be really making love.

It was Alan, in the end, who pulled back, despite their goodnight kiss having reduced them both to panting, passion-filled messes. When Ebony tried to return to the haven of his arms, he forcibly took her hands and held them away from him.

'Let's see how long we can last,' he suggested huskily. 'Call it a game. A new game.'

Ebony cringed at his use of words. She didn't want there to be any kinds of games between them any more. This was for real, forever. 'And what if I don't like this new game?' she said unhappily.

'It won't last for long, I promise you. But please…humour me in this, Ebony. It's important.'

'How is it important? If you love me and I love you, it's only natural that we'd want to make love. I don't understand you, Alan.'

'Might I remind you of what you yourself said at

the beginning of the evening? You wanted to test my love by withholding sex. Maybe I want to do the same with you.'

Her black eyes widened. My God, he actually thought she was some sort of nymphomaniac!

Once again, her behaviour over the past year was coming back to haunt her. What could she do, except go along with him?

'All right, Alan,' she agreed, and, steeling herself, reached up to give him a chaste peck on the cheek. 'We'll wait.'

He seemed pleased. 'That's my girl.'

Ebony went to bed that night telling herself that if she was patient and understanding everything would turn out all right. After all, she had much to be grateful for. Alan didn't love Adrianna any more. He loved *her*. And he wanted to marry her and have babies with her. That was much much more than she'd ever hoped for.

Why, then, as she lay in her cold, lonely bed, was she so worried? Why did she keep thinking that she was fighting a losing battle, trying to gain Alan's trust and respect?

Her final thought before she drifted off to sleep was not quite so pessimistic. It brought a groan, however. Gary was going to kill her when she told him she'd changed her mind again!

CHAPTER EIGHT

As it turned out, Ebony didn't get the opportunity to speak personally to Gary over the next few days. Work took up all Tuesday, Wednesday and Thursday during the daytime, and going out with Alan occupied every evening till nearly midnight. Gary left a message on her answering machine on the Wednesday, complaining that she was never home and that he would leave it up to her to contact him, otherwise he would expect her to arrive at his hotel room around seven on Friday evening.

When Ebony did try to contact him at the Ramada, he wasn't in, so she left a message to say she would see him precisely at seven p.m. on the Friday. She felt bad enough that he had made all those arrangements for nothing, and decided the least she could do was give him her news first-hand, then have a farewell dinner with him.

Of course, there was no question of telling Alan any of this; she was not a fool. But that left the problem of inventing some excuse not to see him on the Friday evening. The matter was beginning to cause her some stress when Alan himself, towards the end of their date on the Thursday night, provided the perfect solution.

They'd been out to dinner and a show, one of those

modern psychological plays which she'd never liked and didn't appreciate. She'd run out of discussion about it on the way home when Alan had turned to her and said, 'By the way, I can't take you out to-morrow night. I have a business dinner which I just can't get out of. Sorry.'

She hoped she had hidden her relief. 'It's all right. I understand.'

'You don't mind?'

'Of course not. My hair's overdue for a treatment and that takes hours, anyway,' she said without any real guilt. Everyone told little white lies to shield the ones they loved from hurt and worry.

Actually, Ebony was relieved about Friday night for more reasons than her dinner date with Gary. Platonic-style outings with Alan had gradually proved to be more of a trial than the wonderfully sweet and romantic encounters she had hoped they might be. The physical attraction between them was so strong that continually denying its natural conclusion be-came a barrier to other forms of communication. Their conversation had become stilted and forced, their goodnight kisses nothing more than fleeting pecks. On these occasions, she longed to throw her arms around Alan, kiss him properly then drag him inside.

Suppressing a sigh, she was off in another world till she found herself opening her front door, Alan standing at her shoulder.

'You were very quiet in the car,' he said. 'Are you

annoyed with me because I can't take you out to-morrow night?'

She turned to lift startled eyes to his. 'No, of course not. Why should I be?'

He shrugged, but his eyes were troubled. His concern touched her. Laying an understanding hand on his cheek, she smiled softly. 'Don't be silly, Alan. I know you're a busy man.'

His hand covered hers and Ebony immediately tensed. 'I love you,' he said. 'You know that, don't you?'

'Yes,' she choked out. Dear God, just go. I can't take much more of this.

But already his mouth was bending and this time his goodnight kiss in no way resembled a peck. Ebony gave a soft groan as his lips flowered open over hers, his probing tongue-tip inviting her to part her lips as well.

No invitation was required. She was already ahead of him, sending her own tongue forward to meet his. The hand on his cheek slid around his neck, her other hand coming to rest on his chest. She could feel his heart beating madly underneath the heat of her palm. His kiss grew fierce and his arms swept her hard against him.

When he broke from her mouth he was literally shaking. 'No,' he astonished her by saying. 'No...'

'But why not?' she protested, half in shock, half in frustration. Dear lord, but she wanted him, and he wanted her. Why should they keep on torturing themselves like this? 'This is crazy, Alan,' she muttered.

His sigh was ragged. 'It's something I have to do.'

'But *why*? We're just not cut out for this kind of relationship, Alan. It's unnatural.'

'There has to be more to a marriage than just sex,' he said firmly. 'If we can't go one single week without it, then what kind of people are we?'

Such thinking fired her very Gallic temper. 'I'll tell you what kind of people we are. We're a man and woman very much in love with each other. And we're not married yet, might I remind you! What further tests will you come up with before we are, I wonder? Oh, go home to bed, Alan,' she threw at him. 'As for myself, I think I'll go inside and drink a whole bottle of wine all by myself. Maybe then I'll be able to forget that the man I love doesn't want to make love to me any more!' And with that, she slammed the door in his face and locked it.

Shock galvanised Alan to the spot for a couple of seconds. Then an answering anger took over. His closed fists lifted to bang on her door, but he stopped himself just in time. Damn it, but she was right, wasn't she? He knew she was right. What had seemed like a good idea at the time had just not worked out. So their love was mainly physical at this point in time. So what? Ebony's intense sexuality was one of the things he loved about her. It fired a passion in him he'd never thought he possessed, made him feel like a man in the most basic and satisfying way.

It was one thing to know how to make love to a woman—something he prided himself on being able to do well—but there was nothing to compare with the woman you loved showing an overwhelming amount of pleasure in your arms, in listening to her unrestrained sounds of satisfaction, in being on the receiving end of such uninhibited and passionate loving.

He ached at this very moment to have those sensuous lips of hers rove all over him. God, the thought of the sensations she could evoke was sending the blood surging along his veins, making his flesh swell even further than it already had.

The temptation to thump on that door was powerful. But there was a stronger force. Pride, probably. Certainly not any notion of testing. He could no longer cling to the hope that this last week of denial had proved a thing. It had, as Ebony had pointed out, been a disaster, not one moment going by when he hadn't wanted to pick her up and take her off somewhere private where he could make mad passionate love to her. To be honest, it had seemed to focus their relationship more on sex than ever before.

The human being was a contrary animal, he realised testily. Forbid it something, and suddenly that thing became even more attractive and imperative than before.

Alan shook his head, turned and walked slowly down the stairs, each step an agony. He would call her in the morning, apologise, then ask her to spend the weekend with him. Maybe he would take her out on his boat; she'd always liked that as a young girl. And being on the water was both private and relaxing. He would cruise up to Broken Bay, and find a secluded cove to drop anchor in. He'd ask her to bring that black costume she'd modelled the other day. Not that he planned on having her swim in it. He didn't plan on her having it on for long at all…

Alan's smile was sardonic as he let himself into his car. This was familiar territory, he realised, though he found a certain irritation in his letting her slip back into the role of mistress in his mind. But damn it all, he just couldn't wait!

It was seven forty-five on the Friday evening, and Alan had been sitting at the cocktail bar in the dimly lit restaurant for several minutes, his dry Martini down to the olive.

Adrianna was late. When she'd contacted him earlier in the week, saying she was coming to Sydney for business and a pre-natal check-up, and expressing a wish to see him while she was in town, he hadn't been able to turn her down. Yet he'd felt vaguely guilty about it, especially when he'd lied to Ebony. He'd felt even guiltier when Ebony had been so trusting, accepting what he told her without even asking a single question. If *she'd* begged off a date with him, saying she had a business dinner, he'd probably have given her the third degree.

Ebony would not be pleased, however, if she found out who Alan's 'business' dinner was with. But there was no reason why she should find out. This place was out of the way and not popular with celebrities or people from the fashion world. He glanced around again to make sure. Nope. No one he knew. Darn it, where *was* that woman?

She breezed in a couple of minutes later, looking as elegant and coolly beautiful as only Adrianna could look at six months pregnant.

'Am I terribly late?' she exclaimed, a cloud of flowery perfume assailing his nostrils as she leant forward to kiss him on the cheek. She hoisted herself on to the stool next to him, her cleverly layered outfit in cream wool hiding her pregnancy completely.

'A Perrier, please,' she told the barman before turning towards Alan. 'The gynaecologist was running late and then my taxi got stuck in some traffic and in the end I jumped out and walked. Am I forgiven?' She pushed back her curtain of sleek blonde hair and flashed him a winning smile.

He smiled back. Just. Oh, Adrianna, he thought. If only I could have fallen in love with you all those years ago, things would have been much simpler.

She gave him a sharp look. 'That's not much of a smile. And you're looking terribly tired. Are you working too hard?'

'Probably.'

'Alan, you bad man. You need someone to take you in hand.'

'I couldn't agree more,' he said blackly.

Her lovely grey eyes widened slightly. She picked up the glass of mineral water and took a sip. 'That doesn't sound like you,' she said. 'The Alan Carstairs I used to know and love was always in control of his own life.'

'You never loved me, Adrianna, more's the pity.'

Her hand covered his where it was resting on the bar. 'That's not true, Alan. I did love you. You were a good friend, and a damned good lover. I still love you. But I'm *in love* with Bryce. There's a difference.'

'Mmm.'

Her laughter was light and teasing. 'Now what does "mmm" mean?'

'Nothing.' He looked over at her, schooling his face into a less troubled expression. The woman was too damned intuitive. 'So tell me, Adrianna, what did you want to see me about?'

'Shall we go to our table first? I could take this with me and you could order yourself a nice bottle of red. A full-blooded claret might cheer you up.'

'No more hedging, Adrianna,' he began again once they were settled at a table in the corner. 'What's up?'

'Nothing, really. I've been thinking a lot about you lately and I had to come to Sydney anyway to have an ultrasound, so I decided to kill two birds with one stone.' She drew in then exhaled a deep breath. 'You'll probably think I'm prying, but I wanted to find out what happened between you and Ebony. Four years ago when you came to my wedding I could have sworn she was as much in love with you as you were with her. No, don't deny it again, Alan. I won't ever believe it was only lust you felt for the girl, despite her tender age. You're just not the type. I've been half expecting to get an invitation to *your* wedding all this time, but it never came…'

Alan clenched his teeth hard in his jaw. He didn't want to play true confessions with Adrianna about Ebony. He wasn't in the mood for a lecture. And Adrianna would give him one if she knew what had been going on this past year. God, yes, she'd really give him a tongue-lashing.

Adrianna was not forgiving when it came to any form of chauvinistic treatment of women. A staunchly independent career woman, she had made some astonishing compromises to marry Bryce McLean. But one could only admire both the woman and her cattle-station-owner husband for the depth of their feelings for each other. It was the type of love that could move mountains.

'Ebony and I did fall out with each other for a few years,' he admitted, thinking what an understatement that was! 'But we go out together occasionally now.'

'And?' Adrianna probed.

Alan shrugged. 'She had a lot of growing up to do, Adrianna. I didn't want to rush her.'

'Well, she's certainly all grown-up now, and so beautiful it's just criminal. Would you believe I saw her tonight?'

Alan tried very hard to look nonchalant, but every nerve in his body had snapped tight. 'You saw her? Where?'

'She was going into one of the hotel lifts as I was coming out. I went to call out to her, but the doors shut and she was gone. I don't think she saw me.'

Alan tried to stop the black suspicions from crowding in. 'Are you sure it was Ebony?' he asked casually.

'Of course I'm sure. How many girls look like Ebony? You know, it's not surprising she's become a highly sought-after model with that face and figure, not to mention that hair! I tried to sign her up for one of my fashion shows not long ago, but she only models black, it seems, and I don't design in black.'

'Yes,' Alan said on automaton. 'But it's worked surprisingly well for her, that black-only business. Still, I think she'd have been successful anyway.'

Adrianna gave him an exasperated glance. 'So when are you going to snap her up, Alan? A girl like that must have plenty of admirers. You wouldn't want to wait too long.'

'I won't,' he said with more feeling than he'd intended.

Adrianna looked surprised. 'That's more like it. Now tell me, how's *your* business going? Better than mine, I hope.'

Alan let the whole meal go by before he was able to ask the one question that was gnawing a jagged hole into his insides. 'I'll take you back to your hotel, Adrianna,' he said as he helped her into her coat. 'Which one are you staying at, by the way?'

She smiled at him over her shoulder. 'The Ramada.'

They arrived back at the hotel by ten—Adrianna had not wanted a late evening. Alan ushered her across the foyer, his emotional state something like a kamikaze pilot. He didn't care if he ran into Ebony. He didn't care if *she* saw *him* with Adrianna. He felt homicidal and suicidal at the one time.

But as fate would have it, nobody ran into anybody else. He delivered Adrianna to her room, kissed her goodnight, and returned to the foyer. On approaching Reception, he asked for Gary Stevenson's room number, vainly hoping that they would tell him he'd checked out days ago.

But he was there all right.

When he asked to be connected by telephone he was told that Mr Stevenson wanted all calls held that evening, but he could leave a message if he liked.

Alan shook his head and turned away from the desk, feeling sick. He went outside into the street and simply walked. After an hour of mindless pacing, he found a telephone and rang Ebony's apartment, holding his breath till it clicked over to her answering machine. He knew from experience that meant she wasn't home. She didn't use the answering machine while she was merely asleep. He hung up and went back to the hotel, finding an unobtrusive spot in the foyer where he could sit and watch the lifts without being seen himself.

By eleven-thirty, he was beginning to think he was crazy, sitting there. Then he saw her coming out of the lift with a leanly built, fairish man whom he immediately recognised. Stevenson had once done a fashion shoot for his Man-About-Town label many years ago. He'd been a womaniser back then. Nothing had changed, apparently.

Alan watched, seething, while Gary placed his hands on Ebony's shoulders and kissed her. OK, so it wasn't a long kiss, but it wasn't a peck either. He saw Ebony wag a finger at him and laugh. But then she went up on tiptoe and kissed him back on the cheek.

Alan ground his teeth, forcing himself to stay right where he was till Stevenson turned to walk back to the lifts and Ebony hurried away. For a few terrible moments he battled with the temptation to go over and mash the bastard to a pulp. But he didn't. He knew who was to blame for what had happened tonight. And it wasn't Gary Stevenson.

A blackness enveloped Alan, a blackness full of jealousy and fury and revenge. She would never do this to him again, he vowed savagely. Never!

CHAPTER NINE

FROM the moment Alan picked Ebony up early on the Saturday morning, she felt something was wrong. Why she should feel that, she had no idea, for Alan was, if anything, extra attentive, a ready smile coming to his face whenever she glanced his way. It almost seemed as if he was trying to hide something, though she could not, for the life of her, imagine what it could be.

'Did your—er—business dinner go all right?' she asked on the drive to his place.

Was she imagining things or did he tense slightly at her question? His mouth was smiling when he looked over at her, but not his eyes.

'Excellent,' he pronounced. 'Most productive and informative.'

'In what way?'

'Pardon?'

'In what way was it productive and informative?'

He gave her another of those unnervingly cold smiles. 'Must you bother your pretty little head about business today? Now that I've put aside all that nonsense about our not indulging ourselves, I'd like you to concentrate on only one subject. *Me.*'

Ebony stared at him. When he'd called and asked her to spend the weekend with him on his boat, she'd assumed they would start making love again. The prospect had both relieved and excited her. Now, however, she felt oddly chilled. Alan's mood seemed dark, even darker than it had ever been when they'd been conducting their love-hate affair.

'Have I said something wrong?' he asked silkily. 'Am I to take it that you're no longer as anxious to have me in your bed as you were the other night?'

Ebony gulped. Suddenly, she didn't know what to say, or how to answer that two-edged question. If she said yes, then she would sound sex-mad. If she said no, then he would think she was a tease and a hypocrite. God, what was the matter with Alan today? Why did she get the feeling he wanted her to feel awful?

'I...I haven't changed my mind about what I said the other night,' she tried. 'I think when two adults are in love, then making love is the most natural, beautiful thing in the world. I don't find my wanting you to make love to me a thing to be ashamed of, Alan.'

'I can only applaud such fine sentiments. But what if you *weren't* in love with me? Would you still be prepared to go to bed with me?'

'But I *do* love you. Oh, Alan, is that what's bothering you today? Are you beginning to doubt my love again?'

He looked taken aback. 'Why do you think something's wrong with me today? I've been perfectly normal.'

She laughed. 'You have to be joking! You're

wound up tight as a drum, and you keep smiling at
me with about as much warmth as the wicked old
witch in Hänsel and Gretel.'

'I see… Is this better?' He flashed her a smile that
was marginally improved, if one ignored the new
overtones of the big bad wolf in Little Red
Ridinghood. But Ebony decided not to mention that.
Maybe he was just as frustrated as she was, but it was
coming out a different way.

'What have you told your mother about us?' she
asked, believing a change of subject was called for.

'That we're going steady, view matrimony.'

She laughed. 'What a quaint term! "Going
steady". Oh, Alan, you're so old-fashioned in some
ways.'

'Am I? Well, that's too bad because I'm not going
to change. I happen to believe in old-fashioned values
like loyalty and fidelity.'

'I should hope so! I wouldn't want my man stray-
ing all over the place like a…a…'

'Man-About-Town?' he suggested drily.

She pulled a face at him. 'I was going to say alley-
cat.'

'Alley-cat's a female term. Women are called
alley-cats.'

'Miaow!' she mouthed, and clawed her hands like
a cat. 'Now tell me what your mother said about us
or I'll scratch your eyes out.'

'What a good idea,' he muttered. 'Then I wouldn't
be able to see any more evil.'

Ebony gave an exasperated sigh as her hands

dropped back into her lap. 'Are you trying to avoid answering my questions? I'm not sure you've told your mother about us at all.'

'I have. Unfortunately…'

She was taken aback. 'Why ''unfortunately''?'

Alan shrugged. 'You know what she's like—runs off at the mouth—though actually she was struck dumb for a moment or two. But when she did find her voice, everything she said was complimentary. She thinks you're a cross between a martyr and a saint for loving me after the way I've treated you.'

Ebony frowned. 'You mean you're still taking all the blame? You didn't say anything about how I treated you?'

His sideways glance was sharp. 'Are you confessing to treating me badly, Ebony?'

'Well, I…I did let you think things that weren't true, and I…I…oh, you know how rotten I was at times. I got some weird kind of pleasure out of making you jealous. I feel quite ashamed when I think about it now.'

'You mean you wouldn't deliberately try to make me jealous any more?'

'Good lord, no, I'd go to great lengths to avoid it. Your jealousy can be quite frightening at times, you know.'

'Can it, now? I think I like the sound of that. Ah…here we are.' He pulled into the driveway, braking while he used the remote control to open the high iron gates that guarded the Carstairses' home. 'I hope you brought that sexy black costume as I asked you to. I've a mind to see you in it.'

And out of it, you lying, treacherous bitch, he thought savagely as he shot the car inside, crunching to a halt beside the front porch. Not a trace of guilt all morning, he noted bitterly. But that was only to be expected. She had no conscience. None at all. She'd been frustrated by the events of the week and had taken the first opportunity to have her insatiable needs satisfied, turning to one of her old flames, someone who would know exactly the sort of wild lovemaking she liked.

The thought of what had gone on in that hotel room last night reinforced his dark resolve to carry through with his revenge. Women like her had to be punished. They could not be allowed to toy with a decent man's feelings. She thought she had his measure, did she? She thought she could marry him, take his money and his love, then sneak around behind his back, screwing whomever she pleased.

When he thought of how she'd fooled him with her tears and her protestations of love…

But he would have the last laugh. He'd take the only thing she had to offer a man, take it and take it and take it over the next two days. And when he'd finally sated his lust—for that was all that was left of his feelings—then he would toss her aside like the disgustingly used creature she was.

'There's your mother coming out to meet us,' Ebony was saying.

Deirdre Carstairs had eagerly awaited their arrival,

and, hearing Alan's car on the gravel, had dashed out of the front door.

Ebony opened the car door and jumped out to meet her. They hugged each other delightedly.

'Ebony! Darling!' Deirdre gushed, and held her away to look at her with love and satisfaction. 'Oh, I'm so happy. You and Alan! Who would have believed it? You did say you wanted a large family, didn't you?' she went on exuberantly while Alan busied himself taking Ebony's overnight bag from the boot.

'Alan,' she called over to him. 'Ebony hasn't a ring yet. Oh, and we should have an engagement party. Yes, that's what we should do. Vicki can help me. She's good at throwing parties. You can leave the ring till then, I suppose.'

'Thank you for your kind permission,' Alan said curtly, guilt assailing him at his mother having to be hurt by all this. He'd been premature in telling her about his new relationship with Ebony. Premature and bloody stupid. All he could do now was try to minimise future hurts and embarrassments.

'Would you be offended if I begged off the engagement party for a while?' he said on joining them on the front doorstep. 'Ebony and I have only just discovered each other, so to speak, and we'd like some more time to ourselves. You must realise she's a celebrity in this city. Her engagement to her guardian would make good copy for the tabloids, and maybe not all of it so good. You get my drift?'

Deirdre frowned. 'I hadn't thought of that. But you're right. They could put a nasty slant on it.'

'You haven't mentioned anything to Vicki as yet, have you?'

'No, I haven't heard hide nor hair of my darling daughter since she scooted out of here last Sunday.'

'Then don't. I'll tell her myself, eventually. OK?'

'I suppose so,' his mother sighed, then shrugged. 'Well, come on inside. Bob's packed a special picnic basket for you to take on the boat. Nothing's too much trouble for his "Mr Alan". And before you ask me if I've told him about you two, then the answer is yes. I'll just have to swear him and Bill to secrecy.'

'I'm not so worried about Bob and Bill,' Alan muttered. 'They aren't big-mouths like Vicki.'

'Speaking of Vicki,' Ebony piped up once they'd moved inside, 'did she patch things up with her boyfriend?'

Deirdre threw her an astonished glance. 'Didn't Alan tell you? He gave Alistair a job in the main factory as assistant to one of the designers—a day shift, of course—so that Vicki's problem was miraculously solved. Wasn't that sweet of him?'

Alan retreated from the admiration in those black eyes as they turned towards him. He didn't want Ebony to admire him. Certainly not today.

'Your son pretends to be tough, Mrs Carstairs,' she said warmly, 'but he's a real softie, do you know that?' She reached out to lay a tender hand on his forearm.

Alan felt an electric shiver run right through him.

Damn her, he thought. Only a light touch and a melting look, and his desire for revenge was weakening. She was like a drug, all of her. Not just her sexuality, but her whole personality. God, but he still loved her despite everything. Still loved and wanted her.

But how could he turn a blind eye to betrayals such as were perpetrated in that hotel room last night? What would happen the next time she was denied sex for a while? Hell, he'd never be able to trust her out of his sight for a moment.

On the other hand, if he didn't marry Ebony, he would never marry anyone, never have children, never give his mother the grandchildren she so longed for. She loved Ebony like a daughter and would continue to love her without reservation, provided he never enlightened her of Ebony's failings. The girl was not all bad, having but the one fatal flaw in her character: she had no conscience about sex.

Could such a marriage work? he agonised. Was he strong enough, bold enough, forgiving enough to take on such a woman?

That was the dilemma facing him. Yet when he looked deeply into her eyes as he was at this moment, there didn't seem to be any dilemma. Her gaze was truly loving, and oddly innocent. Maybe she didn't realise how wrong her behaviour was. Maybe, in her mind, sex and love were two entirely different things.

Her father had been like that. Pierre had seemed to love his wife, yet that hadn't stopped him seducing every pretty girl who came his way. Judith had done her best to keep her husband faithful, always travelling with him wherever he went, but Pierre was incorrigible. He often boasted to Alan that he only needed an hour here and there to accomplish his adulterous adventures. There were some women, he'd claimed, who liked to be treated as sex objects. They enjoyed strictly sexual encounters, the risk of discovery increasing their passion and pleasure.

Alan had not agreed with him. Till now...

Suddenly, his mind was made up, his insides tightening with the acceptance of what he was going to do.

'Being a softie is not always a good thing for a man to be,' he told Ebony brusquely. 'I won't be letting it become a habit. Shall we move along now? I'd like to reach our destination while the sun's still high in the sky and has some warmth in it.'

Ebony thoroughly enjoyed the cruise through the heads of Sydney Harbour and up the coast, loving the feel of the sea breeze and the salt spray in her face. Alan had occasionally taken her out like this when she'd been home on holidays from boarding-school, and they had been outings she'd treasured. Usually it had been in the summer, and she'd loved to watch him move around the boat dressed in shorts and little else. She'd been very aware of him as a man even then, loving the look of his lean male body and dreaming what it would be like to touch it, kiss it.

Her heart squeezed tight and she gripped the railing harder. Alan's body had turned out to be every bit as good as she'd originally fantasised. She'd adored the feel of the steely muscles in his flat stomach, the broad shoulders and hair-roughened chest, the taut buttocks and powerful thighs.

But today…today it would be even better, because it would not only be the body of the man she loved, but the body of the man who loved her. God, but she'd waited a lifetime for that kind of lovemaking.

A shiver of anticipation ran through her and she turned to glance back at Alan, her hair whipping across her face as she did so. He was in the cabin behind the wheel, his dark good looks and tanned skin enhanced by the white shorts and open-weaved white top he was wearing.

Sweeping her hair off her mouth, she went to smile at him. But the smile died before it was born once she saw the way Alan was looking at her. No, *staring* at her. The wind was lifting the beach-coat away from her thighs and buttocks, revealing the high-cut black lace swimming costume Alan had asked her to put on before leaving Double Bay. His gaze was riveted to the revealing costume and the flesh therein, and it didn't look like a loving gaze to her eyes. It was the same way Alan had often looked at her since they'd become lovers—with a combination of lust and contempt.

Shock turned her mind off the necessity to keep a firm hold on the railing, and when the nose of the boat crashed into the top of a wave Ebony lurched sideways, almost losing her balance.

'Hey, watch it!' Alan yelled out to her, his face flashing true alarm. His instant and very real concern brought some soothing to the sickening suspicion that he'd lied about loving her.

But she was not entirely soothed. There remained an apprehensive niggle of doubt, her mind racing to find evidence to support or tear down such a destructive fear.

Alan *had* been very quiet on the trip up. More than quiet. Almost morose. She'd thought he was concentrating on the wheel, but perhaps there was another, darker explanation. Maybe he was feeling guilty at having deceived her. Or maybe he wasn't...

'You'd better go round the back of the boat, Ebony,' he ordered brusquely. 'You almost gave me a heart attack just then. You're usually more sure-footed than that.'

Ebony made her way carefully round to the back of the boat where the sunken decking was a lot safer, but she could not dispel the disquiet in her heart. She tried telling herself she was being neurotic, even paranoid. Of course Alan loved her. Men did not marry these days just for sex.

But he hasn't married you yet, came the insidious thought. He doesn't even want an engagement party. Maybe he'll never marry you...

Ebony turned to frown at Alan, whose back was to her now. He'd been behaving strangely from the moment he'd picked her up, hadn't he?

Suddenly, his head jerked round to find her frowning at him.

'You all right back there?' he asked.

'I...I suppose so.'

'Not seasick, are you? You look a bit off.'

'Maybe a little.'

'You'll be OK in a minute. The sea's behind us now. Only still water ahead.'

When she looked back at the water Ebony saw they were well into the mouth of the Hawkesbury river and the water was indeed calm. Not so her insides.

Taking a deep, steadying breath, she let it out slowly, finally convincing herself she was imagining things. Life had been rotten for so long that she'd lost the knack of being happy, of accepting that dreams could come true. She clung to the fact that Alan was basically a good man who would never deliberately deceive anyone. Their affair had been twisted by unusual circumstances, but now that everything was all out in the open there was no reason to feel this insane fear. No reason at all.

Ebony sighed again, forced a smile to her lips, and determined to be happy.

The river, she noted, was quite crowded with a plethora of pleasure craft, all out for a day on the water. The lack of wind plus an unseasonable warmth made for very pleasant conditions for fishing or cruising or just lying in the sun, enjoying being alive. Ebony was finally relaxing, watching the water and the other boats go by, when Alan suddenly veered right and headed up a narrow and rather out-of-the way branch of the river.

An immediate tension gripped which showed she hadn't totally dispelled her earlier irrational unease. For why should she worry if Alan was looking for a

private spot where they could be together without being observed? It wasn't beyond the realms of possibility that they might like to move around the boat
au naturel. Ebony was not shy about her body and
she knew Alan liked to see her that way.

Now stop being ridiculous, she told herself impatiently. This was getting beyond a joke.

They dropped anchor shortly after noon in a small,
almost hidden cove.

'What an isolated spot,' Ebony remarked, trying to
sound relaxed as she glanced around the secluded
area.

But she wasn't relaxed. The lack of other boats
around, plus the unearthly silence, was unnerving her.
Neither did she like the look of the thick virgin bush
that came right down to the water's edge, or the dark
jagged rocks that lined the shore. Even the water
looked forbidding, cold and deep and ominous-
looking. One could easily imagine monsters lurking
in those dark green depths, waiting to entwine their
tentacles around the legs of anyone foolish enough to
challenge their territory.

A dark shiver reverberated all the way down her
spine.

'You can't possibly be cold.'

Ebony was startled by Alan's sudden appearance
behind her, his hands on her shoulders firm and almost imprisoning.

'Feeling better now?' he went on, his voice husky
in her ear, his hands undoing the buttons of the thigh-
length black and white striped beach-coat. In no time

the garment was being parted by Alan's nimble fingers, and Ebony's pulse-rate was starting to escalate. But so was an accompanying underlying feeling of panic.

Surely he didn't mean to have her right here and now? She'd envisaged a romantic picnic lunch, a bottle of wine, a long and tender foreplay.

The coat had been discarded and already his hands were roving hotly over her body. Already it was responding. Dear God, it knew nothing else, after all, nothing but a wild succession of harsh and impassioned possessions. Never for her a tender or loving union. Never…

A tortured moan escaped her lips when she felt her breasts swelling, felt their erect nipples poking at the confining lace. And then his hands were sweeping back down the length of her body and he was whispering wicked words in her ears, words that should have disgusted her, but didn't. Was she past disgust? Past everything except the need to have his body blended with hers?

Apparently so…

Closing her eyes, she leant back against Alan's body, giving herself up to whatever he wanted. She felt utterly boneless and without will. She felt dazed.

'You're still mine, aren't you?' Alan rasped, his hands skimming the front of the costume, making her shudder as they brushed over those hardened peaks before travelling further down her body. He caressed the smooth white skin of her quivering thighs, first down the outside of her legs then the inside. His fashion-experienced mind quickly discovered the easy velcro opening, and he gave a growl of satisfaction as he gained easy access to the moist flesh within.

Ebony shuddered again, then lay her head back against his shoulder and squeezed her eyes even more tightly shut. 'You must stop,' she groaned after a couple of minutes' exquisite torture.

'Must I? Ah, yes… You want the real thing, *need* the real thing. Nothing else will do for my lovely Ebony.' His hands had stopped their intimate exploration of her flesh, to her intense relief. She could barely think. Now, perhaps, he would turn her round, kiss her, make proper and beautiful love to her.

Instead, he wrapped a strong arm around her waist, holding her captive while there was the rustle of clothes being removed close behind her. And then he was taking her hands and curling them over the top rail, easing her hips backwards, spreading her legs.

There was a moment of confusion at the choosing of a position that prevented any real sense of intimacy. But it was hard to think clearly when one was already on the edge, when every nerve-ending was twisted tight in anticipation of becoming one flesh with the man she loved.

It wasn't till Alan pushed the costume up to her waist with shaking hands that her confusion crystallised into dismay, and she saw this encounter for what it was: nothing different from all their previous encounters.

But already he was inside her, already taking her along that path he'd taken her so many times before.

Her dismay sharpened. This was not what she wanted any more, or what she'd believed this weekend would be like. She'd thought they would make love—*really* make love.

There was no doubt about it any more. Alan didn't really love her.

So why was she letting him do this to her? Ebony agonised. Why was she gripping this railing with a white-knuckled intensity, hating it yet wanting him to keep going, to plunge deeper and harder till she was beyond thought, beyond hating herself for being no more than a faceless receptacle for Alan's lust?

Stop him, her pride demanded. For pity's sake, stop him…

It wasn't till she saw her tortured reflection in the water below that her body listened to her brain, her arousal going as quickly as it had come. Alan must have sensed her emotional withdrawal for he stopped abruptly to pull her upright, holding her tightly against him, their bodies still one. His breathing was heavy and hoarse in her ear.

'You're not with me, are you?' he rasped into her ear, his voice shaking. 'Why, Ebony? This is what you usually like, what you've often craved, this type of sex. Tell me what it is that makes you so lacking in fire today,' he taunted. 'Normally you'd have been over the edge by now. Tell me what's wrong. Are you a little tired, perhaps?'

'No…I…' A sob caught in her throat. 'Oh, please. I…I don't want it like this any more…'

But when she struggled to escape, he scooped her

back against him with ruthless ease. She'd always known he was physically strong, but it wasn't till this moment that she had seriously been afraid of his dominant male strength. She was no match for him out here, and there was no use screaming. All she had as a defence was her mind, and his conscience.

'I...I thought you loved me,' she said broken-heartedly.

'I do.'

'But this isn't making love,' she sobbed.

'Isn't it? Well, we can't have that, can we? How about this, then? Is this better?'

'Oh, God,' she whimpered when he began to caress her again, gently now, despite the other arm wrapped around her waist being as iron-like as ever. And while there was something horribly false about his tender touch, it was also insidiously seductive. God, why did he have to know her body so well? It wasn't fair...

'Yes,' he urged thickly when she shuddered with involuntary pleasure. 'Yes...'

The arm around her waist loosened to find its way up to her breasts and she found herself being bombarded with even more sensations. Nipples were teased till they were tense and aching. All of her was tense and aching. By now all she wanted was for Alan to bend her to that railing once more, to do whatever he wanted, to give her body the release it craved, his oddly derisive tone of a few moments ago quite forgotten.

Till he spoke to her like that again.

'I knew you wouldn't be able to resist for long,' he jeered.

Alan's obvious contempt cut through the fog of arousal that had been blanketing Ebony's pride, forcing her to face the unfaceable once more. He *didn't* love her. His offer of marriage was a sham, and so was this weekend. He'd tricked her into giving him the only thing he'd ever wanted from her, into resuming her old role as mistress.

The hurt was unbearable, the pain infusing her limbs with a crazed strength. With one almighty heave, she ejected Alan from her body, sending him sprawling back on to the deck. Then, without even turning around, she climbed up on to the railing and dived into the murky depths of the river.

CHAPTER TEN

EBONY was not the best swimmer in the world, but adrenalin and the freezing water had her striking out with frenzied strokes for the shore. Not for a second did she turn round to see if Alan had followed her, though she thought she heard a loud splash a few seconds later. This only served to make her swim harder and faster.

She made it to the shore without being overtaken and was trying to find a foothold on the slippery rocks when pain sliced through the ball of her foot, making her cry out in agony. Instinctively, she tried to lift her foot up to see what had happened, the action making her slide back out into the deeper water, and it was then that Alan caught her.

This time she fought him with every ounce of energy she had, thrashing about in the water, slapping, kicking and struggling till she was weak with exhaustion.

'Let me go,' she cried wearily when he scooped an arm around her waist and lay her on her back, life-saver-wise, dragging her slowly back towards the boat.

'To go where?' he snarled. 'Into that bush? Don't be ridiculous, Ebony. Now be quiet till I get you back on board. You might want to kill yourself, but I have no such wish.'

It was quite an effort to get aboard, but they finally made it, Ebony collapsing on the deck into a bedraggled heap, her chest heaving, her long hair plastered down her back. For a few seconds she lay there with her eyes shut, too tired to do anything about the black lace costume which had ridden right up under her bust.

When she opened her eyes it was to find Alan nowhere in sight. Not that this made her contemplate another crazy escape attempt. There was nowhere to escape to, she realised wretchedly. She was here till Alan decided to take her home.

Shivering now, she levered herself up into a sitting position and pulled the costume down into place. It was then that she saw the trail of blood on the deck, and remembered the incident in the water.

Slowly widening eyes surveyed the bottom of her foot and the fresh blood bubbling from it. She stared at the blood for what seemed like ages before the oddest feeling came over her. Having never fainted before in her life, Ebony didn't recognise the warning signs, so a few seconds later she quietly succumbed to the blackness and slipped sideways on to the deck.

When Alan saw Ebony, unconscious on the deck, he nearly died. When he saw the blood, he cried out in horror and raced forward, dropping to his knees beside her.

'Ebony…darling,' he groaned, and shakily picked her foot up to see what had happened.

His relief once he saw that the cut on her foot was only superficial was enormous. If anything terrible had happened to her he'd never have forgiven himself. God, whatever had possessed him to speak to her like that? It was no wonder she'd cut and run. She'd always been proud, his Ebony. Why couldn't he have made all the right noises as he'd planned, damn it? Now he'd blown everything!

A whimpering sound fluttered from her bluish lips when he scooped her up into his arms. An unconscious Ebony was affecting him even more dramatically than a weeping one. Her total helplessness brought out his male protective instinct and he cradled her against him, giving her his warmth, loving her in a way he'd never loved her before.

His Ebony…

Something strong and fiercely possessive curled around his heart as he stared down into the innocence of her unconscious face. Strangely, he knew that, no matter what she'd done with Stevenson at the Ramada, she still loved *him*. Last night did not lessen that fact. That had been just sex.

What she craved from *him* was love. Alan could see that now. That was why she'd reacted so violently to his loveless lovemaking, why it had repelled her in the end. She wanted from him what no man had ever given her before. True love.

Alan struggled to contain his emotion at this thought, but he'd been right in his resolve back at the house. He would marry her and, by God, he'd make it work. She needed him as much as he needed her. He'd watch over her, protect her, keep her safe from other men's dark desires. And her own. Everyone had faults and weaknesses. Hers was clearly sex.

But he had a plan to combat that. He'd give her a baby. Alan reasoned that maturity and the strong maternal instinct he was sure Ebony possessed would probably solve this one flaw of hers. He sure as hell hoped so, because he didn't think he could bear it if she ever made him feel again as she'd made him feel last night. Just thinking about it made him cringe. Still, that was the past, and Stevenson was going back to Paris next week. As damned hard as it would be, he would learn to forget his pain, learn to forgive.

But could he get her to forgive him?

Ah, yes…that would take some doing, if he knew his Ebony.

When she came to, it was to find herself being carried down the gangway in Alan's arms. He was wearing shorts, and nothing else, his manner grimly silent as he manoeuvred his way carefully down the steep steps and through the galley and small sitting-room. Even after several seconds she still felt totally disorientated.

'What…what happened?' she asked when he stopped at the door of the one and only bedroom.

His eyes snapped down to hers. God, but he looked dreadful, she thought dazedly, his face all pinched and strained.

'You fainted,' came his curt announcement.

'Fainted?'

'Yes, fainted. It was probably the blood.'

'The blood?' Her voice sounded weak and shaky. Slowly, she remembered something about a cut on her foot, but when she went to look at it again Alan snapped, 'Don't look! Close your eyes and try to relax.'

'All…all right,' she agreed, and, linking floppy arms around his bare chest, she closed her eyes and sagged back against him.

It was then that the whole scenario flooded back and she froze. What am I doing, hugging this man who doesn't love me, who only wants me for one thing?

If he noticed her sudden stiffening he ignored it, or maybe he was too busy opening the door of the cabin and getting her inside and on to the double bed.

'You'd better take that wet costume off,' he told her brusquely. 'You're frozen stiff. I'll get the first-aid kit. Here's a couple of towels.' He pulled them from the railing of the tiny *en suite* and tossed them over to her before turning and leaving.

Ebony stared at his retreating back. Frozen stiff, was she? Well, it wasn't from cold. It was from shock and horror and total despair.

A deep series of shudders rippled through her, and she realised she *was* cold. An angry desolation invaded her heart as she stripped the skimpy costume from her still damp body and threw the hateful thing into a corner. Wrapping her long wet hair up in one towel, she rubbed her shivering body with the other, then dragged the sides of the quilt around her, careful to keep her foot hanging over the edge so that any drips of blood wouldn't stain the bedspread. The floor didn't matter so much, being polished wood.

Not that she should care about his damned bedspread or his damned anything, she thought despairingly. The man was cruel and callous and so arrogantly selfish that it was mind-boggling. Did he honestly think she would marry him now? She wanted to be his wife for real, not his legal mistress, which was the only sort of marriage he seemed to have in mind, if he had one in mind at all!

Outrage welled up within her as she awaited Alan's return, yet when he walked in looking grim, then sat down to pick her foot up and stroke it with incredible softness, the angry words she'd been rehearsing couldn't seem to find voice.

'I nearly died when I found you lying unconscious on that deck,' he admitted bleakly, 'then when I saw the blood. But at least it doesn't look too deep. Still, it needs looking after...'

A lump formed in her throat while she watched him gently tend the cut, first stopping the bleeding with pressure, then disinfecting it and covering it with a large patch plaster.

'All done,' he said at last, though he continued to hold her foot, continued to touch it and stroke it in ways he knew stimulated rather than relaxed her.

The soles of her feet had always been highly sensitive in an erotic way, something which Alan had discovered and often used to his advantage. He was doing so now, narrowed blue eyes watching her re-actions carefully, showing satisfaction each time she quivered. But the *coup de grâce* came when he lifted her foot to his mouth, kissing and sucking each toe in succession, his heavy-lidded eyes holding hers as he did so. By the time he finally lowered her foot back down on to the bed, she was wide-eyed and breathless.

'I'm sorry,' he murmured, continuing to stroke her feet and ankles with seductive softness. 'I shouldn't have said the things I said earlier. I know how awful they must have sounded. I don't know what possessed me. This past week has been a big strain and I was beside myself with wanting you. Say you'll forgive me, my darling. Say you still love me…'

Ebony blinked and swallowed. Alan had never called her his darling before. Yet some instinctive in-tuition at the back of her mind was whispering to her that this was a very sudden about-face and too good to be true. But to deny what he was saying was to throw away everything she'd ever dreamt about and hoped for. It was much easier to lie back and accept both Alan's assurances and caresses. Much, much easier.

She sighed when his hands began moving further up her legs, parting the quilt as he did so. His en-dearments were as intoxicating as his touch.

'Let me make it up to you, my darling,' he mur-mured thickly. 'Let me love you properly…'

Now he'd reached the area between her thighs and

she moaned. Her mind hazed over and her legs parted on a sigh of bliss.

'God, but you're incredible,' he groaned. 'Any man would do anything to keep you… Anything at all…'

And he bent his mouth to her flesh.

Ebony sighed again. This was what she'd wanted; this was making love. His lips were a delight and a torment, but a very addictive torment. When he eventually moved further up her body to lick sweetly at her nipples, she felt as if she were drowning in sensations hitherto unknown to her. Her love swelled in her breast till it wasn't enough to lie there and let him make love to her. She wanted to make love back, to show him all that he meant to her.

She reached to run trembling hands over his back, lifting her head to kiss his shoulders and neck, to nibble his earlobe and run her tongue-tip around his ear. 'Take off your shorts,' she whispered shakily.

When he was naked, she reached for him, pulling him down beside her, making *him* lie still while she started kissing and touching him all over. Oh, but it was heaven to feel him tremble beneath her hands, to hear his sharply indrawn breath each time her lips moved tantalisingly close to his desire. She knew he ached to have her draw him deep into her mouth, but there was excitement in making him wait, in seeing how far she could extend his need.

She pushed him as far as she could, running her tongue-tip down the sides, then over his thighs and loins till he was quivering with expectation and tension. Only when he gave a raw, tortured groan of pain did she finally do what he so desperately wanted.

'Oh, God,' he moaned as the heat of her mouth engulfed him.

Alan stared down at the stunningly erotic picture of a naked Ebony pleasuring him that way and shuddered in sheer ecstasy. He'd had other women do this to him and had always found it arousing. But nothing could compare with the physical and emotional satisfaction he gained from having Ebony do it. Surely she must love him to make love to him so uninhibitedly. Surely she reserved this intimacy for him and him alone.

Doubts besieged him and he reached down to touch her, only to knock the towel from her head when her eyes snapped upwards. Her hair spilled around her face and she smiled at him through the damp strands. 'You want me to stop?' she teased.

'God, no...'

Now he stroked her head, telling her how much he loved her, his hips lifting and falling in a ragged rhythm of delight as she brought him closer and closer to the edge. She would have selflessly taken him all the way, he knew, but that was not either his plan or his wish. When he could bear it no more, he stopped her, pulling her up and under him so that he could sink deep inside her.

It was impossible to last long, but she didn't need long, her own aroused flesh spasming around him with a fierceness he'd never felt before. He gasped aloud, then climaxed as well, spilling himself into her for what seemed like ages. Afterwards he clasped her to him, knowing that he had never experienced the like before, and equally knowing he would never be able to give this woman up, no matter what.

Ebony sighed deeply and fell asleep in his arms, physically and emotionally sated, her confidence in Alan's love restored. When she eventually woke again, she was alone, and for a split second she felt bereft.

Sitting up, she pushed her hair out of her eyes, but she could not push the niggling feeling of disquiet out of her heart. There was no reason to feel afraid, no reason to feel anything but happy. Alan loved her. They were going to be married soon. Then they would have babies and...

Her gasp of shock sent Alan's face popping round the door. He was smiling.

'So you're awake! Why don't you have a shower, pop a towel around yourself, and come and have some lunch? Watch that foot, though. Hop, if you have to.'

'Alan!' she called after him when he disappeared.

He reappeared in the doorway, all of him this time. He was now wearing his shirt as well as shorts. 'Yes?'

'I just realised. You...you didn't use anything. When we made love...'

His shrug was dismissive. 'I forgot to bring them with me. Does it really matter? We'll be married soon. Besides, you'd have to be unlucky to get pregnant straight away.'

'I...I don't know about that. It's a dangerous time for me...'

Alan came forward and sat down on the side of the bed, taking her hands in his. His eyes were intent as they raked hers. 'I thought you said you wanted children.'

'I do! But I...I—'

'You what?' he said sharply.

Ebony stared into Alan's suddenly cold blue eyes and felt a resurgence of that earlier unease. It wasn't like Alan to forget anything. It wasn't like him at all.

But how could she accuse the man she loved of trying to trap her into a pregnancy? Why would he feel he had to trap her anyway? She did want children, but she'd hoped having a baby would be something they would plan together, a mutual decision made with thought and love. Still, it seemed silly to quibble at this stage. What was done was done.

'Oh, nothing.' She tried a smile, but it felt somewhat forced. 'I guess we'll just have to wait and see, won't we? I might have to buy a specially designed wedding-dress that hides tummies.'

'I doubt that. We'll be getting married within a couple of months.'

'So soon?' she gasped.

'Why should we wait? I'm not getting any younger and I've waited long enough for you, surely?'

'I...I guess so.'

He cupped her face and kissed her. 'I'll take you somewhere deliciously private for our honeymoon.'

'Such as?'

'How about a dungeon?' he said with a dark chuckle.

Though startled, she laughed. 'What are you? The Marquis de Sade reincarnated?'

'Could be, Ebony. Could be.'

She smiled a loving amusement at that thought. 'Not you, Alan. You like to play the big, bad wolf, but underneath you're a sweet, cuddly bear.'

'Even bears can be dangerous, my darling.' He smiled back, and bent to kiss her once more. 'Always remember that,' he whispered, and patted her gently on the cheek. 'Now get up, woman. Bob's picnic lunch awaits.'

CHAPTER ELEVEN

'THIS is the life,' Alan sighed, leaning back against the booth-style seat and lifting the glass of wine to his lips. They'd already finished one bottle of Chardonnay between them and had moved on to the second. Bob's picnic lunch of crispy fried chicken plus his special pasta salad and herb bread had long been reduced to crumbs and bones.

Ebony was sitting opposite, wrapped in a towel, her face washed clean of make-up. She looked about sixteen, Alan conceded, his gut tightening at the thought that she'd probably already been pleasuring men's bodies back at sixteen, or even younger.

For a second he felt fiercely, insanely jealous, but then he took a sharp hold of himself. I'll have to control my jealousy if I'm going to marry her, he vowed. Either that or I'll go stark raving mad.

There again, it's only normal for a husband to want to know all there is to know about his wife. What do I know about Ebony before she came to live with Mother and myself? It's not as though Pierre and Judith lived just around the corner. I was lucky to see them once a year.

Alan stared down into the near empty glass as he twirled it slowly in his hands. A degree of puzzlement filtered in when he realised he'd avoided the subject

150

of Ebony's childhood for years. Why? What was he afraid of finding out?

He looked up, blue eyes hardening as he determined to ask about her life with her parents.

'Yes?' She cocked her head on one side and smiled at him. There was a quality of innocence about that smile that curled around his heart. Damn it all, he didn't want to find out anything that would destroy that illusion of innocence. Not now. Not today.

'Yes what?' he asked with deliberate vagueness.

Her smile became knowing. 'You were going to ask me a question. I saw it in your eyes.'

His own smile felt forced. 'I'm glad you're not a business adversary, reading my face like that. I was simply wondering how your foot was. Is it hurting you?'

'It throbs a little.'

'Do you want some pain-killers?'

'No. Just pour me some more of this wine. It's delicious.'

'It is rather good.' He filled her glass to the brim then emptied the rest into his own. 'That's the last of it, I'm afraid, though I do have some other wine around here somewhere. Not Chardonnay, though, and not chilled. Shall I put a bottle in the refrigerator for later?'

'By all means. Might as well take advantage of the fact that you don't have to drive home.'

'Speaking of home,' Alan found himself saying while he rummaged around in the galley cupboards in search of the wine, 'it must have been hard on you not having a proper home while growing up. I mean…you mostly lived in rented apartments and hotel rooms, didn't you?'

And so much for his decision to let sleeping dogs lie…

Ebony's silence drew him to glance over his shoulder at her. 'Aren't you going to answer me?'

No way could he read *her* face. Ebony was a mistress of deception when she wanted to be. But while those coal-black eyes of hers had glazed into an expressionless void, her body language bespoke a tension that was unmistakable. She didn't want to talk about her childhood. Even having been *reminded* of it was upsetting her.

'Ebony?'

'Really, Alan, haven't we got more interesting things to talk about besides my boring old childhood?'

A surge of something close to panic claimed him. What in hell lay buried in her past that was so ghastly that she had to put on this pretence of cool indifference?

Several ideas infiltrated, all of them horrifying. Dear God, surely she hadn't been sexually abused, had she? He'd read about such victims often becoming promiscuous as a result of either being raped or abused as a child. It seemed too vile to contemplate, although such a tragic background might explain the mystery of Ebony's behaviour with other men.

Alan paled, but kept his face turned away till he found the wine. If she had been abused in some way, she wasn't likely to blurt it out. She would have to be coaxed into telling the truth. Extracting two bottles of white burgundy from the back of the cupboard, he turned to put them in the small gas fridge before sitting back down opposite her.

'It seems only reasonable that I want to know all about you,' he said smoothly. 'I love you, Ebony. Very much.'

His assertion of love discomfited her, or was it his persistence in asking about the past?

'You already know everything there is to know, surely?' she said with a dismissive shrug.

She was hedging, he could tell, her eyes evading his by pretending to look down at the plaster on her foot.

'Not really,' he replied. 'Because of Pierre's and Judith's constant travelling, I didn't get to spend much time with them. Or you. If your parents hadn't had the misfortune to be on that ferry that day when it capsized, I would never have got to know you at all.'

Her eyes jerked to his, smouldering with an intensity that startled him. 'But you did. And you know what? My parents' misfortune was my good fortune. Because it meant coming to live with you and your mother. God, even the boarding-school you sent me to was preferable to living with them.' Her involuntary shudder of revulsion shocked Alan. 'I hated living with them. Maybe I even hated *them*,' she bit out.

Alan stared at her. My God, was the situation worse

than he'd been envisaging? Had the abuse come from within the family? But who? What?

'That's a very strong thing to say about your parents, Ebony.' He managed to sound calmer than he felt. 'From what I could see, they loved you very much.'

Now those black eyes blazed with indignation. 'Did they?' She shook her head. 'Well, maybe Papa did in his own selfish way, especially since I looked like him. But not Mama. She never loved me. She only had me because she thought a child would bind Papa to her forever. She never had any love left over for me.'

Alan almost sighed with relief. This was not as bad as he'd been fearing. Daughters often thought mothers didn't love them, especially when competing for their father's love. He'd heard the same complaints from Vicki when she'd been about thirteen. Still, he had to agree with Ebony that her parents had seemed rather self-absorbed in their lifestyle.

'I'm sure Judith loved you,' he soothed. 'She was a very warm woman.'

'How would you know what Mama was?' Ebony challenged. 'By your own admission you hardly ever saw my parents.'

'Maybe not after they got married, but I knew your mother quite well beforehand.'

'You did?'

'Judith was my father's secretary for years. Didn't you know?'

Ebony was clearly astonished by this news.

So was Alan by her reaction. 'Didn't your mother ever tell you how she met your father?' he asked incredulously.

'Never. She—er—didn't really talk to me about anything much. Neither did Papa for that matter.'

Alan frowned. It sounded as if Ebony's parents had been more than selfish in their treatment of their daughter. Downright neglectful seemed closer to the mark. He recalled his own mother having commented about Ebony's 'withdrawn' manner shortly after coming to live with them. At the time, he'd thought it grief. Now he saw it for what it was: intense loneliness.

God, he must have been blind back then not to notice how grateful Ebony had been for any crumbs of affection and attention. She'd fairly glowed when he and his mother had made the effort to show up for every single one of her school functions, and then whenever he'd taken her out in the holidays. Hell, the child had been literally *starved* for love. He could see that now.

Yet it seemed *Judith* had been the guiltier party when it had come to withholding affection, a fact which surprised him. As he'd told Ebony, she'd always seemed a sensitive woman, not like Pierre, who'd never struck Alan as a man of any great emotional depth. Admittedly, he was charming and intelligent, and his generous loan of money after Alan's father's death had been a godsend. It had come out later, however, that Pierre had been a risk-taker of the first order. He'd made many wild investments. Some had paid off. Others hadn't. In the end, most hadn't, and he'd died stony broke.

'Well, as I said,' Alan went on when he realised Ebony was waiting for him to continue, 'Judith was my father's secretary. That's how she first came to meet Pierre. He was in Australia buying wool for a large French manufacturing company and he visited Dad's clothing factory to see some of the fine woollen garments made here. Dad brought him home for dinner a couple of times. I was only a boy at the time and found him quite fascinating.'

'Papa could be very fascinating,' Ebony agreed drily. 'When he needed to be.'

'What do you mean by that exactly?'

'I mean when he wanted to impress a woman. I presume your father brought his secretary to these dinners to make up the numbers?'

'I think she came to one.'

'And Papa took Mama home afterwards?'

'I can't really recall.'

Ebony smiled a smile that chilled Alan's bones. 'He would have. And he would have stayed the night. What has always puzzled me is why he married Mama at all. It wasn't to have children. He didn't like them particularly, though I think he was almost fond of me.'

'More than fond, I would think. But maybe your mother was not as accommodating as you have presumed, Ebony. Maybe she was not that kind of girl.'

'Or maybe she was simply cleverer than the others. You know what, Alan? I think you're right. I think she refused to sleep with him. That's the only thing that would have got Papa to the altar, of that I'm sure.'

'There is another solution,' he suggested, finding her cynicism unnerving. 'Pierre might have truly fallen in love with Judith.'

'Papa?' Ebony laughed. 'Don't be ridiculous, Alan. He had no concept of true love.'

'He never divorced her.'

'Which wasn't because he loved her, though she did love him, if one could call what she felt—love. I call it a sickness. There was nothing she wouldn't do for him, including turning a blind eye to his bedding every available woman he could get his hands on. Of course, when it was someone under her own roof, she did fire them. Over the years, I lost count of the number of nannies and companions and tutors and housekeepers we had. It wasn't till I caught Papa with one of them in bed that I realised what was going on.'

'God, Ebony,' Alan groaned. 'What a rotten atmosphere for a young girl to grow up in.'

'To be honest, it wasn't the sexual goings-on that upset me as much as not ever being able to form a close relationship with anyone. I dared not bring girlfriends home and I learnt not to make friends with the women Mama employed, because I knew they wouldn't last. People used to think I was weird. I wasn't. I simply chose to distance myself from those around me because it was less hurtful not to care about anyone in the first place.'

Alan felt dismay and sadness that Ebony's life had

been so wretched. 'Wasn't there anyone you could confide in, or feel close to? An aunt or uncle, perhaps?'

'We never visited relatives. As for my parents' friends…they weren't the type of people one could confide in. Why do you think Papa made you my guardian in his will? You were the only person he'd ever had dealings with of any honour, or principle.'

Guilt curled within Alan's stomach. Some principle he'd proved to have. Still, at least he was prepared to marry the girl, despite her appalling upbringing. But no wonder she wasn't normal, sexually. She herself admitted that she hadn't been upset by her father's excesses in the end. Her sense of right and wrong had probably been dulled by constant exposure to immoral behaviour.

'Don't look so serious, Alan. You have to admit living with Mama and Papa gave me a broad mind in certain matters.'

'Judith should have at least put you in boarding-school,' Alan muttered. 'You shouldn't have had to put up with—or witness—the things you did. Your father's behaviour was a very bad example for a growing girl's mind.'

Ebony shrugged and picked up her wine glass to drink, her nonchalance provoking him.

'Can't you see it made you think promiscuity was normal?' he accused.

Her black eyes flashed then narrowed as they met his over the rim of the glass, but she said nothing till she had taken a swallow of the wine.

'You've always believed I was promiscuous, haven't you?' she said bitterly. 'When exactly do you believe I started having sex? How old?'

Now it was his turn to shrug, but it was an uncomfortable gesture, not an indifferent one.

'Eighteen?' she suggested.

What did she see in his face to make her look at him like that?

'Sixteen?' she tried, half disbelievingly.

When he declined to answer, she stared at him.

'My God, how low could I go before I get some sign of agreement?' she went on savagely. 'Fourteen, perhaps? Twelve, even? Answer me, damn you!'

'I'm waiting for you to tell me,' he replied, agitated by her self-righteous anger. Why couldn't she just admit she'd started young? He wouldn't condemn her for it. He could see now she hadn't had much of a chance to be different. Pierre had set the pattern in the household and she had absorbed his morals without even being aware of it.

'If I recall rightly, I told you all this once before, Alan,' she bit out. 'There's only been one man before you, and I was twenty at the time.'

His sigh was full of scepticism and exasperation. Had she honestly expected him to believe that? Even if it *was* true, by some miracle, it didn't alter her present promiscuity. She'd spent most of last night with that bastard photographer, then come away on this boat with him this morning without a qualm.

The memory of Stevenson kissing her goodnight, of her laughter afterwards, speared Alan with a sudden and savage jealousy. It took all his mental strength to gather himself and not confront her then and there with his knowledge.

'So you did,' he replied coldly. 'And was Stevenson a good lover?'

'Was Adrianna?' she countered, not so coldly.

Steely blue eyes snapped to blazing black ones. 'I don't think that's on a par, do you?'

'No, I don't. I didn't love Gary, which makes him far less of a rival for my affections than Adrianna is for yours. You loved her, or so you always claimed. Where does she figure in your life these days, Alan? Is our marriage bed to have a ghost in it, or can I be assured your love is all mine?'

Alan glared frustration at Ebony. Damn it, but the witch was turning things around, twisting the facts. Why should he be made to feel any guilt about his relationship with Adrianna? They might not have been in love, but they had been good to each other. There'd been no mad jealousies or hurting involved, and when it had finished it had finished cleanly.

'Were you in love with her or not?' Ebony persisted in asking. 'I think I have a right to know.'

'Why? What gives you the right to know anything about my life before I became involved with you? Why can't the past be the past?'

'Because it isn't. The past can taint the future. Is my past past for you? If so, why were you quizzing me about it just now? What would it matter if I'd screwed every man I met before you as long as I stopped after I did?'

'But you didn't, did you?' he lashed out without being able to stop himself. 'You used to taunt me with all your other lovers all the time, remember?'

Her face flushed a bright red, but she kept her chin up, her eyes proud and strong. 'I lied. I wanted to make you jealous. And why not? You gave me nothing, Alan, except your body in bed. Not a kind word or a scrap of love. I needed to see your jealousy to soothe my own love, to keep clinging to the thin hope that you did care about me. He wouldn't be jealous, I used to tell myself, if he didn't love me a little.'

Alan jumped up, shaking inside with emotion. 'And were you trying to make me jealous last night when you went to Stevenson's hotel room, when you made love to him for hours on end, when you let him kiss you goodnight in front of everyone, including me?'

Ebony's mouth dropped open, her shock overwhelming. And then she crumpled.

'Oh, God,' she groaned, her head dropping into her hands. 'God…'

'No speech in defence?' he jeered. 'No claim of total innocence or mistaken identity?'

She shook her head, muttering something he couldn't hear.

Well, he'd blown it now, all right. And he didn't care. Goddamn it, what man could have been that noble to forgive and forget such treachery? He certainly wasn't. His crazy idea of marrying her and saving her from herself had been just that. Crazy! Worry over her faithless nature would eventually have torn his guts out.

Just looking at her bowed head—her obvious *guilt*—was sending a raging fury along his veins, making his blood boil and his head pound.

'Look at me, you two-timing bitch!' he spat.

Her head jerked up, her eyes blurred with tears.

'Oh, no,' he mocked with a harsh bark of laughter. 'That won't work this time, honey. I've been there, done that. This time I want to hear word for word what you did with that bastard. I want to hear you explain how you can sleep with him last night and claim you love me today. I've tried to understand it. Maybe I even do, but I can't live with it. I thought I could. I even thought if we had a baby together, then we might have been able to make a go of it, that you would settle down and stop craving sexual excitement. But that wouldn't have stopped you, would it? There would always be a Stevenson in one form or another. You're just like your father, aren't you?

'*Aren't you*?' he screamed at her, thumping the table with a balled fist.

He watched her rise, watched her blink away the tears, watched her gather that steely inner strength that he'd always admired, however reluctantly.

'No,' she denied vehemently. 'I'm not like my father. Not in the least. Not that I expect you to believe me. As for what I did last night with Gary, I'll tell you. I had dinner with him in his hotel room because he's my friend and he's going away. I didn't go to a restaurant because I was afraid someone might see us together and jump to the wrong conclusions, something that has plagued me for years. We ate, we talked—about you, actually,' she added with a sardonic laugh. 'Ironic, isn't it?'

She laughed again, then slumped back down in the seat, her shoulders and head drooping. She felt utterly devastated and totally defeated. Who would have believed Alan would see her and Gary together? What twist of fate would have brought him to the Ramada at that time of night and at that precise moment? God, but life could be cruel…

'Do go on,' Alan snapped. 'Don't stop now. I can see you're as good at lying as you are in bed.'

Ebony looked up at him with desolation in her eyes.

'I have very little else to say. There are some people who don't wish to believe, no matter what the evidence or explanations may be. You're one of those people, Alan. Oh, I appreciate I have played a role in the opinion you've formed of me, but only a very small role. You've always been happy to believe the worst. I could slap a private-detective report in front of you, proving that I was as pure as the driven snow when I wasn't with you, and you wouldn't believe it. Yet it is the truth, Alan. I've never touched another man in a sexual sense since we became lovers.'

'What about the kiss I saw Stevenson give you?' came the harsh accusation. 'That wasn't my imagination.'

'Neither was it anything for you to worry about,'

she replied wearily. 'A goodbye kiss, for pity's sake. The man's been very good to me.'

'But by your own admission, he'd once been your lover,' Alan argued. 'He also asked you to marry him quite recently. And you were going to for a while. Goddamn it, Ebony, I have every reason to be suspicious and jealous. Don't take me for a fool!' And he banged the table with a balled fist, the intimidating and violent action firing an answering fury within her.

'And don't take me for a tramp!' she flung back fiercely, tossing her hair back from her bared shoulders and glaring up at him. 'I'm not. I was a virgin when I went to bed with Gary. I only let him seduce me because I was so lonely and I thought I would never have you. God, I cried and cried afterwards because I'd only ever wanted you, and anything else was second-best. I never loved Gary and I was never going to marry him. I only said that as a desperate escape because I couldn't go on being your mistress. It was killing me, Alan. Really killing me.' Tears flooded her eyes again and this time Alan could not remain unmoved.

Dear God, but all she'd just said had the ring of truth about it. And it stabbed his heart with pain and regret. What if she wasn't lying? He dropped back down on to the seat, the air rushing from his lungs.

'I'm not like my father,' she sobbed quietly. 'All I ever wanted was for you to love me as I loved you. Oh, I know you think I couldn't have fallen in love with you at fifteen. But I did. I know I did. You meant the world to me, right from the first day you brought me into your home. You were everything my father wasn't. You were hard-working and honest and kind. Your family was everything my family wasn't as well, with your loving concern for each other, your warmth and your generosity.'

'You…you didn't seem to like my generosity,' he muttered unhappily, and, picking up a paper serviette, reached over and pressed it into her hand. 'Blow your nose. It's dripping.'

Her smile was softly wry as she did as he told her.

'Most people might conclude I was merely a father-figure to you, Ebony,' he pronounced firmly, trying to keep his head when all he really wanted to do was sweep her up into his arms, to hold her and kiss her and make beautiful love to her. He didn't want to talk about the past any more. He wanted to forget all their misunderstandings and just go forward. But perhaps this was necessary, this purging. He doubted their relationship could survive any more secret revelations.

She was nodding in quiet agreement. 'And they'd probably be right. To begin with. But you soon became much more, Alan. I didn't want you as my father for long. I wanted you as my lover.

'Oh, yes,' she swept on, seeing his knee-jerk reaction to her statement. 'It's true and I'm not ashamed of it. By the time I was seventeen I was wanting you in my bed. I lay awake many a night thinking about it, fantasising about all the things we could do together. Maybe in that I am like my father. I don't think of sex itself as shameful, only how people abuse and misuse it. Sex is a very powerful and natural drive, and, while people seem to accept that young men have it on their minds all the time, so do young women, believe me. I wasn't at all unusual. Most of my girlfriends at school were just as fascinated by the subject.'

'Maybe so, Ebony, but sex is not love. I can understand that I might have been the object of your youthful romantic fantasies. What other man did you have in your life, after all? No one. But you weren't in love with me. Not back then.'

Her laughter surprised him. 'Dear Alan, how naïve you are sometimes for a grown man. Don't you think I met boys down the street, or at the beach or the school discos I went to? I had plenty of opportunity for experimentation, if that was all I wanted. Then after I left your home to live by myself in a flat I had oodles of very attractive men throwing themselves at me, doing everything they could think of to get me into their beds. They didn't succeed because I didn't love them.'

'Stevenson succeeded.'

Ebony closed her eyes. 'Yes...'

'Why was he different?' Alan asked bleakly. 'You said you didn't love him.'

She sighed and opened her eyes. They were still blurred, he saw, and his heart turned over.

'I liked him.' She shrugged. 'We'd been working together for a long time. And he caught me at a vulnerable moment.'

'Vulnerable in what way?'

'I...I'd been over to the house to visit your mother

the day before. I don't know if you recall the occasion, but you…you looked up at me when I came in—you were having lunch at the time—and you didn't say a single word. You just put down your serviette, stood up and left. I know why you acted that way now, but I didn't then, and it…it was my birthday, Alan,' she choked out. 'My twentieth birthday…'

His groan was full of pain. 'Your birthdays have really been disaster days where I'm concerned, haven't they? God, Ebony, I'm sorry…for everything. I've really made a mess of things, haven't I?'

'No more than I. We have to learn to forgive ourselves, Alan, and appreciate the favour fate did us by throwing us together. I know you still think you're too old for me, but you're not. You're perfect for me.'

His smile was wry. 'You have a penchant for older men?'

'I think I do,' she replied quite seriously. 'After watching my father's womanising for years, I needed a strong, stable man who would make me feel totally secure in his love. Could a man of my own age do that? I doubt it. And you know what? I think one of the reasons you fell in love with me was *my* age. I think you responded to my youth because it revived in you what circumstances forced you to miss—*your* youth, with all its lust and passion. I brought you alive, Alan, as no older woman could bring you alive.

'Even Adrianna,' she finished with a tight squeezing of her chest. Lord, would she never get rid of her jealousy over that woman? Would it always hurt that he had loved her first, loved her better? Oh, it wasn't the sex part. She could cope with that. It was Alan's heart she coveted, his soul. She needed to feel he was *all* hers, not just his body. She'd meant it when she'd said she didn't want a ghost in bed with them.

'Adrianna,' he repeated with a dark frown, and Ebony felt a stab of something akin to real panic. What was he thinking about to make him look so worried, so…guilty?

Ebony didn't feel she could let the moment go. She had to know. *Had* to!

'What is it?' she asked quite sharply. 'What haven't you told me about you and Adrianna?'

His glance was more than worried now. 'I have something I must tell you which I hope you'll understand.'

'What?' she managed to ask in a strangled tone.

'Last night, I—er—well, the truth is that—um…'

Ebony didn't need him to say it. The truth—for want of a better word—jumped into her brain with crystal-clear clarity. The businessman Alan had had dinner with had not been a man at all. The ghost who walked had walked back into their lives.

'You had dinner with Adrianna,' she said flatly. 'It wasn't a business dinner at all…'

His face told so much. 'Don't jump to conclusions, for God's sake.'

Don't jump to conclusions? What kind of conclusions? That he'd slept with her? It was hard to think he'd slept with her in a restaurant. Unless…

Various pieces of the puzzle of last night began to

slide into place. Ebony's eyes widened with horror and understanding. 'She was staying at the Ramada, wasn't she?' she accused. 'You brought her back to the hotel after dinner, didn't you? That's how you came to be there to see me with Gary.'

'Ebony, don't do this. Remember the false conclusions I jumped to with Gary. You'll be just as wrong if you start thinking anything happened between Adrianna and me last night. She's a happily married woman. She's six months pregnant. I did not sleep with her or do anything wrong. I gave her a goodnight peck on the cheek, that's all.'

Emotion impelled Ebony on to her feet, her black eyes blazing down at him. 'I don't believe you!' she flung at him heatedly. 'You kissed her, you bastard. You went through the roof about Gary and me, when all the time you'd been in that woman's arms yourself. You *do* still love her. You'll always love her. Stop denying it!'

The pain behind her accusation became a scream in her head and she couldn't bear it any more. Scrambling out from behind the table, she fled for the gangway in a blind rush, unsure of where she was going or what she was about to do. Her reaction when Alan grabbed her ankle from behind before she could reach the top of the narrow staircase was both violent and wild. Swinging round, she kicked out at him, but he side-stepped and somehow scooped her unbalanced self up off the steps and into his steely arms.

'And where did you think you were going?' he demanded harshly. 'Into the river again? There'll be no more blind running away, Ebony. And no more misunderstandings between us. We're going to talk this out, and, by God, you're going to really listen to me this time!'

And so saying, he carried her down the narrow walkway into the one place where talking was the last thing they'd ever done. The bedroom.

CHAPTER TWELVE

ALAN kicked the door shut behind him, more from lack of room than temper. Ebony was an armful. Angling himself down the side of the built-in bed, he would have lowered her gently on to the quilt if she hadn't chosen that moment to struggle.

'Let me go, you brute. I've had enough of your manhandling tactics, not to mention your hypocritical and typically male double standards!'

He dumped her on the bed. A silly thing to do. The towel that had already been slipping precariously down over her breasts burst asunder. Alan groaned silently and tried to put his mind on the problem at hand.

Which was what? Damn, but he could hardly remember.

'Cover yourself up,' he growled, and spun away to drag in a steadying breath before turning to face Ebony once more.

She lay there, the towel now draped across the middle of her body as if she were awaiting a massage, her chin tipped defiantly up at him. But her eyes... Dear God, her eyes revealed a despair he hated seeing.

I've done this to her, he agonised. I've misjudged

her, tormented her, crucified her. I've taken her love, taken her body, taken her pride.

No, he amended. Never her pride. Never that…

'I'm waiting, Alan,' she snapped, her pride and spirit very much intact. 'Make it good, though.'

He frowned. 'Good?'

'The reason why I should believe there was nothing between you and Adrianna on Friday night, whereas *I* was condemned as a whore over my date with Gary. After all, you loved Adrianna once enough to ask her to marry you. Whereas *I*…I turned down Gary's offer of marriage because I'd never loved him!'

He groaned and grimaced at the same time. Hoist with his own petard! He should never have given in to the temptation to keep fuelling Ebony's jealousy with his supposed love of Adrianna. It had been cruel and so unnecessary. He bitterly regretted it now, because it made convincing her of the truth all the more difficult. Yet he had to try, didn't he?

Alan came forward, Ebony flinching with fear when he sat down beside her on the bed. He'd always used sex to get his own way with her. And she'd always surrendered in the end. But dear God, not this time, *please*…

Everything inside her tightened when he picked up her hand. But he simply held it within both of his and started speaking in a low, measured tone.

'I realise this probably comes too late. But they say ''better late than never''…'

Ebony was astonished to see his mouth soften into a rueful yet touching smile. 'I did ask Adrianna to marry me, I admit. But it wasn't because I loved her. We were good friends and we drifted into an affair, but we were never in love. Neither of us. Just two lonely people reaching out to each other as you reached out to Stevenson.'

Ebony blinked her astonishment. 'But…but *why* did you ask her to marry you, if you didn't love her?'

'Why, indeed? Can't you think of a reason, my darling?'

She shook her head, her fluttering heart still not used to Alan calling her his darling. And to think he'd never loved Adrianna. But dared she believe him? What was this mysterious reason?

'I asked Adrianna to marry me to protect the sweet innocence of a girl I believed was too young for love, a girl who twisted my heart and body into knots every time I saw her.'

Ebony stared, her heart leaping. So she'd been right all along. He *had* wanted her back then.

'Yes, it was you I really wanted, Ebony, not Adrianna, you I loved, even though I could not accept that at the time. Maybe if you'd been anyone else other than my ward, I might have seen what a surprisingly mature young woman you were, and that you were as capable of giving true love as receiving it. As it was, I was consumed by guilt at desiring an innocent who'd been entrusted to my care. So I set about saving you from my carnal lust, protecting you from my dark desires…'

His low laugh carried a wealth of remembered pain. 'I imagined a wife would be the perfect antidote for my forbidden feelings. But the best-laid plans of mere mortal men come unstuck sometimes. When Adrianna married Bryce McLean instead, I had to resort to whatever tactics would keep you safe. I was rude and cruel and hurtful. Every time you came within a hundred feet of me I deliberately drove you away. I was almost insane with frustration, and eventually it began to come out in the worst possible way...'

He shook his head, his expression grim. Ebony carefully extracted her hand from where he'd started squeezing her fingers tightly through emotion. It brought his eyes up with a worried jerk, but she merely smiled at him and wiggled her fingers. 'They were going to sleep.'

Alan was moved by her sweetly loving smile. God, but he'd been a stupid bastard to believe all the rotten things he'd believed about her. But that was what he was trying to explain now. Would she listen? Would she understand? Would she forgive him? What if she didn't? What if...?

No, no, he couldn't think like that. She would understand, his Ebony. She would understand and forgive, because she really truly loved him. He gulped down one last lump of anguish and went on.

'I tried to hate you,' he confessed. 'I wallowed in every scrap of scandal and gossip I heard about you. I filed them away in my tormented mind, exaggerated them, hugged them to my ever increasing need to justify the feelings I hadn't been able to conquer. She's wicked, I told myself. A corruptress. A seductress. A pagan goddess. It's not my fault I want her as I do.

All men want her. And she wants all men. I could have her if I really wanted her. But how could I possibly want someone so cheap and disgustingly easy? Oh, the lies I kept clinging to in order to stop myself from doing what I was dying to do.'

Ebony's eyes were wide upon him, appalled yet fascinated.

'Perhaps if I'd gone to bed with another woman. But I didn't *want* another woman! You were all I wanted all those years, yet all I did was make you miserable. My Ebony, my love, and I was *vile* to you.' He shook his head, his shoulders sagging. 'God…'

'Alan, stop,' she said gently, reaching to take his hand in hers this time. 'Let it go.'

'Let what go?'

'The guilt. We've found each other now. I love you and you love me and it's futile to torment ourselves with the past. I've done crazy things too. Look at the way I tortured *you* with my innuendoes about other men. No matter how sorry I am for that now I can't take it back. We were both wrong. We must forgive ourselves, as well as each other. We must go on and resolve to be happy together. We deserve it.'

Her smile was like a physical blow to Alan, because it meant so much. She forgave him. She understood him. She still loved him.

And then she did something so bold and brave and beautiful that he almost cried. She swept aside that towel, held her arms out, and simply said, 'Darling…'

The next half-hour would live in Alan's mind forever as an example of the most perfect lovemaking.

Yet there was no wild passion, no torrid mating, no Kama Sutra position or exceptionally erotic foreplay. It was as though they were making love for the first time and it was enough to just hold her and stroke her softly, his fingers trembling slightly as they traced the glorious shape of her body, revelling in the knowledge that she would always be his and his alone.

The splendour of her love kept washing through him in waves of bittersweet emotion, and eventually he had to bury his face in her breast to hide his eyes lest she think him a fool. But she would have none of that, cupping his face and lifting it to hers so that she could kiss his damp cheeks and his suddenly tremulous mouth.

'I adore, you,' she whispered, and kissed him again. 'Now give me that baby, my darling. But give it to me slowly...'

He laughed, feeling heady with desire as he eased his aching flesh into her hot velvet depths. God, but she felt incredible. *She* was incredible.

I'll make it up to her, he thought as he set up a steady but powerful rhythm. I'll give her anything she wants, anything at all. Nothing will be too much trouble.

Her gasps brought him back to the present and as he saw her eyes shut and her lips part on a soft moan of ecstasy he thought he would never hear anything so satisfying as the sounds of her pleasure. But then his own pleasure took control of his mind and he was drowning in their love, drowning in *her*, simply drowning...

Afterwards, he held her close, and promised her the world.

'If you like,' he murmured, 'I'll even buy us a new house to start our married life in. I know Mother can be a bit interfering and—'

'Oh, but we couldn't do that!' Ebony burst out, pushing away from the warmth of his broad chest to stare up at him, her face aghast. 'She'd be devastated! And so would poor Bob and Bill. Why, you're their world, Alan, don't you know that?'

'I wouldn't go that far…'

'I don't mind living with your mother. Really I don't. In fact, it would be good to have a built-in baby-sitter. We could still have weekends away together, and…and…well, quite frankly, Alan, I…I have some other plans as well. For a career.'

Now Alan was frowning at her. 'I thought you said you would happily give up modelling. Oh, my God, you're not thinking of becoming an actress, are you?'

'Heavens, no. I don't want to see another camera ever again. Or a catwalk, for that matter. What I want to do is go back to college and become an infant teacher. I realise you'd have to support me while I did that, Alan, but I'd pay you back. Really I would. Once I was working, I could—'

'Stop!' he ground out, both his hands reaching up to rub his temples.

'What's wrong? Are you ill? Are you in pain?'

'I have a feeling I'm going to be in pain for the next fifty years,' he groaned.

Ebony felt bewildered as Alan's hands dropped

away to take her firmly by the shoulders. 'I don't want to hear one more word about your paying me back,' he told her sternly. 'For *anything*. I am a rich man and I love you. Let me bestow my worldly goods on you as the marriage vows say. Let me love you and cherish you as a slightly old-fashioned husband wants to love and cherish his wife.'

Ebony's heart turned over. 'That's what I want too, Alan,' she whispered. 'To be loved and cherished in an old-fashioned way.'

'Good. Now put your head back down here and shut up. I like cuddling with my wife-to-be.'

'I like my husband-to-be cuddling me,' she laughed softly.

With a sigh, she settled back into his arms, listening contentedly to the sound of his heart beating strongly in his chest. Her eyes closed and she felt the love pulsate between them.

'Ebony,' Alan whispered after a while.

'Mmm?'

'I don't really want you to become old-fashioned, you know. I like the woman you are. I like your rampant sexuality and your—'

'My *what* sexuality?' she broke in, clearly bewildered.

'Rampant.'

She lifted her head to look up at him, but her hair fell into her eyes. Moving to straddle him, she sat up, pushing the tangled strands back from her face and shoulders with unconsciously sensual movements. 'What does rampant mean?'

Alan's breath caught in his throat when she bent forward to kiss him lightly on the mouth, her erect nipples brushing his chest.

'Is it good or bad?' she asked with the most arousing ingenuousness.

'Good,' he rasped.

'But what does it *mean*?'

'I'll tell you afterwards,' he growled, and, splaying both his hands up into her hair, he pulled her mouth down hard on to his.

Deirdre Carstairs was stretched out on the cane lounger in the sun-room, browsing through the Sunday papers and having a late, leisurely brunch when she saw Alan and Ebony making their way, hand in hand, up the back steps and across the terrace. The sun was just setting, throwing a warm glow over their dark heads. They stopped once to kiss lightly, smiling their happiness at each other.

Deirdre's heart swelled with joy and wonderment. She could not have chosen a more perfect spouse for her son. God had been very good to her the day that he'd directed Ebony into their household. As a mother, she'd been so afraid Alan would never get married and have children, that she would never have grandchildren. But one look at those two together confirmed her suspicion that it wouldn't be long before there was the patter of little feet around these empty old rooms.

Suddenly, she noticed that Ebony was limping

slightly. Rising, Deirdre hurried to meet them just as they were coming through the French doors.

'Ebony, dear, have you hurt yourself?' she asked straight away.

'Just a small cut on her foot, Mother,' Alan reassured. 'She's fine, aren't you, darling?'

Deirdre just stopped herself from staring at her son. He just wasn't the type to call anyone 'darling'. It just showed how much in love he was. 'You had a nice relaxing weekend, then?'

'*Very* relaxing,' Ebony said, and flashed Alan an incredibly sexy smile.

Deirdre beamed with satisfaction. This beautiful young thing was just what the doctor ordered for Alan. He'd been in danger of turning into somewhat of a stuffed shirt before she had burst back into his life. His claim that she'd shamelessly seduced him on the night of her twenty-first was probably a blatant exaggeration. Deirdre suspected Alan was a bit of a prude where sex was concerned. That Adrianna he'd got mixed up with had been a bit of a cold fish. Ebony was completely the opposite. There again, French girls were notorious for their sensuality.

'By the way, Mother,' Alan began, 'go right ahead and plan that engagement party. As soon as possible too. Ebony and I are getting married as quickly as the law allows.'

Now Deirdre could not hide her surprise, or her smugness. 'Is there—er—some reason for the hurry?'

'We're not sure yet, but better safe than sorry, wouldn't you say?'

'Yes, indeed. Next weekend for the party, then? I'll organise everything.' She clapped her hands excitedly. 'Oh, how exciting. I'll go tell Bob and Bill. They'll be tickled pink. Then I'll ring Vicki and…'

She was still bubbling away as she left the room, after which Alan turned to draw Ebony into his arms, kissing her resoundingly. She pulled back at last, laughing with soft surprise at this new and rather shameless Alan. He didn't even seem to mind who knew what they'd been up to all weekend.

'Your mother was pleased,' she said.

'Who wouldn't be, having a daughter-in-law like you?'

She flushed with pleasure at his words.

'You are so giving, my darling. Not many women would care about their mother-in-law's happiness, only someone as special and sweet as you.' His hands curved softly around her face, lifting her chin so that her lips tipped up to his. 'Of course, you do have another side to your character,' he murmured softly into her mouth. 'One which will remain for my eyes only…'

When the telephone ringing interrupted their kiss, Alan glared at it for a second before disentangling himself from Ebony's arms and resignedly snatching up the receiver. 'Alan Carstairs,' he announced a touch brusquely.

'Alan, it's Vicki.'

'Vicki! I'm glad you rang. I have some news for you.' Smiling over at Ebony, he reached out his arm to enfold her against his side, so close that she could hear Vicki's chatter.

'Have you?' she was saying. 'Well, it'll have to wait a sec, because I've got some news of my own and I think I'd better get it over with first.'

'Don't tell me you've left Alistair again,' he sighed. 'Or has he left you this time?'

'Neither. I know this might come as a shock after all I've said about marriage and stuff, but it seems I made a big boo-boo with my pill a couple of months back and…well…the upshot is I'm going to have a baby and Alistair insists we get married straight away. I told him he didn't have to, but he's gone all strait-laced on me since going to work for you. He's threatening to get his hair cut and start listening to classical music if I don't marry him. Well, I ask you, what's a poor girl to do?'

Alan and Ebony both had to cover their mouths to smother their laughter, the result being an awkward silence.

'Alan? Are you still there? Speak to me, for heaven's sake!'

Alan gulped a couple of times before continuing with a straight face. 'That's wonderful news, Vicki. I couldn't be happier. And I'm sure Mother will be thrilled.'

'Are you sure? I thought she'd be appalled. I mean, she never liked Alistair much, but he has changed, you know.'

'I do know. I'm very pleased with his work.'

'You are? Goodness! Well, maybe he has really changed, then.'

Alan's eyes softened as they travelled over his beautiful Ebony. 'Love changes everything, Vicki, don't you know that?'

'Why, Alan, what a romantic thing for you to say!'

'Maybe I've changed too, sister, dear. Maybe I'm in love.'

'You, Alan? I don't believe it. You're not the type. Besides, who would be stupid enough to fall in love with a workaholic like you?'

Ebony took the receiver out of his hands. 'Me, Vicki.'

'Ebony? Is that you?'

'It is indeed.'

'But…but…but…'

'Perhaps you and Alistair had better come over to the house, Vicki. I'm sure your mother will want to talk to you at length.'

Ebony hung up, and, snaking her arms around Alan's waist, pulled him close. 'Your sister was speechless with delight.'

'So I heard.'

'Give her ten minutes and she'll be knocking on the front door.'

'Ten? I'll give her eight.'

'Did I hear the telephone?' Deirdre said on coming back into the room.

'It was Vicki,' Alan informed her.

'Vicki! Why didn't you call me? I wanted to speak to her.'

'Don't fret. She's coming over. She has some good news for you.'

'Vicki has some good news? Did you tell her *your* good news?'

'We did.'

'And?'

'She was…surprised.'

Deirdre grinned. 'I'll bet she was.' Her grin faded to a puzzled expression. 'I wonder what her good news is? Do you know?'

'We do.'

'Can't you tell me what it is?'

'Should we, Ebony?'

She nodded.

'You're going to be a grandmother, Mother.'

'Well, I already suspected that might be the case, but I… Oh, my God, you mean Vicki. Vicki's having a *baby*?'

'That she is,' Alan announced with a wide smile on his face. 'And Alistair is insisting she marry him. So I think, Mother, we might plan a double wedding in the near future, don't you?'

Deirdre looked as if she might pass out for a second, then rallied. She looked from Alan to Ebony to Alan again, tears glistening in her eyes. 'A double wedding,' she choked out. 'Who would have believed this a week ago? Oh, I must be the luckiest person in this whole world.'

'No, Mother,' Alan refuted, loving blue eyes gazing deeply into shining black ones. 'That honour definitely goes to me.'

Susan Napier was born on St Valentine's Day, so it's not surprising she has developed an enduring love of romantic stories. She started her writing career as a journalist in Auckland, New Zealand trying her hand at romantic fiction only after she had married her handsome boss!

Susan had her first book published by Mills & Boon® in 1984, and since then she has written nearly thirty books, which have been distributed worldwide. Now she still lives with her most enduring hero, two future heroes—her sons!—two cats and a computer. When she's not writing she likes to read and cook, often simultaneously!

THE CRUELLEST LIE
by
SUSAN NAPIER

For Liz Pollack
The Parkroyal Hotel, Wellington

CHAPTER ONE

'The cruellest lies are often told in silence.'
Robert Louis Stevenson

'YOU'RE pregnant!'

Claudia, who had found precious little reason to laugh over the past few months, looked down at the small mound under her flimsy, faded cotton sundress and felt a thrill of amusement lift her embattled spirts.

'My goodness, so I am!' she declared in tones of mock-horrified discovery to the black-browed stranger frowning at her from her doorstep. 'And to think of all that money I've been wasting on Weight Watchers!'

Instead of amusing him, her flippancy deepened the frown, the man's crooked, surly mouth tightening ominously. He was tall—quite startlingly so—and correspondingly lean, with close-cropped midnight-black hair contrasting with surprisingly pale skin and a shadow on his jutting jaw that added to the general aura of menace radiating from eyes grimly slitted against the afternoon sun. In fact, if it weren't for his achingly elegant grey suit and a discreet silk tie that whispered of extravagant wealth and excellent taste, Claudia might have been afraid. As it was she assumed that he must have knocked on the wrong door.

'Very funny.' Perversely, his acid reply made Claudia even more amused.

'Thank you, I thought so, too. Do you usually start conversations with total strangers by stating the obvious?'

'If anyone's being obvious here, it's you… *Very* obvious.' The clipped pronouncement of distaste and pointed reference to her swollen abdomen tempered her amusement with annoyance. He was obviously too stuffy to appreciate her teasing. On the other hand nobody liked being laughed at for an honest mistake and it wasn't really fair of her to play on his ignorance, but she couldn't resist one more dig.

She sighed loudly. 'OK, I'll bite. What are you selling? Vaccum cleaners? Encylopaedias?' She gave him the cynical once-over of a typically harassed housewife, knowing that he couldn't possibly be a salesman, let alone one of the door-to-door variety. For one thing he was clearly lacking in the main essential—ingratiating charm.

Sure enough he stiffened at the very suggestion.

'I'm not selling anything.'

'Not to me, at any rate,' she agreed. 'First day on the job, huh? You really must do something about that technique of yours if you expect to make a living door-to-door...'

'I am *not* a salesman!' The crisp consonants vibrated dangerously against the growling vowels and Claudia decided that she was in danger of letting her unaccustomed frivolity run away with her. Now was the time to smooth the savagely ruffled male ego with some of her famous tact.

'Of course you're not—' she began soothingly, only to be cut off by his furious hiss.

'Don't patronise me—*Miss* Lawson!'

The emphasis on her single status, as well as the realisation that he knew her identity, was like a dash of icy water in her face, washing away the dregs of humour and clarifying the reasons for his accusing contempt.

Claudia felt a dreary, dispiriting, and totally unreasonable disappointment in her unexpected visitor. She had faced narrow-minded prejudice often enough lately to recognise its stony façde. The half-smile which had softened the pinched lines of her narrow face congealed into a grim line. She suddenly felt exposed by the harsh light of the hot summer's day, and hated him for making her aware of her terrible vulnerability.

Was he a reporter? No, no more than he was a salesman. Newspapers didn't pay their journalists enough to afford thousand-dollar suits.

'Then get to the point, Mr...?' She lifted her eyebrows in a gesture that she knew emphasised the natural haughtiness of her delicate features. Chris had called her beautiful and, even though she thought that her face was too sharp for conventional prettiness, he had made her believe it. These days it was even sharper, refined by the nausea that constantly blighted her appetite and the sheer strain of putting on a brave, unconcerned face for the world.

He ignored her implicit command. 'Is Mark in?'

'Mark?' As she had been expecting another oblique attack on her morals, his innocent query about her boarder took her off-guard.

'Mark Stone.'

'Mark Stone.' She repeated the name slowly to give herself time to think. Innocent? This man? Definitely not. Was he ferreting for information about her or about Mark? Was *he* the reason that the young man had been acting oddly guilty in the past few weeks? Had Mark got into some kind of trouble and not wanted to add to Claudia's burdens by worrying her with his personal problems?

Claudia looked again at her visitor, who was waiting with unconcealed impatience for her reply. Overt evidence of wealth was no guarantee of honesty and integrity, as she had very good reason to know. On second glance the slickly formal clothing didn't disguise the threat of that crookedly sneering mouth, the coldly narrowed eyes or the tension in the muscles of his neck and the set of his shoulders under the slim-fitting jacket. He had come expecting trouble and was prepared to handle it aggressively. Ruthless was the descriptive epithet that sprang to mind.

Was he a con man, or some kind of heavy, come to collect on an outstanding debt? Her eyes flicked past the scowling stranger to the car parked outside the gate of her small suburban home. A silver Jaguar as coldly sophisticated and sleekly solid as the man in front of her.

She made her decision. 'He's not here,' she said bluntly.

Not surprisingly, he didn't make a gracious expression of regret and politely leave.

'I know he lives here.' His grating statement challenged her to deny it.

'Well, I'm sorry, he's not at home,' she replied, not trying to hide her satisfaction at thwarting him.

'Really?' Neither did he try to hide his disbelief. 'Not at home, or just not at home to *me*?'

'Since I don't know who you are I guess it's both,' she said crisply.

'I'll wait.'

'You do that.' Little gold flecks of malice shimmered in her caramel-brown eyes. She hoped he would roast in his stuffy suit waiting for a victim who would never arrive, though no doubt his expensive car had air-conditioning.

'Thank you.' Before she realised what he was doing he had whipped past her with an agility astonishing in someone so tall, and was striding down the cool hall, looking into the rooms on either side.

'Hey! What do you think you're doing?'

She had left all the internal doors in the house open to help circulate the turgid summer air and by the time she had caught up with her uninvited guest he had swiftly inspected the empty kitchen and bathroom and the two bedrooms, one of which contained a double bed, the other a divan and a partly assembled rocking cradle along with a desk and chair.

Knowing that there was no way she could stop him by force, Claudia stormed into the compact, L-shaped livingroom ahead of him. Energy boiled inside her, banishing the weary lethargy that had been a constant companion to her pregnancy.

'As you can see, Mark isn't here!' she reiterated sarcastically. 'Perhaps you'd like to check the cupboards and pull up the carpets in case he's hiding in the cellar!'

'Do you have a cellar?'

Claudia blinked at his hard suspicion. Was the man utterly devoid of any sense of humour or proportion?

'No!' she bit out. 'I wish I did. It would be somewhere to lock you until the men in white coats come and fetch you!'

'You think I'm mad? You haven't seen anything yet, Miss Lawson.' So he *could* smile, but it was no consolation. In fact, the crooked quirk of his lips was most unnerving. There was no softening of humour in it and certainly no intention to amuse. Even more unnerving were his eyes. Now they were no longer squinted against the sun she could see that they were a gorgeous, breathtakingly intense blue. The blunt features and hard jaw were almost unattractive in their ruggedness, but those eyes were almost hypnotic in their vivid splendour.

'Where is he?'

With difficulty she tore her gaze away from his drilling stare. 'Why should I tell you?'

'Because I ask?'

She almost laughed. 'You call this *asking*? I call it arrogant bullying and invasion of privacy.'

'I didn't know you had any privacy left to invade, *Miss* Lawson.' Again that cynically contemptuous emphasis, accompanied by the piercing stare. 'The way you and your famous lover cavorted for the Press I doubt that you even know what the word means.'

Claudia wished that she could icily refute his sneer but the truth was that Chris *had* revelled in the fame that his race-driving career had brought him. Loving and being loved by him had meant embracing his fame, sharing a large chunk of their relationship with his devoted public, accepting her place in the limelight beside him, if not whole-heartedly then at least with dignity and grace.

In the first few months after he was killed in a race-track crash the publicity had been even more intrusive and wildly speculative but Claudia had simply withdrawn, and her resolute refusal to feed the old gossip or provide any fuel for the new had led to her present blissful anonymity. But she would not allow this narrow-minded bigot to belittle what she and Chris had shared just because he believed what he read in the scandal rags...

'Thank you for that illuminating insight into your petrified morality—'

'On the contrary,' he cut her off sharply. 'I have a very modern flexibility on the subject of morality. For instance I don't subscribe to the old-fashioned notion that a child is condemned by illegitimacy. If you think that my son is going to marry you just because you've cleverly managed to get yourself pregnant you have another think coming!'

A light as dazzling as his vivid eyes switched on in her brain. Of course! The black hair, the lean physique, the deep crushed-velvet voice! Only there the resemblance ended. Mark's eyes might only be a motley hazel but otherwise his face had a male-model perfection that he had not inherited from his father. It was no wonder that she hadn't guessed straight away. Somehow Mark had given her the impression that his father was much older, but this man looked barely forty. And no wonder he had looked so shocked by her pregnancy when she had opened the door! She almost grinned. This time she knew for certain that he had made a mistake. But in view of his anger she didn't think that he'd find it any more amusing than he had their misunderstanding on the doorstep.

'If I thought your son wanted to marry me, I'd run screaming in the other direction, Mr Stone,' she said drily and with perfect truth. 'It *is* Mr Stone, isn't it?'

'You know damned well it is,' he snarled.

'Oh, and how would I know that? As I recall you didn't bother to introduce yourself before you barged in.' From what she had gleaned from Mark, such arrogance was par for the course for Morgan Stone.

Mark had told her very little about his background other than that he was from Wellington, and that his mother had died when he was young, leaving him to be brought up by a wealthy, autocratic, perfectionist father whose expectations of his only child and heir were increasingly rigid and unrealistic. A business student at Auckland University, Mark had had a final blow-up with his father six months ago and had broken off all contact. Confronting the powerful image of his father in the flesh, Claudia could sympathise with Mark's desperate need to assert himself by proving he could make it by himself.

'If tests confirm that your child is Mark's I'll naturally arrange financial support during your pregnancy,' Morgan Stone continued coldly. 'If you wish to bring up the child yourself I'll establish a trust fund. My lawyer, as trustee, will approve expenditure strictly in the interest of the child so don't expect to be able to live the high life on my account. If you don't want to be bothered with the baby I'll make the appropriate arrangements—'

A chill of unnamed fear shuddered down Claudia's spine. She placed both hands over her swollen stomach and fought to control a sudden surge of nausea at what she thought he was implying, appalled by his cold-blooded recital and suddenly deeply aware of her physical fragility. She knew that she was unusually small—her doctor was constantly urging her to put on more weight—but she had seemed to do so only at the expense of the rest of her body so that while her bosom and stomach had continued to slowly bloom the rest of her had seemed to shrink, her face and arms and legs losing their formerly rounded contours. She might not look the picture of blooming motherhood but she wanted this child, she *needed* it...

'If you're suggesting an abortion,' she said raggedly,

'you can forget it. It's too late. This is *my* baby. It's nothing to do with you—'

'If it's my grandchild, it has everything to do with me,' he countered grimly. 'And my moral flexibility doesn't happen to include accepting abortion as a belated form of contraception, especially for a woman as sexually experienced as yourself. I meant only that I would take custody of my grandchild, if you proved unwilling or incapable of providing a secure home...' His fathomless blue eyes moved down her body as he spoke, studying her with blatantly hostile curiosity. Was he wondering what his son saw in her?

The dress Claudia wore was very thin, the humid Auckland summer heat being as taxing to her slim reserves of strength as was her nausea. This morning she had uninterestedly pulled on the coolest thing to hand, which was not actually a maternity dress at all. The spearing glance made her acutely aware of the feminine ripeness of her body, the way the flimsy bodice strained across her breasts, barely containing their lush bounty, the tautness of the fabric across her burgeoning stomach. There was nothing leering in the look and yet Claudia could feel herself flushing wildly. The placid maternal acceptance of the radical changes taking place within her body was momentarily swamped by the sensual realisation that, like the crude stone carvings of a primitive bygone era, she was to male eyes a brazen symbol of fertility, of voluptuous female sexuality. When this man looked at her, it was with the sure knowledge of her intimate experience.

A strange shock quivered along her bones. This hard, virile man a *grandfather*? Grandfather to *her* child? The first idea was almost laughable, the second utterly repugnant.

He took a step towards her and she gasped and lurched backwards, almost falling when the arm of a chair caught the back of her knees. Only his hands locking on her thickened waist saved her. She instinctively grabbed at his powerful wrists and tried to wrench them free.

'L-let me go.'

'What did you think I was going to do, hit you?' he growled roughly. 'I don't hit women—let alone women in your condition. You went very pale for a moment there; I thought you were going to faint. You'd better sit down.'

'I don't—' Even as she protested he was pushing her back into the chair, holding her there in spite of her squirming. He was not only strong, he was also extremely stubborn.

'You blanch at the idea of an abortion and yet you seem to have no problem with the concept of starving your baby in the womb,' he told her tersely. 'I suppose you're too worried about losing your figure to eat a properly balanced diet. What are you—about four or five months along? Yet you barely weigh anything and your arms are like twigs.' He bent to demonstrate his blistering point by wrapping his hand around her upper arm, his fingers overlapping on her smooth flesh.

'I'm naturally small-boned,' said Claudia defensively, loath to go into the dreary details of her difficult pregnancy with this unfeeling man. She was going to enjoy immensely seeing him eat crow when she told him the truth. 'Now will you please remove your hand? I don't like being mauled by ham-fisted male chauvinists. You know nothing about my pregnancy—' She twisted her body and he let her go, straightening to loom over her.

'I know that there are risks a woman of your age having her first baby should take care to avoid—'

'A woman *my* age!' Claudia's intention of boldly slapping him with the truth was ambushed by outrage. 'What has my age got to do with it? I'm only twenty-four!'

'A good six years older than Mark,' he took the opportunity to point out smoothly.

'I know how old he is!' Claudia gritted. When she had

offered room and board to a university student she had been thinking in terms of a girl but when an eighteen-year-old Greek god had turned up on her doorstep six months ago with his wistful tale of family rejection she had let him talk his way into her life. She had never regretted the decision. His cheerfulness and fierce energy and optimism had rescued her from the dangerous inertia of grief into which she had been sliding.

'But I'm surprised *you* do,' she added tartly. 'You didn't even send him a card on his birthday.'

Mark had told her he hadn't expected any softening from his father, but she had seen the veiled disappointment in his eyes when the minor rite of passage had passed unacknowledged by his family.

'Because he didn't see fit to inform me of his whereabouts at the time, and no doubt you wouldn't have urged him to make contact. Not before you had him well and truly hooked—'

'Don't be ridiculous!' Claudia tilted her head to glare up at him, struggling to retain her dignity in her inferior position. She was glad that the heat had prompted her to twist her waterfall of straight black hair into a top-knot instead of leaving it to brush her shoulders casually as she usually did. It gave her a much needed air of sophistication that might go a little way towards counteracting her the rest of her dishevelled appearance. Thanks to her swollen ankles she wasn't even wearing *shoes*, for goodness' sake!

'Mark is a responsible, intelligent young man—'

'With the emphasis on *young*—'

'Who is quite capable—insistent, in fact—of making his own decisions. Perhaps if *you* had been more receptive to his feelings he wouldn't have—'

'Run off the rails into your eager arms?'

'Will you *stop* putting words in my mouth?' Claudia rose defiantly, albeit with a little difficulty, to her feet again.

'Mr Stone, if this is the way you conduct your personal affairs I'm not surprised that you're having difficulties—'

'And you, of course, are famous for conducting affairs. When he was alive you were trumpeting Christopher Nash as the great love of your life and yet here you are only seven months later, shacked up with a boy half his age, newly pregnant to him and bleeding him dry of every cent he can lay his hands on.' His scathing voice raking her expression of surprise with contempt, he added, 'Oh, yes, I know that he's taken on two part-time jobs to buy your expensive loyalty, regardless of the fact that his studies are suffering! He's too blind to realise that your loyalty is assured by his surname. Why should you care if he gets his qualifications with honours or not at all? It's not what he could be but who he is that interests you. I bet you've calculated his net worth as a Stone down to the last dollar! But know this: if he marries you he won't get a single cent of my money!'

Claudia was speechless with guilt and dismay. Mark had been stubbornly adamant that he would not touch the trust-fund living allowance that his father had allocated for his studies—'apron strings', he had called it, and she knew that he paid her for his room and board through his job at a pizza takeaway, but she had not known about a second job. In her self-absorption she had vaguely protested when he brought her pretty fripperies—perfume and flowers and luxurious titbits to tempt her meagre appetite—but he was so cheerfully determined for her to enjoy them for their own sake that she had closed her mind to the implications of his having spare cash to spend on her.

She took a deep breath. This had gone quite far enough. 'Mr Stone,' she said huskily, 'you have it all wrong. Of course I'm not in love with your son—'

He laughed harshly. 'You're not telling me anything I don't already know. A pity I didn't come with a tape recorder; I'm sure Mark would find this very enlightening.'

'And he is not in love with me,' she continued steadily. 'He only thinks he is? Oh, yes, I know that too, Miss Lawson. That kind of infatuation makes him very easy to manipulate, doesn't it? Your years as a racing groupie obviously serve you well when it comes to insinuating yourself where you don't belong. A pity you encouraged the love of your life to spend so much on you when he was alive—he might not have left you so destitute when he died. This place must be quite a come-down from the five-star hotels you and your drunken groupie friends used to regularly smash up during race parties—'

Claudia clenched her hands at her sides to stop herself lashing out at his mocking face, her whole body trembling with a violent, repressed rage. It might not be much in *his* eyes but she had struggled hard against tremendous odds to make a home for herself here, to build a secure background for her baby in the midst of a shatteringly insecure world. He had no right to taint it with his contempt. But she would not beg for his understanding. No, he deserved to suffer a little of the torment he had offered her!

'Do you always believe what you read in the papers, Mr Stone?' she attacked. 'I wouldn't have thought you so gullible—'

'It's my son who's the gullible one. He always was too soft for his own good.'

The casual disrespect for Mark was another reason to hate him. 'For his own good—or for yours? You know, Mr Stone, the ironic thing is that I didn't really believe him when he told me about you. I thought he was exaggerating. I even suggested that he get in touch with you to try to work things out.'

The blue eyes looked stunningly unimpressed by the information. 'You suggested a reconciliation? How touching! And how profitable for you if Mark could be welcomed back into the family bosom…and bank-balance.'

It was like hitting her head against a brick wall. No—a

Stone wall, decided Claudia hysterically. Who could have believed that a simple misunderstanding could mushroom into a confrontation of such nightmare proportions? The labyrinthine conversation had taken so many twists and turns away from the clearly illuminated path of the truth that she felt dizzy and disorientated. He confused and enraged her, standing there so perfectly groomed, so perfectly righteous so…so *perfect* while she floundered in the hopeless knowledge that nothing she could say would convince him that she was anything but a mercenary, opportunist tramp.

'But perhaps there is another alternative,' he murmured into the sizzling silence. 'One that might be just as profitable for you…'

'If you're going to offer to pay me off you can forget it!' said Claudia fiercely, the headache that had dragged her out of bed that morning returning with a vengeance. 'I want you out of my house. *Now!*'

'*Your* house?' The mirthless smile reappeared. 'I understand that it belongs more to a finance company than to you and the repayments must take a large chunk of your benefit money. You *are* on a welfare benefit these days, aren't you, Miss Lawson? You certainly seem to have made no attempt to find a job in the last few months. I suppose you decided that getting pregnant was a good way to avoid having to earn a living in the foreseeable future now that the government is tightening up on persistent free-loaders on the welfare state. I wonder how the welfare people would view your cohabiting with a man who is obviously supporting you with money and gifts?'

'I am not a cheat!' Claudia flared, lifting her pointed chin, the flecks in her eyes blazing angrily. It was shaming enough that because of her difficult pregnancy she had been forbidden to work and had to accept what she saw as charity to live. To have him rub her nose in it was doubly humiliating. 'The social welfare department knows all

about Mark! So don't think you can blackmail me if your
bribes fail.'

'If?' He was swift to pick up her slip of the tongue. 'So
you *are* willing to consider a bid—if it's high enough?' He
named a figure that took her breath away. Unfortunately it
also exploded the last shreds of her self-control.

Later, the sequence of events played themselves over and
over in her agonised head—her attacking him with all the
vile words that had used to make her blush when she heard
Chris use them at the track whenever he lost a race through
someone else's incompetence. Her shoving at his immov-
able bulk, raining blows on his impervious chest, his catching her elbow to try and calm her hysteria, her wrenching
away, slipping, falling jarringly on her side...

She lay, dazed, on the threadbare carpet as he dropped
to his knees beside her, that pale, implacably stony face
exhibiting the first jagged cracks of emotion, the blue eyes
icing with shock as his hand hovered above her hip.

'Are you all right?'

'Don't touch me!' If he touched her she would shatter.
The fear that had haunted her since Chris's violent death
solidified into an agonised certainty that she had been too
terrified to entertain before this moment. Since the incessant
vomiting of her first month of her pregnancy she had been
waiting, dreading, hoping and praying that this moment
would never come. The moment when she would have to
pay for the sins of her past. But not this way, please, God,
not this way... She moaned.

'Miss Lawson—Claudia, are you hurt?' She heard the
reluctant horror in his voice, the grudging concern.

'Go away, leave me alone...' A ripple of pain shuddered
through her body, breaking her words up into fragmented
syllables as she closed her eyes and turned her head away
from him, away from the cruelty of the world.

'I can't do that. Not when you might be hurt. Is it here?
Is it your baby?' His hand lightly feathering against her

swollen belly made her convulse with a pain that was more mental than physical. She sobbed and heard him curse under his breath and shift, felt the skirt of her dress delicately lifted. Her eyes flew open, a little mew of humilitated protest dying on her dry lips as he carefully tucked the fabric back over her curled legs and leaned closer to stroke the damp strands of hair back from her sweaty brow as he murmured reassuringly,

'There's no blood, Claudia. You're not bleeding and your waters haven't broken. Don't cry—you're not alone. I'll take care of you. Who's your doctor?'

Oh, God, he was as implacable in his gentleness as he was in his rage, even though he despised her. Claudia's head swam and her bones ached and at that moment she gave up hope.

'I'm going to be sick—' she gritted through clenched teeth.

She was, miserably, and afterwards he lifted her very gently on to the firm couch, sitting beside her, stroking her shuddering body soothingly as he made an emergency call on the cellphone that he had produced from his inside pocket.

When the call was finished he bathed her face with a cool, damp cloth and talked softly to her, not seeming to care that she wasn't listening, her blank eyes shuttered, her whole being focused inside herself, preparing for the pain that she knew was to come.

He rode in the ambulance, too, and for some inexplicable reason she instinctively clung to his hand, only letting him break away when the hospital emergency staff finally persuaded him that his insistent presence in the examining-room was interfering with her treatment. The rest of that day and part of the night degenerated into a blur of pain and horror so that when next she woke she thought it had all been some unlikely nightmare.

Then she registered the cool white room, and explored

the exhausted emptiness inside her and knew it had all been real. Too real. She closed her stinging eyes and when she opened them again the doctor was there. Not the young emergency doctor but the consultant gynaecologist from the hospital's pregnancy clinic whose special patient she had been.

She received his kindly expression of sympathy apathetically, remaining dry-eyed at the information that her baby had been a son. Only when he sat on the chair beside the bed and began to question her about her activities in the last few days did she show a flicker of emotion.

'Had you noticed the baby moving much, Claudia, recently?'

She looked down at her fingers, picking at the bleached white sheet folded across her breasts. 'Was he perfect? I mean—he wasn't…?'

'Deformed? No, Claudia. But there was no heartbeat when they brought you in—that's why the Ceasarean was necessary—speed was of the essence.' He paused, and then continued, more gently, 'I don't think you'd felt him moving for quite a while, had you, Claudia?'

The tears that had been stinging in her eyes were hot on her cheeks. 'He—he was never a very active baby during the day…it was at night that he used to kick—'

'And the last few nights?'

She blanked out the unease that she had dismissed as a pregnant woman's fancy. 'I—I've been very tired, sleeping heavily recently—I don't know. I—when I fell it must have—'

He took her restless hand from the mangled sheet. 'It wasn't the fall, my dear. I think that perhaps in your heart you know that. It wasn't anything that was any fault of yours. All the fall did was to start your premature labour. But all the indications are that your baby had been dead for several days—'

'No!' She wrenched her hand away, placing it over her

flattened stomach as she denied the secret terror that had stalked her dreams. 'No—I would have known something was wrong—I would have done something—'

'I doubt that there was anything anyone could have done, Claudia. Sometimes these things happen—'

'What things? You said the baby was perfect—so it must have been me! What did I do wrong?' she cried in tearful anguish.

'You did nothing wrong, my dear,' he reassured her patiently. 'And I agree that the baby appeared physically perfect but we don't know about the rest. I did warn you at the beginning that there were some disturbing aspects to the pregnancy that could indicate that you might not carry to full term…'

'But I did everything you said,' whispered Claudia wretchedly.

'I know you did. You did everything you could for your baby, Claudia, I know that. But sometimes it's just not enough. Perhaps later, when I know more, I'll be able to give you precise reasons.' Claudia quickly pushed away the awful implications of those words. 'Meanwhile you should get as much rest as possible. Losing a baby in the later stages of pregnancy is much more traumatic than earlier miscarriage. And I know you probably don't want to hear this right now, but you need to know that the emergency doctor said that there was no indication of any chronic physical complications that would jeopardise future pregnancies. There is every chance that next time you will deliver a normal, live, healthy baby…and you won't necessarily have to have it by Caesarean…'

'*Next* time…?' Claudia couldn't imagine ever risking this kind of heartbreaking agony again.

'It was a mistake, you know!' she remembered achingly. 'I didn't mean to get pregnant—it was such a shock—I—do you think—?'

'No, I don't, and nor should you,' the doctor said sternly.

'Whatever your feelings at the beginning, you fought long and hard to have this baby, Claudia, and now you'll have to fight to accept this and go on. Now, shall I tell your friend he can come in and see you for a few minutes? The nurses tell me he's been out there all night pestering them, wearing a groove in the waiting-room…'

'Friend?' With Mark away she couldn't imagine who would have come to see her. Only Mark and her parents in Australia were listed as contacts on the information sheet she had filled in when she had first attended the hospital clinic.

'The very appropriately named Mr Stone. Sister Dawson says that he's as stubborn as a rock. He's not satisfied with the brief bulletins she's given him and is demanding to talk to your doctor. The emergency man has been flat out all night, and I've had a few other calls to make, but if you like I could explain to him now what's been going on—'

'No!' Claudia's voice was shrill with panic. Suddenly she had a source for all her pain. A perfect repository for all her rage and guilt. *Perfect*. How she hated that word. Hated him for being there when her body had rejected her own baby. 'No. I don't want you to tell him anything! He's not a friend—I hardly know him. I don't want him to know anything about me!'

The consultant eyed her cautiously. 'He already knows that we operated and the baby was born dead. In view of the fact that he was with you when it happened, don't you think—?'

'No, I don't.' Her agitation increased to borderline hysteria. 'Promise me you won't tell him! You have to have my permission to discuss my medical details with him, don't you? I don't give it. I don't want him here. Tell him to go away!'

He had no option but to agree, and, after a few more minutes inspecting her stitches and assessing her condition, he left. Claudia lay painfully on her side, her body curled up around her achingly empty womb. Tears seeped slowly from her under her tightly closed lids. After the gradual blossoming of joy inside her over the past few months it was a cruel shock to have her happiness snatched away as the illusion it was.

'Claudia?'

She opened her eyes to find Morgan Stone bending over her.

Even in her slightly drug-confused state she was shocked by the change in him—his rumpled haggardness, his hair uncombed, eyes red-rimmed with fatigue and the elegant suit decidedly rumpled. Then she was viciously pleased at the evidence of his long, desperate wait. He *should* be feeling desperate. *He* should be the one lying stiff and cold somewhere in the depths of the hospital, not her darling, innocent baby son…

'What are you doing here?' she demanded, smearing away her tears with an angry hand. She might have known he would arrogantly ignore the doctor's message that she didn't want to see him, she thought bitterly. The only wishes Morgan Stone cared about were his own.

'I had to see you. To see how you were. To see if you needed anything—if I can get you anything…' His mouth was a thin, crooked white line of tension.

'Yes, there's something I need—my baby back, alive and well,' she spat at him with searing contempt, trapped into the confrontation by the pain that pinned her to the bed. 'Can you do *that* for me, Mr Stone, or are you going to admit that there are *some* things your precious money will never be able to buy—like love?'

The sickly, greyish cast to his rigid, mask-like face bloomed with a dark colour across the hard, high cheekbones; like a livid badge of shame, she thought cruelly, and yet he wore it with a kind of shattered dignity, his eyes steadily unwavering as they met the silent accusation of hers, the compassion in them causing her to recoil in a jumble of confused emotions. In her precariously vulnerable state his compassion would be even harder to bear than his contempt.

'No, I can't do that.'

'Then why are you here? My baby is dead and I feel as if I've been ripped apart with blunt knives. Is *that* what you're waiting to hear? Is that punishment enough for my daring to even exist on the same planet as your darling son, let alone share a relationship with him?'

The previously smooth, dark shadow of his jaw was now roughly uneven but beneath the overnight growth of salt-and-pepper stubble Claudia could see the clenching ripple of muscle as he absorbed the full force of her acid hatred. His tired eyes were navy with a deep-seated torment she refused to recognise as he said raggedly, 'God, no—Claudia, it was an accident. You can't believe I meant anything like this to happen—'

'Can't I?' she taunted him bitterly. 'Doesn't this very neatly resolve one of your problems? One less skeleton to sweep into the family closet. One less parasite to detach from the Stone fortune? Of course, whether Mark will thank you for murdering your own grandson to try and stop him marrying me is another question entirely!'

The blue eyes went opaque with shock and she felt a tiny sliver of guilt. But it was only what he deserved, she told herself with grief-distorted logic. Morgan Stone had taunted her with her fickleness, when in reality she had been completely faithful to Chris, even at those times she had not been so certain of his equal faithfulness to her. In fact, if he hadn't been killed they would have been married by now, in the typically flamboyant ceremony that Chris had been planning at the time of his death. Now Chris was beyond pain, denied forever the fatherhood that had been barely anticipated in his last few weeks of life.

'Is that what you're going to tell Mark?' Morgan Stone

asked in a voice that sounded as hollow and echoingly empty as she felt.

'It's the truth, isn't it?' she said icily. 'You pushed me— I fell—I lost the baby. *You killed my baby*!' Her need to blame someone, anyone but herself, was desperate—essential for her survival.

'Claudia, please—'

'Oh, don't worry,' she sobbed wildly. 'You don't have to beg. I won't tell him. And if you have any feeling left for your son you won't either. You think I want to hurt him like that? You think I want him to carry around that crushing burden of guilt for the rest of his life—knowing what you did because of his friendship with me?'

She didn't want Mark hurt. The only person who should suffer, who *must* suffer, was the man whose arrogant contempt had destroyed her baby.

'Claudia—I—' He stopped, and made an inarticulate sound, gesturing helplessly with his lean hands. For all his fierce self-restraint he looked…lost. And suddenly she felt a terrifying surge of unwelcome empathy—the sharing of that most basic parental fear of loss of a child—whether baby or a grown adult. No, oh, no, she couldn't let herself share anything with him, feel anything for him…she had to make him go away—*now*…before she weakened any further…

'Just get out. I feel violated by your just being in the same room as me,' she told him in a listlessly pale voice suddenly drained of all life. 'And you don't have to worry about Mark and me. We're not going to get married. There was never any question of it anyway—I would have told you that in the first place if you hadn't bullied your way in like a cheap thug and started flinging insults around. I would have told you, too, that he's gone away for a week with friends—won't be back until next Sunday…'

Morgan Stone shifted sharply and, in case it was with triumphant relief, she gave the knife one last, deliberate twist. 'So I guess that for the want of some patience your grandson was lost. Maybe one day I'll be glad that I didn't bring another child of your blood into the world. Right now, the way I'm feeling, I really don't care if I never see you or your son ever again.'

CHAPTER TWO

CLAUDIA looked into the bleary eyes of a famous female
rock star and endeavoured to make her lie as sincere as
humanly possible.

'I'm sure nothing is going on. The maid must have mis-
interpreted a perfectly innocent gesture from your husband.
She was upset, she knew she was somewhere she wasn't
supposed to be—so she blurted out the first thing that came
to mind to divert attention—'

'Well, it was a bloody lousy thing to say. Silly bitches
like that shouldn't be allowed to work in hotels. If you
won't fire her I'll talk to the general manager. He sure as
hell won't ignore me—'

'Naturally the girl will be removed from her duties,'
Claudia lied smoothly, endeavouring not to wince at the
raw language. It was mild compared to the rock star's initial
outburst, compounded of tears, rage and, Claudia suspected,
a dangerous mixture of alcohol and exhaustion. Eliza
Mitchell was on the last leg of a world tour which had
begun in her native England and the pressures were obviously catching up with her. On one level Claudia sympath-
ised with the famous guest's outraged feelings of betrayal
but privately considered that they were being vented on the
wrong person, and she had no intention of allowing what
was evidently an ongoing marital war to jeopardise the job
of an innocent and hardworking member of the hotel staff.

It took a further twenty minutes to smooth things over,
and by the time she let herself out of the suite into the
fifteenth-floor corridor Claudia was beginning to feel a little
frazzled herself. The hotel security guard outside the door
grinned at her reappearance. He had had a ringside seat

when the ruckus started and had called down to the security
office while defending the unfortunate maid from a hail of
hotel furnishings.

'Oiled the troubled waters, Miss Lawson?'

Claudia sighed. 'Would you mind calling down for
Housekeeping to send someone *experienced*—and prefer-
ably middle-aged—up to replace the vase and chairs in the
penthouse suite? But wait until Miss Mitchell and her husband have gone out; she's due at a Press conference in
forty-five minutes.'

'Will do, Miss Lawson. You know, you should have
been a diplomat!'

'I don't have any languages,' she said, and then smiled
wryly. 'Although I think Eliza Mitchell just taught me a
word or two I didn't know before.'

She nodded to the two extra security men flanking the
glass lift and exhaled in relief as she began the smooth
descent to the ground floor. She didn't enjoy lying even
when, as now, it had been made clear to her that a lie was
the correct and required response to Eliza Mitchell's hysteria. The woman knew the truth but was unwilling to admit
it to herself or anyone else. So Claudia had obligingly provided her with the opportunity to avoid facing it. As public
relations co-ordinator for the Baron HarbourPoint she often
had to soothe over awkward situations with a view to the
hotel's reputation but today's lie had probably been the
biggest and most distasteful she had ever been called on to
produce.

Her eyes darkened and she turned to look out over the
panorama of Wellington harbour revealed by the glass wall
of the lift, blankly unseeing of the armada of small boats
welcoming several naval frigates sailing into Wellington for
navy anniversary celebrations.

No, not the biggest lie. The biggest lie she had ever told
had been the ugly one she had flung at Morgan Stone in
that spare hospital room two years ago. A lie soon regretted

but never redeemed. She had preferred to push it away. Pretend that it—and he—had never existed. But even the pretence was a lie. In a dark, unacknowledged corner of her mind she knew that she had committed a crime against an innocent man and, just as she had condemned him to carrying the death of a child on his conscience, so she had condemned herself to the perpetual burden of remembrance.

The lift doors opened and Claudia's heels clicked against the polished marble floor as she crossed the wide foyer towards the curving reception desk.

'Claudia? *Claudia*?'

A firm male hand on her arm halted her progress. Claudia turned, staring blankly at the man who had accosted her until he grinned familiarly.

'I know it's been a long time, Claudia, but not *that* long, surely? It's me—Mark Stone, remember? We used to live together.' And as she still failed to react to the joke his handsome face sobered. 'Hey, I didn't mean to rake up bad memories or anything, but it's just so great to see you again…'

Claudia was so appalled by the apparition that she had conjured up by her brooding that it took her a further few seconds to adjust to the fact that she was facing solid reality, not a fantasy from her own guilty conscience.

'Hello, Mark,' she said huskily, forcing a smile as she looked up into his incredibly handsome face. It was almost two years to the day, she realised with a pang, since she had seen him. 'I'm sorry, my mind was elsewhere. I— What are you doing here?' Her heart was suddenly fluttering with panic as her eyes slid nervously around the foyer.

'Business appointment—I'm meeting someone who's staying here. What are you…?' He looked down at her clothes and did a discreet double-take at the name badge she wore. 'You *work* here—at the hotel?'

Her smile came naturally this time, the fluttering in her

chest subsiding a little. *He was alone.* 'I'm in charge of public relations for the hotel.'

'That's fantastic! And you live in Wellington now. Why haven't you looked me up? I told you to, if you were ever in town...'

'I've only been here a couple of months; I'm still getting my bearings,' Claudia prevaricated. She could hardly tell him that she had tried to refuse her transfer from the Baron LakePoint in Auckland to avoid just this eventuality. However, her request for another posting had been denied and she had told herself that she was being unnecessarily cautious. New Zealand's capital city was a big place and it was hardly likely that she would run into Morgan Stone or his son.

'You never replied to any of my letters either,' Mark continued. 'I worried about you, you know—whether you were mad at me for leaving so suddenly and so soon after your—you lost the baby...'

'Of course not; I understand,' she murmured, her heart sinking at the hint of hurt in his expression. The last thing she needed was to shoulder another burden of guilt!

Unfortunately, she had understood all too well why Morgan Stone had suddenly decided to mend fences with his son, offering the imminent prospect of a business partnership if Mark would move back to Wellington. Mark's swift departure, three weeks after she had lost the baby, had followed his sheepish explanation that he had visited his maternal grandparents during his holiday and they had persuaded him that his father might be willing to compromise after all.

'Things were pretty hectic for me after you left—taking that hotel course, deciding to sell the house—and I'm afraid that letter-writing got pushed on to the back-burner,' she said, trying not to let her eyes waver from the innocent enquiry of his. She had been taken aback by his uncomplicated pleasure on seeing her but now she could afford to relax a little. He knows *nothing*, she realised with relief. She had never told him about his father's visit that day or the circumstances of her miscarriage, and now it seemed that Morgan Stone had been equally silent on the subject.

'Well, you're looking great now, I must say. Terrific, in fact!' Mark still had all of his youthful enthusiasm and in spite of herself Claudia was warmed by his outrageous flattery, although she could hardly have looked worse than she had during the time that he knew her! She knew that she looked a different woman from that pale, sickly creature. The cream and navy hotel uniform for female front-of-house staff suited her dark colouring and slim-hipped, long-legged figure and thanks to the hotel gym and the excellent meals provided for live-in staff she was stronger and healthier than she had ever been in her life.

'You're looking pretty good yourself,' she said, noting the beautifully cut suit that enhanced his Greek-god looks and the sleek grooming that had superseded the casual sloppiness of his student days. 'Quite the sophisticated man-about-town.'

He grinned at her teasing. 'You must be mixing me up with my father—he's the sophisticate; I'm just a pup in comparison.'

The easy reference set Claudia's nerves on edge, as did the thread of pride interwoven through Mark's humorous words. Was this the same young man who'd used to rail against his father's rigid intransigence and despise him for his manipulative coldness?

'Hey, how about we meet later and have a chat about old times?'

Old times? Claudia flinched inwardly. She looked at her watch, and automatically dropped into her professional persona. 'Er—well, I'm really pretty busy, Mark. I have a few meetings myself and then I'm conducting a back-of-house tour for some of our guests and then I have to attend a champagne-tasting we've arranged for a few of our regulars…'

To her surprise and relief, Mark accepted her brush-off without argument, a little spark of mischief glowing in his hazel eyes as he shrugged.

'OK. Some other time, perhaps. Lovely to see you again, Claudia. Cheerio!'

Slightly stunned at the ease with which she had evaded what could have turned into an awkward and painful encounter, Claudia watched him go. She couldn't believe it was that easy.

It wasn't.

Six hours later Claudia was laughing over a glass of Charles Heidseick with a tall blond man of greyhound elegance when she felt a presence at her elbow. She turned, the remnants of laughter glimmering in her brown eyes.

'Told you I'd see you again, Claudia.' Mark was full of glee at his surprise.

'If you're boasting about gatecrashing, Mark, I should warn you that this is Simon Moore, our general manager,' Claudia said wryly as she introduced the two men, briefly mentioning Mark's status as a student boarder in her home.

Mark lifted his hands. 'I'm strictly legit. Your invitation to guests said they were welcome to bring a couple of guests. I'm one of Tony's.' He pointed out his stocky, middle-aged companion, already talking with keen interest to one of the unattached women attending the tasting, as the man he had earlier met for lunch.

'Don't worry, he's also legit,' he added wickedly when he saw Claudia's glance flick to the other man's left hand, wrapped around the stem of his glass. 'He's divorced and up for grabs. If you like, I'll introduce you, Claudia.'

'You may as well forget the matchmaking,' Simon commented with his easy smile. 'Claudia's as married to the hotel business as I am, for which I'm grateful. She's certainly a dedicated employee—she's always brimming with ideas and she's done wonders for the HarbourPoint's image in the short time she's been here.'

'Why, thank you, Simon,' Claudia murmured sweetly, thinking he was laying it on a bit thick.

His brown eyes twinkled. 'Just indulging in some good PR, my dear. As you so frequently point out, blowing one's own trumpet produces a single, often discordant note, but blowing each other's creates a harmonious orchestra. Well, I suppose I'd better keep circulating.' He patted Claudia on the shoulder as he nodded to Mark. 'It was interesting to meet you, Mr Stone. I hope you enjoy your visit to the hotel.'

'I'm sure I shall,' Mark murmured as the other man moved away. 'Is there something going on there, Claudia?'

'He's my boss, Mark.' Claudia was startled by his suggestion. She and Simon got on extremely well but there had never been a hint of anything more personal between them.

'So? He's single, isn't he? And good-looking, and a smooth talker. Or are you already involved with someone else?'

'No, I'm not, nor do I want to be—'

'Mmm, maybe he is just a little bit *too* smooth,' he commented considering, eyeing Simon's effortless integration into the small crowd. 'It would be hard to know whether he's sincere or not. Maybe you're right to ignore any interest from that quarter.'

'Mark!' Claudia protested laughingly. 'There isn't any interest, from either side.' From the way he had slipped back into his teasing protectiveness it was as if the intervening years had never existed. But they had. And they precluded any closer friendship now. 'And if there were it would be none of your business,' she pointed out mildly.

'Just taking a friendly interest, Claudia,' he grinned. 'So…' he cosied up a little closer and tapped her glass with his '…here's to renewing old friendships. Now tell me, what have you been up to for the last two years, while I've been becoming a mini-tycoon? I guess that hotel course paid off in spades for you, huh?'

She glanced around, thinking to tell him that she was here on duty rather than for private amusement and ought to circulate herself when her gaze collided with a frigid blue one across the room. There, talking to the man she could remember only as Tony, was Morgan Stone, and as she looked at him he broke off his conversation and began to move. Towards her.

The world and everything in it vanished, except for that approaching blue void. She was tumbling; weightless, helpless as it rushed towards her, swallowing her will to speak, to think, to move. She was cold, so cold that her hands and feet felt like lumps of ice.

She heard Mark say something, and tried to turn to him but she couldn't, trapped by that approaching nightmare. She had imagined this moment often, but always it was with herself in control, prepared, braced to do what she knew had to be done. Not like this. Without warning. She felt a strange cold tingling creeping up the back of her skull and knew it was a symptom of shock. For one cowardly moment she wondered if she was going to be able to escape humiliation by fainting, but her natural resilience was too strong. Colour flared violently back into her white face as Morgan Stone halted in front of them.

'Well, Mark, I'm here. And this, I presume, is my surprise.' His voice was as deep, as crisp and darkly sardonic as she remembered.

Surprise didn't even begin to cover it. As Claudia's mind began to function again she could interpret the tightness of his jaw, the pin-point narrowness of his pupils stranded in the ice-pack of his eyes. His shock was as great as hers; he was just a little better at handling it.

'Yeah. This is the lady I lived with for a while when I was in Auckland.' Mark put his arm across her shoulders.

'She was a real darling. I couldn't have wished for a more accommodating landlady.'

Claudia wished he could have worded it differently. His innocent words were more bricks in the wall of misunderstanding.

'An accommodating landlady is an experience that every student should be granted on his road to maturity,' his father agreed blandly.

Oh, God, what did that mean? Claudia's icy hands began to sweat. She loved her job. She didn't want to lose it over an ugly public scene. She licked her dry lips, and then found Morgan Stone staring at her mouth. His eyes slid further, to her neat breasts, cloistered behind the navy jacket and the flat stomach revealed by her tailored skirt. Was he remembering her body as it had been, over-ripe to bursting with her child? Claudia couldn't help a tiny defensive movement of her hands and his eyes rose to her face again. This time there was something smouldering there that made her afraid. Was he going to challenge her? Was her lie at last going to catch up with her?

'Well, Mark? Aren't you going to introduce me to the lady?'

Was there just the tiniest hesitation before *lady*? Claudia didn't care. She only knew that she had received a temporary reprieve. He was willing to pretend they'd never met.

'Dad, I'd like you to meet the lovely Claudia Lawson. She's the public relations co-ordinator here at the hotel. Claudia, this is my father, Morgan Stone.'

Her worst nightmare held out his hand and Claudia had no choice but to take it politely. His palm was hot in contrast to her cold, damp one, and she saw his eyes flicker at the realisation. She half expected him to smirk at the betraying evidence of her nervousness but instead he did something that shocked her to her toes.

He lifted her limp hand to his mouth, pressing his lips

against the blue veins tracing beneath the skin from the back of her wrist to her knuckles, his thumb moving gently, almost reassuringly, against her palm. Claudia's eyes widened on his bent head and when he rose to his full height again she felt her flush deepen, struggling against the impulse to snatch her hand out of his and wipe it against her skirt. He had to be mocking her, he *had* to be!

'Cut it out, Dad,' Mark chuckled, seeming to see nothing odd in his arrogant ogre of a father performing a gracious, old-fashioned salute to a strange woman. 'You're making her blush. And you're wasting your time trying to impress her because she's already spoken for.'

'Oh?' Morgan Stone still held her hand and his fingers tightened, his eyes moving sharply between his son and his flustered captive. He was just as big and hard and masculine as she remembered but now she saw that there was a distinct frosting of grey in the short, midnight-dark hair, a few more lines radiating out from his unforgettably brilliant eyes.

'He means the general manager just told him I was wedded to my job,' Claudia said quickly.

'I see. Then you're not married?'

Was that a dig at her past? 'Not yet,' she said, extremely wary of his pleasantness.

'Oh. Does that mean that you're engaged?'

She wished she had a convenient fiancé to stop this polite interrogation in its tracks.

'No,' she admitted stiffly.

'I see.'

What did he see? Claudia pointedly flexed her fingers and he relinquished his warm clasp. At least she wasn't cold any more. She was distressingly hot—and thoroughly confused by his blandness.

'Did you move to Wellington recently, Claudia?'

His use of her first name was disconcerting, as was his innocent expression of enquiry. That hauntingly contemptuous 'Miss Lawson' still lingered in her memory. 'I was transferred from the Baron LakePoint in Auckland two months ago,' she said tautly.

'By your request?'

The implication was unmistakable. 'No—I was quite happy at the LakePoint,' she said firmly. 'It just happens to be part of management policy to regularly rotate staff to other hotels within the group.'

'An offer you couldn't refuse?' he murmured reflectively. 'Is this your first visit to Wellington?'

What was he getting at? Did he think she might have been regularly sneaking into town to see Mark behind his back? Her answer was clipped with angry frustration.

'Yes.'

'I see. And where are you living at the moment?'

'Here, at the hotel, but it's only a temporary measure while I settle into the job. I'm looking for a suitable place of my own to rent...' Her cool façade slipped as she realised how much she was revealing and she demanded with equal bluntness, 'Where do *you* live?' She would make a note to steer well clear of the location.

'I have a home over on Marine Drive.'

So he lived in one of the hillside residences on the opposite shore of Port Nicholson. Claudia was surprised. She would have thought that the kind of workaholic Mark had painted him as would prefer to live in the city centre, at Oriental Bay or one of the other exclusive, convenient, inner-city suburbs. There was the view, of course, and the eastern bays were within comfortable commuting distance of the city by car or ferry, but for a man who apparently spent little time at home and had no hobbies but his work she thought the view and the beaches were probably wasted on him.

'And are *you* married?' She followed up his calm reply with another goading question.

His dark eyebrows ascended sharply and Mark made a

muffled choking sound that could have been laughter. The answer, when it came, was a deliberate parody of her earlier one.

'Not yet.'

'Oh, does that mean you have someone in mind?' she cooed, equally mocking. 'Who's the un—er—lucky... lady?'

He looked at her consideringly for a long moment, until she began to regret her stupidity in challenging him. Then suddenly he smiled, making him look all the more dangerous.

'I regret to say that underneath this urbane exterior beats the crude heart of a commoner,' he said, laying a hand across the breast of his dark suit. 'If and when I marry again it'll be to a woman rather than a lady. Ladies are for pedestals; women are for wives. It's a fine line but a definite one...rather like the difference between men and boys.'

'I didn't know there was one,' said Claudia crushingly, looking down her haughty nose at him, a difficult deed to accomplish since he was at least six inches taller than her, even though she was wearing her party heels.

'Really?' he drawled, completely uncrushed. 'My dear Claudia, you *have* been running with the wrong crowd.'

So intent had she been on the silent interchange which shadowed the verbal jousting that she had quite forgotten Mark, until he shifted uneasily beside her.

'Hey, you're not arguing, are you? I thought you two would get on like a house on fire. After all, you both have something in common—me!'

His feeble joke produced a tiny, telling silence, and Claudia was about to rush into the breach with something foolish when Morgan Stone spoke again, still in that slow, easy drawl.

'Oh, there's a fire all right, Mark, isn't there, Claudia? We're just not sure whether to douse it or feed it.'

'Huh?'

'Speaking of dousing, Claudia is out of champagne and I haven't tasted any yet.' The soft comment jogged Mark into over-eager action, the sophisticated air he had been busily projecting dissolving in his puppyish desire to please.

'Oh, hey, let me get that for you...' He removed the empty glass from Claudia's nerveless fingers and slipped away. She didn't even remember having drained it and now she suddenly felt light-headed as she confronted Morgan Stone without the protection of his son's presence. What had he meant about a fire?

'You're looking very beautiful—no wonder he's so enchanted to see you again.'

'I—I beg your pardon?' Claudia was sure she must have misheard that husky ripple of sound.

He ignored her wide-eyed shock, studying the way her silky black hair shaped her head and flared out around her neck in a thick, blunt bob that just licked forward at her jawline. 'No, perhaps not beautiful. Very lovely. Another case of subtle but definite difference. You look younger with your hair short—young and carefree.'

Carefree was the last thing she felt right now and maybe her expression told him as much for he stopped looking at her in that disturbing fashion and said quietly, 'You never told him what happened. You could have used the information to widen the breach between us, but you didn't. I thank you for that.'

'I—I thought *you* might,' she stumbled, disorientated by his stunning boldness in cutting to the heart of her unease.

'You said you didn't want me to,' he said simply.

'And what I want *mattered*?' she said incredulously, adding sarcastically, 'Of course, it had nothing to do with suiting your own interests.'

His blue eyes never flinched. 'I don't deny it. If he'd talked to me about it, perhaps I would have told him. But he has never confided in me. We weren't on close or comfortable terms with each other for quite a while after he came back. There were…adjustments to be made on either side. When he talked about you it was always in general terms. He mentioned your losing a baby, but he never admitted or indicated in any way that it had been his. In fact he seemed so willing and relieved to come home that I thought what happened must have shocked him out of his infatuation. I thought it was kinder to both of you not to interfere—'

'Not interfere! What did you call pestering me in the hospital? And suddenly offering Mark a partnership when you'd refused to even discuss letting him have any sort of involvement in your business.' That was as informative as Mark had got about the argument that had caused the split.

'Being humanly fallible. Being willing to admit I was wrong. I wanted him to have choices—'

'Knowing that he'd choose not to stay with me—'

'If he'd loved you he would have stayed—or brought you with him,' he said bluntly. 'It was his decision to come back alone. And you had admitted to me that you didn't love him.'

She looked away. Why was she arguing with him? Compounding the lies that she already regretted?

'However much you resent me, Claudia,' he said quietly, 'I only did what I thought was best at the time for my son. And, looking at you now, I think that perhaps it was also best for you…'

'I suppose you think it was best for my baby, too!' she blurted fiercely, the ache of emptiness that she thought had been filled momentarily returning to haunt her.

Some of her pain must have shown in her face because he placed his hand on her waist, turning her so that she was facing him directly, her back to the room. 'I'm sorry. I wasn't being dismissive of your loss. I, of all people, know how much you suffered. That was why I visited you. I wasn't pestering you. No one else came to see you.'

'I didn't need your pity then and I certainly don't need it now!' she denied proudly.

'No. But you did need something from me. Money. Quite an outrageous amount of it, in fact,' he pointed out pitilessly, in direct contrast to the gentle restraint of his touch on her waist. Claudia felt her defiance flee before her shame.

Morgan Stone hadn't gone away meekly when she had ordered him to. He hadn't left her alone. For three days he had continued to visit, bringing flowers and fruit and news of the outside world, even though Claudia had resolutely refused to even look at him, closing her eyes and putting on the headphones that hung above her bed.

When she had recovered sufficiently to realise that she was in a private rather than public hospital and that Morgan Stone had arranged to pay her bills she had further reason to fiercely resent his manipulation of her life. She could never have afforded the extravagance of private care for herself and the envelope that he had handed her as he left on the third day turned out to be the final, supreme humiliation. When she had listlessly opened it she had found inside a cheque for several thousand dollars and a brief note suggesting that she reconsider her relationship with his son in the light of her financial independence...and the fact that Mark would be dependent on his father's goodwill for the foreseeable future. The fact that the cheque wasn't post-dated had merely underlined his certainty as to her greed.

Claudia hadn't had the chance to throw his conscience-money back in his arrogant face. She'd never seen him again, and, cheated of the chance to salvage her pride, the only revenge left had been to keep his money, to extract payment for his imagined sins in the only way he seemed to appreciate: cold, hard cash.

Later she had realised the reason for his abrupt departure. He had discovered that Mark was at his parents' home and had flown back to Wellington to protect his investment!

Mark had been so over the moon about his father's startling and apparently unique reversal of his earlier decision that Claudia had quietly relinquished her futile fantasies of furthering her revenge against an innocent man, and sent him on his way with her best wishes for the future.

'Did you expect me to refuse your blood money in some grand gesture of defiance?' she sneered defensively. 'Well, I didn't. I spent it, every last cent!'

'So my bank-statement informed me,' he said calmly, his eyes on her flushed face. 'I hope you used it wisely.'

'Of course I did. I spent it on clothes and jewellery and having a good time,' she answered flippantly.

'Did you, Claudia?'

Why did she get the feeling that beneath his gravity he was amused? She glared at him. He couldn't possibly know that she had used the money to pay for her hotel course at the technical institute and to support herself until she'd gained the qualifications that got her her job with Baron's.

'Isn't that what you expected a cheap tramp like me to do?'

'Oh, not cheap, Claudia, never cheap,' he murmured. 'I think that whatever you thought I expected you to do you would do the exact opposite, just to punish me for my presumption.' His perception was as unnerving as his calmness. 'As you pointed out at the time, I didn't know enough about you to make any judgements on your character.'

'But you did it anyway!'

'As I said, I'm fallible,' he shrugged. 'I have a strong will and a hot temper. It can be a lethal combination. It's what caused me so much strife when Mark grew old enough to challenge my authority. I like to think that I've mellowed a little with age...'

'*Mellowed*?' Claudia struggled with a quite inappropriate desire to laugh. A few grey hairs were one thing, but she couldn't imagine a genial Morgan Stone, however venerable his years.

'You think I exaggerate?' he murmured crookedly.

'I've seen no evidence of it!' She looked him up and down in an insulting fashion, trying not to notice the way his lean, densely muscled body was flattered by the tailoring of his suit. If anything he looked physically even tougher than he had two years ago.

'That's because you're afraid to look. You're too busy hiding from the past. Why don't you come out from behind your defences, Claudia? You might be surprised at what you find—'

'Where's Mark with that champagne?' she interrupted shrilly, totally unnerved by his unwillingness to fight.

'He's very diplomatically giving us time to get acquainted,' Morgan replied, shifting to block her view of the room. 'He wants us to like each other. It seems to be important to him. Don't disappoint him, Claudia.'

It sounded almost like a warning. 'Or what?' she demanded acidly.

'Or I might feel obligated to explain the real reason for your lack of enthusiasm for meeting me...'

'You'd tell him—*now*?' Claudia was stunned by the suggestion.

He shrugged. 'Why don't we discuss it over dinner?'

She was even more stunned. '*Dinner*? With *you*?'

'And Mark...with his fiancée, of course.'

'Mark's engaged?' Her question jerked out involuntarily.

'He hasn't told you?' The cynical gleam in his narrowed eyes switched on a light in her overheated brain.

'We've hardly exchanged a few words. We only met again this morning,' she said stiffly. 'I have no intention of seeing him again if that's what this is all about. So whether he's engaged or not is irrelevant.'

'What if he wants to see you?'

'I'll tell him no!'

'And if he doesn't take no for an answer?'

'Why, is it a family trait to ride roughshod over people?' she said snidely. 'Look, Mr Stone—'

'Morgan. My name is Morgan. He's coming back to-wards us.' His voice lowered and this time the threat was shockingly succinct. 'If you don't want me to rake up the awkward past I suggest that you co-operate.'

'That's blackmail!' Claudia gaped at him. He must be insane. All that unbridled power over the destinies of other people had evidently rotted his reason. 'Morgan,' she purred, suddenly taking great pleasure in the familiarity, a heady sense of her own power overtaking her former wariness, 'haven't you got this completely the wrong way round? You have far more reason to fear the truth coming out than I do. *I'm* the one who could blackmail *you*!' Her triumph was ineffably smug and resulted in an indefinable tension in the man opposite.

'You could, Claudia, but would you?'

She lowered her dark lashes as if thinking, her eyes shot with gold as she studied his impassive face through their silky screen, savouring her dominance over him. Her smile curved in secret satisfaction, revealing a dimple in her left cheek, and she heard his sharp intake of breath as she lifted her head to stare boldly at him, all honey eyes and taunting, rose-pink mouth, unknowingly sensual in her very feminine arrogance. 'I might!'

'I dare you!' he said softly, and before good sense could rescue her from her unaccustomed attack of recklessness Morgan Stone had side-stepped her and was accepting a glass of champagne from his son and toasting her with it.

'Claudia was just suggesting that we dine together this evening. What do you say, Mark? Perhaps you can call Serita and we can make a night of it!'

CHAPTER THREE

'WHY are you doing this?' Claudia demanded fiercely, trying to disguise her temper with a polite smile as she moved stiffly across the polished floor.

'Dancing with you? You said you liked to dance.' Morgan Stone turned her with a delicate but firm pressure of the strong hand splayed across her naked back. What on earth had possessed her to wear a halter-neck gown?

'I was talking about this...this *farce* of a dinner!' Claudia gritted.

'You have only yourself to blame for that, Claudia. I did give you the option of meeting on neutral territory...but you took the coward's way out and your lies were what compromised you, not me...'

Coward. Lies. The accuracy of his thrust cut deeply into her pride. Those two words summed up her whole relationship with Morgan Stone. If only she hadn't panicked earlier, when he had come out with that outrageous remark about dining together, but she had been terrified of what he might say next if she denied suggesting it. Calling the bluff of a man as tough and seasoned as Morgan Stone had been a very bad mistake. Instead she had pretended to remember that she was supposed to be working, making sure that the first night of a week of theme dinners that she had arranged in the main restaurant in conjunction with a floral festival being held in the city ran smoothly.

'Perfect—we can eat here at the hotel,' Morgan Stone had interposed smoothly into her hasty explanations. 'What better way for you to check the effectiveness of the atmosphere than to experience it yourself? And you'll be on hand if there are any problems...'

'Oh, I don't think—'

'If you like I'll square things with Simon.'

'Simon?' Claudia was visited again with the peculiar sense of disorientation that Morgan Stone seemed to engender in her brain.

'Moore. Your boss. We're business acquaintances. In fact we went to the same private school...'

'Oh, no!' Her exclamation was a totally involuntary breath of horror and the piercing blue eyes narrowed in humourless appreciation of her dilemma.

'I assure you the old-boy network is quite a legitimate business tool,' he commented silkily. 'Don't you approve?'

Not when the net was a poison spider's web and she the poor, struggling fly caught in its sticky embrace!

'No—I mean, you needn't bother Simon...' she said hurriedly. Especially since he would expose her excuse for the sham it was. The overall concept of the floral theme in the hotel this week had been Claudia's, and she was responsible for publicising and co-ordinating the various events, but the head chef, a temperamental man at best, would have something to say if he thought she was trying to horn in on his jealously defended territory.

'You're sure? I wouldn't like to get you into trouble,' he murmured innocently.

God, he was a mocking swine! He knew very well she had just been trying to wriggle out from under his thumb. Claudia summoned up a chilling smile.

'I'm sure. But I was going to say that I doubt we'll be able to get a table at this late stage.' She turned her attention deliberately to Mark, her voice unconsciously softening in deference to their former friendship as she tried to inject some sincerity into her regret. 'Our Nautilus restaurant is so popular it's usually booked out days in advance, especially on Friday nights during special events.'

She might have known that the truth would be no more effective than lies where Morgan Stone was concerned.

What he wanted he got. She didn't care to know what form of threat, bribery or influence he had used but he hadn't merely got them a table, he had got the best in the house, in a corner of the glass-fronted restaurant where it jutted sharply out over the harbour, giving diners the feeling that they were on sea rather than land. Claudia hadn't even tasted the meal; she had been far too busy concentrating on walking the tightrope of conversation with Mark, conscious of Morgan watching her like a hawk, observing every word and move. She had been rather voluble in her nervousness, talking a lot about her career because it seemed a nice, neutral topic, not caring that she might sound ambitious to the exclusion of everything else.

'But it wasn't an option, was it?' Claudia remembered sourly now, trying to ignore the envious feminine looks that she was garnering on the dance-floor. She returned an envious look at a woman who was dancing with a plump, cheery little man. How uncomplicated other people's lives seemed to be compared to her hopelessly tangled skein of affairs. 'I didn't want to have dinner with you *anywhere*— let alone dance with you.'

'You would rather have danced with Mark?'

'He didn't ask me.'

'But he was going to.'

Her brooding gaze snapped from the contented couple twirling past them to the blunt, dark-shadowed jaw and from there bounced up to the compelling blue challenge. So that was why he had suddenly swept her into the crowd. Her impatience got the better of her.

'So what? For goodness' sake, what do you think can happen in the middle of a dance-floor?'

'You have to ask?' With a suddenness that took her by surprise his hand slid from her shoulder-blades to the hollow in the small of her back and he drew her hips against his, making her aware of their sinuous, rhythmically evocative movements, the slight arch of recoil Claudia made only emphasising the intimate fit of their lower limbs. The hand that had been decorously holding hers dropped to his lower chest, drawing her entwined fingers down between their shifting bodies, trapping them there as he leaned his chest back into her outraged torso.

'What do you think you're doing?' she whispered fiercely, feeling the heat flare under her creamy skin.

'Dancing.' His voice was a soft rumble against her ear, his hard jaw tucked against her skull. 'Why the outrage, Claudia? After all, what can happen in the middle of a dance-floor?' He spun her deftly, his thigh sliding in between hers and lingering for a fraction of a second, enough to unbalance her so that she stumbled slightly, giving him an excuse to secure her even more tightly against himself. If she hadn't been aware of him as a man before, she certainly was now. He felt as strong as he looked and held her easily, skilfully...

'Very amusing,' said Claudia, and on her next step deliberately planted her slender high heel square on the soft Italian leather of his shoe and ground it deeply. This time it was he who staggered and came to an abrupt halt in the middle of the dance-floor, swearing under his breath.

Claudia stood straight in the prison of his powerful arm, trying not to let him see how helpless she felt against the threat of his undoubted masculinity. 'Had enough already, Mr Stone? I thought you had more stamina.'

He looked down at her from his considerable height. 'Is that a challenge, Claudia?' he asked softly.

She instantly backed down at the hint of relish in his voice. 'No, of course not. I just don't like being— being—' She floundered, trying to think of a word that adequately described what he was doing to her.

'Danced with?'

'Oh!' She glared at him furiously.

'Isn't that what we're doing with each other? Dancing around the main issue?' he continued, with a shrewdness that dismayed her. 'That issue being your unresolved feelings about the past. You say you have no intention of getting involved with Mark, but what if he also has unresolved feelings…?'

'It wasn't *my* fault that his fiancée couldn't come tonight.' Claudia was instantly defensive.

'If he even asked her…'

Claudia's eyes widened. 'That's ridiculous.'

'Is it? He leapt at the chance to come to dinner but what sensible man would want his current girlfriend and his ex-mistress sitting at the same table?' She wasn't even aware that they had started to move again, and that his hold on her was as secure as ever, her steps a fluid match for his.

'Current girlfriend? I thought you said they were engaged…'

'He and Serita have known each other for over a year and have been dating exclusively for the last six months. She's a bright and beautiful girl, warm and sweet and very good for Mark…'

Whereas Claudia had emphatically not been, was the implication.

'And how did Mark happen to meet this paragon of virtue?' she responded tartly. 'I suppose *you* introduced them…'

'As a matter of fact her father did; he's Michael Glenn, the MP…'

'And no doubt you went to school with him, too.' Claudia knew she was being bitchy but she couldn't help it. The knowledge that this man didn't consider her good enough for his son still rankled.

'Actually he did attend the same boarding-school, but not at the same time. Michael is a decade older than I am.'

'He must be near the parliamentary retirement age, then,' Claudia jabbed wickedly. 'You might not have the advantage of his political influence much longer.'

Instead of being offended Morgan laughed, the first time she had heard him do so. It was a warm, husky sound that resonated in her senses.

'If I admit that I'm going to be a creaking forty next month will that please your vengeful soul?' he grinned, seemingly untroubled by the prospect.

'You were only eighteen when Mark was born?' Claudia blurted out the startled realisation.

'Yes.' His smile tightened to the familiar crooked line. 'The same age that Mark would have become a father if your baby had survived. And I was as ill-prepared to assume the responsibilities of fatherhood as he was.'

'W-what did you do?' she asked, unwillingly fascinated by the notion of a Morgan Stone unprepared for anything.

'Married her, of course.' He met her shocked eyes coolly as he confirmed her stunned comprehension. 'Yes, I got my girlfriend pregnant when we were still students. Why do you think I was so determined to make sure that Mark wasn't condemned to repeat the mistakes of the past? Twenty years ago marriage was the only option in the society in which we moved. We were both just out of high school. Marina had no immediate family and mine refused to provide any support, financial or moral, unless we got married. So we did—but I refused to grovel for my parents' approval. I dropped my university plans and went to work to support us. It was not a success. We wanted different things out of life. If Marina hadn't died we would have been long divorced by now.'

Claudia looked away, stricken anew by the unavoidable conclusion that this man was not the ogre of her indefensible imaginings but a living, breathing human being who had endured suffering and emerged the stronger for it. A man of honour.

She swallowed. 'Morgan, I—'

'Mind if I cut in?'

Would she have told him the bald truth, right there in

the middle of a public dance-floor? Claudia didn't know as she glided away with Mark, conscious of a surge of weak relief at the fresh reprieve.

'What were you talking about so intently? You hardly had two words to say to each other at the table...' Mark's curiosity obviously had more to do with his decision to cut in than a desire to dance, thought Claudia wryly. It was true she had consciously directed most of her conversation towards Mark this evening, keeping firmly on the subject of trivialities, but it had been a tactic born of fear. Morgan Stone's mere presence was enough to disrupt her normally polished self-confidence.

'I thought you wanted us to get on together,' Claudia protested lightly, turning her head so that she couldn't see the man who had relinquished her with a brooding reluctance still standing at the edge of the dance-floor.

'Get on, but not get it on,' Mark punned outrageously, his grin hinting at an uncomfortable resemblance to his father. 'I should warn you, Claudia, that Dad doesn't have a very good track record with women. He has this fatal flaw, you see. He's very competitive. He just cannot resist a challenge, but when he's conquered it he seems to lose interest...'

'You think he might see me as a challenge?' Claudia questioned with an inward shiver.

'Well, you do look have a certain touch-me-not air about you, even in that invitingly touchable dress,' he teased, running his hand over the slinky leaf-green fabric on her hip. 'And Dad can't bear being told what not to do...'

'Somehow I can't picture your father as a womaniser,' murmured Claudia uneasily, aware that if Morgan was watching them he was sure to misinterpret that stroke of her hip. 'For one thing he hasn't got the looks...'

Mark laughed. 'You, of all people, should know you can't judge a book by its cover. But you're right, he didn't used to be. The thing about Dad is that he's always been extremely single-minded. Whatever he wants he goes after with a vengeance. A lot of women find that aura of controlled aggression a real turn-on. I used to bring girlfriends home and they'd take one look at Dad and fall over themselves to get him to notice them.'

'And did he? Is that one of the reasons you fought?' Claudia couldn't help asking.

'Maybe—subconsciously it might have been...' Mark admitted slowly, as if he'd never considered the possibility before. 'Not that he ever did anything to encourage them. In those days I guess his aloofness was part of the big attraction, the way he kept everyone at an emotional distance—even me. Oh, he gave me attention when he could spare it and I got the best of everything, but I never really felt part of his real life outside in the real world—the business one he seemed to find so exciting and fulfilling. And because he had this hang-up about the expectation of inheritance making me soft I knew he'd never let me in without a fight. I would always be his son, his duty, his responsibility—never his equal, never someone to share that responsibility with. He was incapable of delegating, he always had to be in total control. I guess I made his life hell for him for a while, trying to get his attention but at the same time break away from that control. You didn't know him before so you just wouldn't realise how much he's changed in the past few years. I can hardly credit it myself. He's learned to play as hard as he works...he seems, I don't know...less aloof and restrained, more...more—'

'Mellow?' Claudia suggested wryly.

'Mellow. Yeah, I guess that's it. Mellow! More... *accessible*. That's what I meant about the women...he seems to pursue his social life these days with the same drive and aggression that used to be directed into work.'

'You almost sound disapproving,' said Claudia, amused

by the role-reversal. 'Now you're finally working for him, don't you think he's got enough of his mind on the job?'

'Not *for* him, *with* him—my name's on the business now, too,' Mark corrected her, his hazel eyes glittering with youthful arrogance. 'I couldn't believe it when he agreed to add that "And Son" to the company logo. No, I just don't see why he expects *me* to want to settle down when *he's* having such an obviously good time playing the field.'

Uh-oh. 'Serita,' Claudia guessed.

Mark's dark head lifted as if prepared for criticism, then he shrugged sheepishly. 'She's a nice girl, but if Dad thinks I'm going to marry just to provide him with grandchildren while he's young enough to enjoy them—'

Claudia blanched and stumbled and before she could re-cover Mark had swept her out of the swaying crowd. 'Sorry, have you had enough of rolling us Stones around the floor? I see our desserts arrived so we may as well go back and join the old man...'

Claudia allowed Mark to seat her solicitously in front of a mouth-watering concoction of fresh raspberries decorated with stems and leaves of white and dark chocolate to look like a sheaf of roses across her plate. Her appetite, however, had deserted her.

Morgan poured her the last of the bottle of red wine which he had ordered with the superb main course.

'You look as if you need this more than I do,' he murmured provocatively. 'Your years must be catching up with you. In your salad days I believe you used to dance away the entire night...on table-tops, no less!'

'Once!' Claudia's response was swift and fierce. She tempered her tone as she lifted her glass and took a calming sip, willing herself not to over-react. '*One* table-top—after Chris won the drivers' championship. I think I was entitled to a little exuberance.' In truth it was Chris, never one to deny a photo opportunity to the attendant Press, who had swung her up on to the table and urged her to pose for the cameras.

Mark looked from one to the other, hesitating. 'I didn't realise you knew about Claudia and Nash, Dad...'

'I knew all about Claudia the first time I ever met her,' his father returned smoothly, not taking his eyes off her pale face. 'I didn't realise it was supposed to be a secret.'

Claudia tensed. Was he going to explain when that first time really was? Intense blue eyes measured her nervous apprehension.

'It's not, it's simply that the Press gave Claudia a really rough time after Nash died and she had to practically go into hiding in order to live a normal life again,' said Mark when she remained silent. Her knight in shining armour— little did he know that while he still defended her honour she had deliberately tarnished his.

'I presume you mean the fuss about his earnings—embezzled by his manager, weren't they? And didn't his family kick up a fuss about the prospect of you inheriting his fortune—non-existent as it turned out to be?'

Claudia inclined her head stiffly. His source of information two years ago had obviously been newspaper files so it was hardly surprising that he had had a distorted view of her character.

At first, insulated by Chris's love, she had been amused at the ridiculous stories about her that had circulated regularly in the gossip columns. It was a joke between them that she was seen as some kind of jet-setting *femme fatale* whereas when they met she had been a rather quiet, serious-minded twenty-year-old whose country upbringing had rendered her painfully naïve about the glamorous world her love for Chris catapulted her into. The naïveté had soon been crushed, but the intrinsic nature of her personality had not changed. In spite of the pressures, and the fact that her parents had never forgiven her for shaming them by flagrantly living in sin with her famous lover, Claudia had

never succumbed to the temptation of believing her own
Press.

'Did they ever manage to get anything back after they
caught up with him, Claud?' Mark asked. 'I read in the
papers that the case went to court in the States. You know,
in the circumstances, you would have had a strong case
for—'

'No!' Claudia quickly cut across his concern, her eyes
willing him not to continue in the same revealing vein.
When he appeared not to get the message she forced herself
to say steadily, 'No, I—he was apparently no better at managing money for himself than he was for Chris…and anyway I just want to put all that behind me…'

Mark finally registered her tension and reacted with an
unsubtle haste that made Claudia groan inwardly. He cast
a guilty glance around as he leaned forward and put his
hand over hers on the table, giving it a reassuring squeeze.
'Oh, sure…I understand…'

His voice was loaded with significance and she realised
thankfully that he was assuming her former paranoia about
the Press finding out that she had been expecting Chris's
baby was the reason for her reluctance to talk. It was just
the kind of sob-story that would make screaming headlines
in the tabloids, even after all this time, but somehow the
fear of a ravening horde of reporters baying for news was
less immediately threatening than the man sitting across the
table.

His fixed, suspicious gaze on their warmly clasped hands
was a fresh reproach to her uneasy conscience. He was no
fool; he must have realised that some sort of silent communication had just taken place and God knew what fresh
misinterpretation he was dwelling on. She had to make sure
that this was the last time that she encountered either of the
Stones.

Deep in her guilty subconscious she had always believed
that if she saw Morgan Stone again she would handle the

meeting with quiet dignity, taking the opportunity that fate obviously intended to tell him the truth and express remorse for her actions. But one look into those breathtaking blue eyes and her courage had failed her. His effect on her was all mixed up with emotions she didn't even dare try to untangle. He just made her feel…angry, threatened, guilty, spiteful—all the things that she knew she shouldn't, that she had no right to feel. For some wicked reason, knowing that she could shock him, shake that arrogant self-confidence of his was necessary to her battered pride…

She used the excuse of picking up her glass again to extricate her hand naturally from Mark's.

'What circumstances were those?' She might have known that Morgan would not let the subject politely drop. She glared at him and drank, defying both him and the slight fuzzying of her brain from the reckless amount of alcohol that had helped get her through the nightmare evening.

'Er—well, there are a lot of palimony precedents in the US lawcourts,' said Mark awkwardly, obviously casting for a plausible red herring. 'And Nash being a US citizen, Claudia could have claimed a percentage of his earnings from the years they were together…if there had been any left to claim…'

'How long did you and Nash live together?' Morgan's bald question made her association with Chris sound casual and sordid. As if he didn't know the answer already.

Claudia pinned him with her most contemptuous look, the gold flecks in her eyes burning brightly with anger and pride. 'Four years,' she said slowly and succinctly. 'Four *wonderful* years.' And she promised herself that he would never discover otherwise.

'They must have been wonderful. Chris Nash wasn't known for his constancy. You must have had something very special to hold his interest so long.' His eyes raked the deep cleavage of her green halter-neck gown, the suggestion that it was her body she had used implicit in the insulting boldness of his stare.

'Dad!'

Mark's shocked protest wasn't noticed by either protagonist. Claudia, when she had recovered the wits that had fled at the blatant sexuality of that hot blue gaze, leaned forward defiantly, aware that she was making her gown even more revealing, but feeling a fierce pleasure in flaunting herself.

'We did. It's called love,' she said softly. 'You know what love is, don't you, Morgan? It's when two people make a commitment to respect and trust each other in a relationship…'

'A relationship?' he drawled. 'Oh, you mean your *affair*. It's a pity that neither of you loved strongly enough to make a formal commitment to your future.'

It was on the tip of her tongue to tell him they *had* decided to get married, but she doubted he would believe her. She had no proof and it would seem as if she was trying to ingratiate herself.

'Formal? Oh, you mean *marriage*?' she said with acid sweetness. 'But these days marriage is no guarantee of life-long commitment. People get married for all sorts of reasons, some of which have more to do with respectability than love.' She half regretted her vicious use of his earlier confidence when his eyes flickered briefly to his bewildered son and dark colour appeared on his cheekbones, making her aware that, like his mouth, the right was slightly higher than the left.

But instead of lashing back at her with equal ferocity he sat back, lifting his half-empty glass in a cynically mocking salute. '*Touché*. Has anyone ever told you that you're beautiful when you're bitchy?'

To Claudia's disgust she blushed at the stinging compliment and he laughed.

'Has anyone ever told you that your vocabulary is as clichéd as your mind?' she said, trying to recoup her losses.

'No one as beautiful as you, Duchess.' He sipped his wine, watching her over the rim with those mesmerising eyes. 'If I'm a little blunt tonight it's because you take me by surprise. I apologise if I offended you. I'm just trying to reconcile the jet-setting racing driver's pampered mistress with the cool, classy, hardworking career-woman image you're working so hard to project.'

What was he trying to do now? Claudia stared at him suspiciously.

'Dad... What's the matter with you? You're embarrassing her.' Mark was suspicious too, and, from his expression, not entirely pleased by the way his father was monopolising her attention.

'No, I'm not. Am I, Claudia?'

She met the challenge boldly. 'No. Once you've been harassed by sleazy journalists and groupies of both sexes the occasional crude, loud-mouthed businessman is a fairly insipid threat.'

'Insipid? I can see I'm going to have to work hard to change your opinion of me,' he murmured, the gleam of anticipation in his blue eyes sending a shiver down her bare spine.

'Now, Dad, remember you're supposed to be a *reformed* workaholic.' Mark tried to draw their attention back to himself. 'I was just telling Claudia earlier how much more relaxed you've been in the last couple of years...'

'You mean since I stopped behaving like a petty tyrant,' his father said drily, obviously echoing words that had been thrown at him by his son in the heat of temper, 'and risked bankruptcy for the sake of boosting your boyish ego.'

'Risked bankruptcy!' Mark grinned. 'You know that sales have improved since I joined the business. You obviously needed a bit of fresh young blood among all your old fogies...'

The fact that they could banter about what, at the time, had been a bitter estrangement that had driven their relationship to the brink of destruction was an indication of the genuineness of their reconciliation, Claudia thought, and yet there was also an underlying tension to the teasing that hinted at potential conflict. Mark didn't see it in himself but he was as fiercely competitive in his way as his father, and as proud. It was Morgan's compromise that had paved the way for the resumption of their father-son relationship. How would Mark's masculine ego react if he discovered that that compromise was just another form of paternal manipulation, that both Morgan and the woman he had thought of as a friend had lied to and about him? She felt guilty enough already; no way did she want to add to that guilt by destroying the basis of their new accord.

'Of course the sales improvement had nothing to do with our increased public profile,' Morgan said mildly. 'It was we arch-conservatives who arranged the sponsorship that you're now reaping such rich rewards from, not to mention the vicarious thrills.'

Arch-conservative? Claudia couldn't help smiling to herself. In spite of the impeccable dinner-suit and the polished ease of his manners that reflected his private-school upbringing, to her Morgan Stone seemed anything but conservative.

'I didn't realise the second-hand car business was so exciting,' she couldn't help murmuring.

The two men looked at her, startled, and Claudia's faint smile faded as the silence stretched; she wondered what on earth she had said now.

'Second-hand cars?' Morgan's voice sounded strangely stifled.

'Yes. Is-isn't that what your company does?'

'Which one?'

'I didn't realise there was more than one,' said Claudia, confused as much by Mark's pained expression as his father's blandness. 'I just—Mark mentioned that your money came from second-hand car dealerships...' Her voice petered out as the blue eyes which had narrowed with scepticism on her flustered face suddenly switched thoughtfully towards his son.

Mark cleared his throat but didn't say anything.

'Is that all he told you?'

'Well—yes. We didn't talk much about his background, or you, and what there was wasn't very flattering,' she added stiffly, annoyed at being put on the defensive.

For some reason that set a smouldering spark of amusement in the coolly speculative gaze. 'No, I don't imagine you spent much of your time together *talking*...' Before she could take issue with that blatantly suggestive comment he continued, 'Yes, I own a string of franchised dealerships, but our flagship is the importation of Lamborghinis and Ferraris, Jaguars and Porsches—all kinds of classic exotic cars, both new and used. We also sponsor racing cars.'

'Racing cars?' Claudia closed her eyes briefly as she felt an echo of the rumbling vibration of the earth under the assault of thousands of horsepower, tasted the sharp, heady aroma of kerosene in the back of her tightening throat, the acrid stench of burnt rubber. The excitement had, in the end, repelled her more than it had fascinated her. Even before Chris had been killed it had taken all her courage to go to the race track, let alone smile for the cameras as he had strapped himself into one of the potentially lethal machines that he had lived to race—and ultimately loved more than life itself. She opened her eyes as Mark hastened to reassure her.

'Not Formula Ones, Claud, not what Chris used to race. Sports cars and Group One production cars. But I never mentioned it to you because I knew how upset it made you to talk about anything or anyone connected with any kind of motor racing. You felt trapped even being *in* a car for a good while afterwards. I'm sorry—Dad shouldn't have sprung it on you like that.' He gave his father a reproachful look.

Claudia smiled tensely. 'No, it's all right—honestly,' she added more convincingly as she saw his frown hover. She refused to include Morgan in her field of vision, sure he must be gloating at the sediment of her life that he was shrewdly stirring up. 'I got over that ages ago.' She pulled a face as she admitted, 'I had to. In the hotel PR trade you learn to use what connections you have and I have quite a few friends in the racing world who can add cachet to special events—'

'Rather like the old-boy network,' murmured Morgan drily, and, when she looked reluctantly at him, said quietly, 'If I caused you pain just now it was not intentional. Forgive me.'

God. Just when she was enjoying hating him he hit her with something like that. Forgive *him*? Surely it should be the other way around.

'There's nothing to forgive,' she said truthfully and made a valiant effort to prove it by acting like the consummate professional she was supposed to be, maintaining the fiction of her work by having a few words with their waiter and the *maître d'*, smoothly winding down the conversation until she could gratefully withdraw.

Her attempt to set the evening on a less personal footing by signing on her expenses for the bill when it arrived was thwarted by Morgan's stubborn insistence that she was *his* personal guest. She was frustrated and he amused when Mark circumvented the argument by picking up the pressed-flower folder containing the bill and walking off to the cashier to pay for it himself.

'While he's exercising his ego, perhaps I can walk you to your room?' suggested Morgan, standing politely behind her chair as she rose, flushed with irritation at the world in general.

'I wouldn't dream of taking you out of your way,' she

said frostily, seeing it as just another tactic to keep her away from Mark.

'Oh, but you're not. I'm heading upstairs myself. Come on, you can say your farewell to Mark at the desk.' His hand on her narrow waist was as implacably firm as his words as he ushered her out of the restaurant. Claudia simmered as she walked, conscious of his towering strength at her back, forced to behave like a gracious lady when she wanted to kick and scream like a vulgar shrew.

'If you think I'm going invite you into my room for coffee you can forget it,' she snapped through a rigid smile as she responded to the friendly nod of a cabinet minister who was one of the restaurant's regular patrons. After tonight she would make very sure that their paths never crossed again!

She felt Morgan's breath feather warmly across her naked shoulder as he dipped his head to murmur, 'I was going to invite you to mine...' He clicked his tongue, laughter threading the dark, throaty purr as her haughty back stiffened, braced for whatever new outrage he was intent on perpetrating.

'Dear me, Duchess, didn't you know that our company maintains a permanent suite in this very hotel? When it's not occupied by visiting personnel or clients I sometimes use it myself if I don't want to bother driving home...'

He gave a mock yawn that raised taunting images of that long, hard, restless body twisting sensuously among the crisp white hotel sheets. 'And I certainly don't feel like bothering tonight. In fact, in the circumstances, it might be a good idea for me to move in for the duration. As you're a dutiful employee of the hotel dedicated to further its reputation and—er—*relations* with the public, I predict that you and I will be seeing a great deal of each other in the future...'

CHAPTER FOUR

'OVER my dead body!'

Four days later Claudia's shocked response to his silky taunt returned to haunt her.

She smiled grimly as she emerged from the shower and roughly towelled her gently steaming body. Her body was very definitely not dead; it vibrated with an unwelcome life at the very thought of *that man*! She had suspected he was a dangerous threat to her hard-won pride and precious equilibrium; now she knew he was…the memo laid out on her dressing-table confirmed it in black and white.

The tingling that enveloped her skin had more to do with the violence of her thoughts than the friction of the impatient drying and she cast a moody glance at her slender, rosy nakedness as she discarded the monogrammed white hotel towel and stalked from the small *en-suite* bathroom into the bedroom of her temporary residence. Damn that man—even in her thoughts she couldn't get away from him!

For the third night in a row Morgan Stone had evidently decided that he 'couldn't be bothered' to drive home and had stayed at the HarbourPoint. Not that Claudia had done anything more than glimpse him at a distance, but just the knowledge that he was somewhere around, effectively haunting her territory, made her uneasy. She had just started to feel comfortable in her new surroundings and now she had to brace herself every time she went out of the door of her room.

Still half inclined to think he had been baiting her with the threat of his unwelcome presence that first night, Claudia had shut the door to her room sharply in his face

and immediately got on the pone to the night telephonist,
who was known to disdain the gossip that generally ran rife
in the back of house and therefore could be trusted not to
speculate on the reason for Claudia's interest. Joy Castle
was a small, bird-like woman in her mid-thirties with an
unexpected deep and sultry voice and she and Claudia had
clicked instantly at the staff briefing at which they had been
introduced.

'Joy, have you ever heard of Morgan Stone?'

'Honey, you can't live in Wellington and *not* hear about
the man! I think that's his plan. He's the personification of
brand-identification. Think Morgan Stone, think cars. Are
you in the market for a Ferrari?'

Claudia shuddered. One of the pleasures of living-in was
that you didn't need a car. 'On my salary? No, I just wondered—I haven't noticed any Stones on our permanent client list but I understand he has a permanent suite…' She
trailed off and Joy obligingly filled the gap.

'Not him personally, his company—Morgan and Son—
R5. Had it for about five years. Sends quite a bit of trade
through the hotel, some of it real glamour stuff—you know,
famous racing drivers, visiting celebrities, that sort of
thing.'

Claudia's hear sank. R5. Although the hotel was fifteen
storeys high it didn't actually possess a thirteenth floor,
because many guests were superstitious about the number.
Instead the hotel's gymnasium, sauna and spa were located
on the thirteenth floor, and it was designated R, for recre-
ation, on the lift controls and information sheets, rather than
by its number. As well as the recreational facilities there
was also a small restaurant located there, and five double-
sized suites.

Morgan and Son. She had probably come across the
name somewhere in the client lists during her orientation
week at the HarbourPoint but had not registered it as sig-

nificant. *Stone*, on the other hand, would have had all the alarm sirens blaring.

'I see... And does he often stay here himself?'

'I think he spends the odd night and sometimes, when he has a personal friend in residence there, he might stay a bit longer...'

'Personal friend? You mean—like...women...?'

There was a briefly startled silence, then a burst of more laughter. 'Claudia? Are you asking me if he uses his company's suite for assignations of an—er—illicit sexual nature?'

'No, of course not,' said Claudia hurriedly. 'I don't expect you to—'

'Relax, I was only teasing. I know you're not digging dirt just for the sake of it. He's single, anyway, so there's nothing actually illicit for him to hide. Some of them have been women, I guess, but the guy has class, if that's what's worrying you. He's got it but he doesn't have to flaunt it, if you know what I mean. He's not going to drag the hotel into disrepute—'

'No, of course not,' said Claudia hastily again, thinking wretchedly that she was more likely to do that than Morgan Stone. Although her ex-celebrity status was useful, it could also backfire if she wasn't cautious in her dealings with the Press. Fortunately she had begun building up a fairly good rapport with the Wellington media.

'Er—does he ring down for any regular special services?' she asked, trying belatedly to sound professional.

Joy wasn't fooled. 'Are we still on the same subject here?' came her droll rejoinder.

'*No!*' Ridiculously, Claudia could feel herself flushing at the gibe. From what Mark had said Morgan would be more likely to be paying women to stay away than vice versa... 'Joy—'

'Secretarial services, the masseur when he's worked out in the gym—he's a member of the health and fitness club—

he sometimes runs conferences in the boardroom and has functions in the restaurant,' Joy listed cheerfully. 'I guess the only facility he *never* uses is the limo service,' she added with a chuckle. 'Anything else you want to know? I have a dozen calls on hold here.'

'Oh, no—thanks, Joy.' Claudia had hung up on the hasty lie. What she had learned already was disturbing enough. Morgan Stone was probably more familiar with the hotel than she was. It was obviously only sheer luck that she hadn't run into him before now. *Good* luck...which had evidently just run out!

Claudia pulled on her underwear now, and sat at her dressing-table to dry her hair quickly, trying to ignore the explosive memo lurking at the edge of her vision as she began to apply the make-up that presented the correct, confident image to the world.

Her dark colouring suited clear, vibrant colours and she had learned to use them skilfully to flatter her patrician features when she had lived with Chris. He had been surrounded by so many beautiful women that it had been a matter of sheer survival to learn how to look as attractive as possible at all times. Fortunately some friends who had been models had been willing to share a few tricks of the trade, but Claudia had found the constant emphasis on her appearance irksome. After Chris died Claudia had shovelled her make-up into a drawer and sold most of her expensive designer clothes with a sense of relief.

It was only when she went to work at Baron Hotels that she came to realise how valuable that rather tiresome training had been and how useful her image-enhancing skills could be if she astutely applied them to her job. As her self-confidence in her ability had grown she had actually found herself enjoying being on the other side of the publicity fence, controlling the flow of information rather than being the victim of it!

Her make-up finished, Claudia dressed with inordinate

care, donning the protective armour of her uniform with meticulous attention to the lie of her collar and the fastening of every button. She brushed her hair until it crackled in protest, putting off the moment when she would have to walk out of the door.

She looked at the cursory memo from Simon that had been slipped under her door the previous evening.

Meeting in my office tomorrow morning at nine sharp with Morgan Stone. He has a very exciting proposal to make!!

Claudia had blanched at the last sentence with its two screaming exclamation marks, wondering for one insane moment whether Morgan Stone intended to blackmail her into marriage. Then reason had asserted itself and she had gone to bed, tossing and turning all night, furious with herself for the ludicrous assumption and torturing herself with dread at what the morning might bring.

She took one last look at herself in the mirror and almost groaned. In spite of the professional paint-job her eyes looked slightly bruised through lack of sleep, the tiny, distinctive downward droop at the outer corners accentuated by tiredness, the gold flecks amid the brown dulled by apprehension. Determinedly she pinned on a smile. Not the warm, magical one which delighted her friends but the cool curve which fended off all-comers.

Claudia's cubby-hole work-space was among a rabbit warren of administration offices behind the ground-floor reception area and distinctly unglamorous compared to the outward trappings of the hotel. She went there first to check her messages and run through her appointments for the day, fortifying her breakfastless state with a strong black coffee before she walked along the windowless corridor to Simon's office.

She was deliberately early, hoping that she might be able

to have a few quick words alone with him to prepare herself for whatever was going to blow up in her face, but as she approached his open door she could hear the low rumble of masculine voices, one of which made her toes curl in her navy shoes. Instead of her practical everyday pumps she was wearing heels as high as she dared. With her chin and eyes up, shoulders back, and a glittering smile stamped across her stiff mouth, she swept into Simon's office and promptly shattered the dignity of her entrance by almost stumbling over Morgan's briefcase set down squarely in the middle of the carpet.

'Sorry.' Morgan sounded more amused than apologetic as he rose from his chair and steadied her with an unwelcome hand on her arm, tucking the discreetly monogrammed case under the overhang of Simon's desk as she whipped her arm away and sat down in the second chair, clinging on to her composure by the skin of her teeth.

She crossed her legs, and then followed Morgan's narrowed gaze to discover that, by accident or unconscious design, her toe had tipped back until her long spike heel pointed directly at the man who had re-seated himself opposite.

'Armed and dangerous,' he murmured, and his gaze flickered up the full length of her leg and lingered for a moment on the outline of her hip in the immaculate narrow skirt before drifting up to her prim face—thinking to discompose her. She let her own gaze drift disdainfully over him. Now, if only she could find something to disdain!

For a man who wasn't very good-looking he knew how to look good, she allowed grudgingly. While Simon was attired in his usual dark suit, Morgan was dressed for the fresh and glorious summer day that already blazed outside the window. A linen sports jacket the colour of old roses worn over a plain white silk shirt, open at the neck, and white pleated linen trousers created a crisp elegance that was effortlessly casual. His shoes were white, too, canvas trainers that twitched as she looked at them.

'The curse of the second-hand car salesman,' he said, snatching her gaze back to his, adding, 'Flashy white shoes,' with a grin, knowing as well as she did that what he wore was far removed from the fancy polished leather implied by the popular cliché.

'And a personality to match,' Claudia was unable to resist adding.

'I didn't realise you two knew each other so well,' Simon said slowly, and Claudia opened her mouth to tell him that they didn't, then closed it again when she realised that it had been more of a warning than an idle comment. If she was going to trade insults with an important client Simon would want to know why.

'Oh, we share a few memories, don't we, Duchess?'

'Duchess?' Simon looked at Claudia's uncomfortable expression. 'Don't tell me you've even got a title tucked away in that glamorous past of yours?'

'It's just Mr Stone's little joke,' she said stiffly, making it clear she didn't find it very funny.

'You can drop the Mr, Claudia, I don't think Simon is fooled,' Morgan horrified her by saying. He leaned back, slewing sideways in his chair so that his body was angled towards hers, one arm casually draping over the back. 'Claudia and I knew each other a couple of years ago. In fact we had dinner together here just a few nights ago.'

'Oh, I see,' said Simon, who evidently didn't, but he was clever enough to pick up the undercurrents. 'Is there—is that going to be some kind of problem?' he asked delicately.

'Not for me. Claudia?'

She glared at her tormentor, trapped, knowing that he had created a totally spurious impression of their former relationship and realising that if she didn't act just as casually Simon would start getting a *very* wrong impression.

'Of course not.' Simmering at the gleam of triumph the appeared in the mocking blue eyes, she added unwisely, 'It's actually Morgan's *son* whom I was friendly with and the three of us were at dinner the other night. Morgan and I don't know each other at all, in fact have only met twice, very briefly—'

'But memorably,' said Morgan with a smooth mock-gallantry. 'Let's just settle for calling you a friend of the family, mmm? Which suits me well, because as you know, Simon, I like to do business on a relatively informal level. With Claudia I know exactly where I am.'

Claudia only wished she did. 'Perhaps one of you would like to tell me what this meeting is about,' she said sweetly, hoping to get the conversation back to less dangerous topics.

'Sure. Morgan, would you like a cup of coffee first? And you, Claudia? You don't look too bright this morning. Heavy date last night?'

Claudia managed a jokingly evasive answer to his teasing, uneasily aware of Morgan's sharpened glance. She was not going to confess that she was having trouble sleeping and thereby open herself up to more awkward questions.

'Now, Claudia, not being a local you may not know that Morgan is sponsoring this year's Sport Five Hundred; that's the annual five-hundred-kilometre sports car race around the streets of Wellington,' said Simon, dispensing with the stilted—on Claudia's part at least—small talk that had occupied them until his secretary brought in the coffee.

'In the past it's been sponsored by an oil company but this year Morgan and Son have taken over the major responsibility and naturally Morgan wants to make the most of the publicity that it offers his company. Since most of the overseas drivers are going to be staying here at the hotel, any publicity he generates is going to affect us and vice versa, so he's suggested that in order to prevent us doubling up on costs we link up to organise a week of race-orientated functions—rather like the floral festival ones you did last week. They were an enormous success by the way, Morgan, although the fact that you've asked for Claudia's input on this means I obviously don't have to sell her talents to you...'

'Quite.'

The dry one-word reply was such a marked contrast to Simon's expansive enthusiasm that Claudia felt herself blush. Fortunately Simon didn't seem to notice her discomfort.

'In fact, if this co-operative effort is a success we might well be able to get other businesses involved and turn it into an annual event—call it the automotive festival or something. What do you think, Claudia?' he urged. 'Excited at the idea?'

'Excited isn't the word for it,' she said weakly.

'Thrilled? Stirred? Stimulated? Hot and bothered?' offered Morgan slyly, reminding Claudia with this that his cleverness was not confined to selling cars. He had been bound for university before pride and circumstances intervened and she had a suspicion that he could tie her in verbal knots if he really brought that formidable intelligence to bear.

'I was thinking more along the lines of mildly interested,' she lied crisply. Terrified was an even better word!

'Really?' He leaned back in his chair, extending a leg so that he could thrust one hand casually in his pocket, the other holding his coffee-cup to his mouth. He looked the epitome of lazy relaxation but his eyes gave him away; they were like bullets of blue steel, firing silent questions at her. 'You don't sound like any PR person I've ever known. At this point a normal publicity agent would be swamping me with eager ideas...'

'Claudia's style is a little different,' Simon smiled, undismayed by the implied criticism. 'That's what makes her so good. She doesn't get carried away with the froth. She's cautious and ultra-practical—always looks at all the angles before she leaps. If she takes something on it's because she is certain she can build it into a success for the hotel. And she's never had a failure yet! Her track record is one of the reasons we were so glad she was transferred here—'

'Cautious? You do surprise me,' murmured Morgan, who hadn't taken his eyes off Claudia's stiff expression. 'I would have thought that Claudia was a bit of a firebrand, a creature of passion and impulse…'

Simon laughed. 'Claudia was right, you obviously *don't* know her very well. Rest assured, Morgan, that if she does decide to take this project under her wing you'll have her full and devoted attention.'

Morgan's crooked mouth curved faintly as a fleeting look of horror crossed Claudia's face at Simon's ill-chosen words.

'I'll look forward to that.'

Enough was enough. '*Decide*? Do you mean I actually have a choice?' Claudia asked sourly.

Simon looked a little puzzled by her sarcasm but it was Morgan who spoke.

'Of course,' he shrugged, 'if you don't think you're capable of handling it…'

She knew what he was doing. He was thrusting an adolescent challenge under her nose, thinking to manipulate her into accepting it. He must think her stupid.

'I *know* I'm capable,' she responded coolly, determined to prove to him that passion and impulse no longer held sway over her intellect. The last time she had allowed emotions to distort her reason had been two years ago and look where that had landed her! It had been the graduating lesson in what she now saw as her six-year course in maturity. Her expectations of life were greatly different from the expectations of that naïve, emotionally reckless girl who had considered the world well lost for love. 'I don't have to prove it to my ego by taking unacceptable risks—'

As soon as the word slipped out she regretted her choice, but it was too late.

'Risk? That's an interesting word for you to use.' His eyes were wide with cerulean innocence. 'What element of risk are you talking about? It's not as if I'm asking you to drive one of the cars yourself.'

Now Simon was definitely wary as he cleared his throat. 'Er—Morgan, did you know that Chris Nash—?'

'Yes, I'm fully aware of Claudia's background, but she's assured me that she's over the trauma of the crash that killed her lover,' Morgan cut across his tentative phrasing with a bluntness that took his challenge from merely provocative to utterly flagrant. 'If I didn't believe her I wouldn't be here. However, I don't believe that risk of a race accident is the hazard that Claudia is referring to...'

'Oh.'

Simon was rarely at a loss but this was clearly one of those rare moments.

Claudia looked helplessly from him to Morgan's coolly determined face, knowing she couldn't hold out any longer and still retain her dignity. She had known from the beginning that the deck was stacked against her but that knowledge didn't make conceding his victory any easier. She wondered exactly how to back down from her defensive position without looking more of a petulant fool than she did already.

'Well, I—'

'Perhaps if I took her away and explained my concept to her in detail—the way that I explained it to you—I might be able to alleviate her concerns...'

Once again Morgan had beaten her to the punch. Simon looked relieved.

'Good thinking, Morgan—'

'That won't be necessary,' said Claudia levelly, relieving him even more. She made herself smile brilliantly into her boss's puzzled eyes. 'I guess playing the devil's advocate isn't my scene. Actually I can see that there are some good possibilities here, for the whole of the Baron chain, not just the HarbourPoint. Why don't you let me work up some ideas—?'

'Us.'

'I beg your pardon?' She spoke to Morgan, carefully directing her gaze to the top button of his shirt.

'Not you—us. You and I.'

Still she refused to look at him as she tried to firmly put him in his place. 'Naturally I'll discuss your requirements with your advertising agency before I—'

'Not necessary. Their involvement will be in other areas. As I've already mentioned to Simon, I prefer to handle this particular promotion myself. *Personally*,' he added after a slight pause, so that she couldn't possibly misunderstand the threat.

He leaned abruptly forward so that his face slid into her deliberately narrowed field of vision, his features lit with a sardonic amusement that made her itch to slap it off. 'In this technological age I still think the personal touch has a lot to recommend it, don't you?'

'Oh, but surely your agency will want to be fully involved? I mean, many heads and all that...' said Claudia feebly, recoiling from the thought of exactly what his personal touch might entail. The more the merrier as far as she was concerned. If she could she would put the whole population of Wellington between herself and this man.

'Democracy is all very well but in this case I'm inclined to be autocratic,' he replied with the easy arrogance of absolute power. 'We only have two more months before the race so it'll be much more efficient for you to deal with me directly. I'm sure that between the two of us we can come up with some ideas that are sufficiently unusual to...excite your mild interest into something more profitable for us both...'

If Claudia had been feeling more like herself she might

have laughed. He had a positive genius for wicked *double entendres*. But her sense of humour had been sorely tried these past few days and in Morgan Stone's company she was too often confronted with an unpredictable 'herself' she hardly recognised.

'Naturally I concede to your wishes as a client,' she bit out, unable to resist adding, 'Even though I happen to think that this time you're wrong.'

'Not client—*partner*,' he said, with silky satisfaction, holding out his hand as if he was the perfect gentleman. 'Do we have a deal?'

She took it, hiding her reluctance from Simon but not from the man across from her. Her eyes, which had been dulled with fatigue when she had walked into the room, glittered with repressed fury. She wouldn't have been surprised if he had tried to disconcert her even more by kissing her hand as he had when Mark introduced them, but his handshake was as firm and uncompromising as a promise. Her slim fingers were completely enwrapped by his, and the sensation of being trapped was stronger than ever. Claudia wondered uneasily just what kind of deal she had committed herself to as she withdrew, mentally and physically, from the hard physical reality of his confident grasp.

'Great!' Simon was eager to cement the alliance. 'I'll leave it up to you two to work out the details. You'll keep me fully posted, won't you, Claudia? We'll need to get head office approval since this will naturally reflect on our international image, but I can't see it being a difficulty, given that this is such a prestige event.'

'Meanwhile, I'll do as you suggest and bring Claudia up to date.' Morgan rose and turned towards her. 'Your office or mine?'

'I'm afraid I have a very full diary today,' Claudia was grateful to be able to inform him with perfect truth. She needed time to assimilate the unexpected turn of events, review her fast-diminishing options…

His blue eyes were mockingly sceptical as he towered
over her. 'I'm a fairly busy man myself. Could you not
perhaps spare just a minute or two for me now, out of your
very full day…?'

Conscious of Simon's restless movement, Claudia capit-
ulated. She might as well get this over and done with as
soon as possible. If she did her job well, she might be able
to keep their meetings to an absolute minimum.

'My first appointment isn't for another twenty minutes,'
she allowed stiffly as she stood, determined to be crisp and
businesslike. Even in her heels her eyes only came level
with his chin—and a stubborn and pugnacious chin it was
too, she recognised glumly. 'If you don't mind being rushed
I suppose we could do enough groundwork for me to start
drafting a plan.'

'Twenty minutes is ample time for what I have in mind,'
he murmured blandly, sending shivers up her rigid spine as
he followed her out of the doorway.

She stalked down the short hallway, conscious of
Morgan prowling at her heels. As soon as he entered her
small office it suddenly seemed claustrophobically smaller
and Claudia hurriedly invited him to take a chair, hoping
that the width of her desk would provide a bulwark against
his intimidating aura of arro-gant masculinity.

But as she brushed past him he caught her by the elbow
with deceptively gentle fingers and her momentum swung
her around to face him.

'Headache?'

He was so close that she could smell the heat of his skin,
the scent of his maleness a confusing counterpoint to the
softness of his deep voice. As she stared at him uncertainly
one hard, square-tipped finger came up to stroke the crease
between her brows and, before she could protest, his thumb
traced the faint circles beneath her eyes. 'I know you didn't
go out last night, so these must be due to something else.
Conscience keep you awake?'

'I—no—as a matter of fact I slept like a baby,' she snapped furiously, trying not to tremble under his touch. Her damned conscience was so burdened; what did another lie matter? His answer, when it came, was devastating.

'Babies sometimes wake crying in the night,' he murmured with the bittersweet knowledgeability of parenthood, and his thumb moved delicately, as if wiping away imaginary tears from the darkened skin beneath her defiant eyes. 'Do you sometimes weep for your lost child, Claudia, in the still of the long, lonely nights?'

Claudia felt as if he had struck her to the heart. She jerked her head back from his disturbingly gentle touch, but his hand on her elbow restrained the violence of her recoil.

'You have no right—'

He answered her choked whisper with a whisper of his own. 'Who has more? Who else knows about your baby? We share a grief, Claudia, a secret sorrow. You haven't forgotten it any more than I have. You've just tucked it away, where other people can't see, can't hurt you with their casual compassion or curiosity. But you and I know it's there between us. And one day we're going to have to talk about it—to resolve the conflict—'

'No—' In her panic she tried to twist free, to goad him into revealing that his empathy was feigned, another trap to disable her reason.

He controlled her struggles easily, overpowering them simply by drawing her against his powerful body.

'Don't—' Her plea was muffled against his chest, her flushed forehead cradled in the warm hollow of his throat bared by his open collar.

'Then stop fighting yourself. I said one day…not today. We haven't established the ground rules, yet.'

She didn't dare try to interpret that cryptic remark. 'Let me go!'

'When you've calmed down. You're trembling and your heart is beating like a wild thing.'

She became acutely conscious of her breasts pressing against the hardness of his ribs and the thick, slow, steady beat of his own heart somewhere just below her ear. A strange and unwelcome tension entered her body, strengthening her fear. Wild. That was how he made her feel. Pursued and captured. And alarmingly safe.

One of his arms was wrapped around her waist, the other pressed vertically between her shoulder-blades, his firmly hand cupping the back of her skull. He enveloped her even more completely than he had on the dance-floor, holding her with an intimate familiarity that said a lot about him as a man and a disquieting amount about her as a woman. It was nearly three years since she had sheltered in such an intimate embrace and even then it had not been the tender cherishing she had needed when she had discovered she was pregnant. On the track or off, Chris was a man who had lived at top speed and even though she had loved him Claudia had sometimes felt left behind in the tumult of his whirlwind passions. Never had he had time in his headlong rush through life to just hold her, for no reason other than to be close. In his world hugs and kisses were casual currency between friends and acquaintances but if he tenderly put his arms around Claudia it was because the cameras were clicking, or as a prelude to lovemaking.

The dangerous drift to her thoughts pulled her up. She imagined what a stranger would think, walking into her office and seeing them now. She drew in a deep, uneven breath and her taste buds tingled at the salty male fragrance that filled the back of her throat in a suffocating rush of shocking awareness.

'I'm all right now,' she said, willing herself to sound calm, not to let him sense the subtle alteration in her resistance.

The hand that had been cupping her head slid around to

tilt up her chin and he inspected her narrow face and wide, guilty brown eyes. His lashes screened the direction of his gaze as his lids drifted down but Claudia felt his look like a touch on her solemn mouth, and it lingered there until her lips began to hum with a curious warmth and a tide of colour rose up her throat.

He let her go then and sat down, an expression of blatant satisfaction on his face as he watched her scrambling retreat behind her desk, so much at odds with her former air of haughty command.

'I— How do you know—that I didn't go out last night?' she blurted shakily, and then silently cursed herself for not returning immediately to business.

If anything, his satisfaction increased. 'I asked,' he said simply.

'Who? Why? How dare you spy on me?' Her voice was annoyingly breathless when she had intended it to sound firm and angry. When she got upset Claudia's vocal cords had an irritating habit of betraying her resolve, making her sound weak and kittenish when she wanted to roar like a lioness.

'Careful, Claudia, you know how irresistible I find a challenge,' he murmured provocatively. 'I dare because I care. You look far more human vibrating with outrage than you do dressed up in your air of cool indifference. I told you we were going to see a lot of each other. You should have believed me. From now on you will. I don't lie.'

With effort Claudia managed not to cringe. 'And I've already told you that I'm no threat to you and Mark. As your spies no doubt told you, I haven't seen him since that night at dinner— '

The phone rang on her desk and Claudia snatched it up with inordinate eagerness.

Her face froze when she heard the voice on the other end. She swivelled her chair as far as it would go in the arc of her desk, turning her head until only the sharp purity of her profile was presented to the man sitting opposite, her tone clipped and careful as she answered in monosyllables.

'I know you've been looking for a nice flat. It's in a perfect location for someone who doesn't have a car, only a fifteen-minute bus-ride from the city. What do you say? Why don't I pick you up at lunchtime and I'll drive you out for a look—or after work this evening? You'll need to snap it up if you want it because once a place this good is advertised it'll go like a shot...'

Claudia suddenly realised why Mark's voice was reverberating oddly in her ears. Her head snapped around and she saw Morgan's finger depressing the loud-speaker button on the console of her telephone. There wasn't an ounce of apology in his crackling command, 'Tell him no.'

Claudia covered the receiver with her hand in a futile attempt at protecting her privacy. 'I'll handle this myself, if you don't mind.'

'I do mind. Your resistance appears to be nil where my son is concerned—whatever he wants you seem to give him and to hell with the consequences. Well, I'm here now. You may not be able to deny him but I can. Tell him that this time your answer is no. You won't allow him to set you up in a convenient apartment...'

'How dare you—?'

'I warned you about saying that to me, Claudia,' Morgan said grimly. He leaned forward to speak into the console microphone. 'Sorry, Mark, the lady has other plans for her day—and for her future accommodation. She doesn't need any extra help. Have you told her yet that you're leaving for Italy next week? No?' He allowed his son the bare minimum of garbled response. 'Well, don't worry, I'll make sure that Claudia is kept fully informed of all your obligations.'

He delivered the final *coup de grâce* in a mercurial switch from brusque dismissal to sensuous warmth as he neatly confiscated the receiver from Claudia's nerveless hand and continued his outrageous monologue with more privacy than he had accorded her.

'What was that you said, Claudia, darling? Oh—she wants you to know that she's absolutely swamped with work herself, Mark, so she probably won't have time to see you again before you go. Oh, and by the way, don't expect me home tonight. I'm staying at the hotel. Yes—*again*. No, I don't think you do need to ask why; you've obviously leapt to all the right conclusions. Yes, of course I'll give her your love—as long as you realise that, while yours is necessarily platonic, mine is not. Goodbye, Mark.'

And with that he hung up.

And Claudia began to yell.

CHAPTER FIVE

'CAN I help you?'

Claudia's hand stilled on the glossy car roof and she turned to smile wryly at the nattily dressed young salesman who had approached her.

'I've never seen one of these before,' she murmured, still admiring the sloping lines of the aggressive two-door sports car.

'Beautiful, isn't she?' grinned the young man, not taking his eyes off Claudia. 'A Bricklin. Ford V8 engine with a top speed of 187 kph. Matches your nail-polish.'

Claudia was amused as much by his sharp eyes as by his flattery. She hadn't even noticed that the hot ginger was indeed the exact shade of her neatly manicured nails. 'You think I should buy it for cosmetic reasons?'

'It's as good a reason as any, but actually I don't think it's really your style.' He was young, barely more than twenty, and she suspected fairly new at his job.

'Oh?' Claudia raised her eyebrows, playing his game. Since she was the only person in the spacious marble show-room he was probably seeking to relieve the boredom of a slow day. Or perhaps her white ribbed cotton top, dressed up with a coral jacket and flared white cotton piqué skirt looked chic enough to seem expensive. The jaunty narrow-brimmed coral sunhat she had taken off as she entered probably added to the illusion of class. If she had been wearing her uniform instead of the 'civvies' she wore when she worked outside the hotel he would have placed her immediately as a non-customer. 'And what would you say *is* my style?'

'Something a little faster, maybe?' His eyes drifted south

of the flirty hem of her short skirt and Claudia was acutely conscious of her bare legs. Thankfully they were tanned just enough to give the illusion of wearing tights. As with her arms, that pale tan had taken all summer to acquire through natural exposure to the elements. In spite of her dark colouring, Claudia's skin was so fair that she had years ago given up the drudgery of sunbathing.

'How about a Ferrari?' He ushered her over to the steel-grey, open-topped vehicle which occupied pride of place on a low ramp in the corner of the showroom.

She decided to tease him a little. 'A Ferrari is so awfully...*conventional*, don't you think? Middle-aged men drive Ferraris. Haven't you got anything a little more... flamboyant?'

She hid a smile at the expression of outrage that flitted across his face. He *was* young. And no doubt he, as any sensible young macho man would, lusted dreadfully after a Ferrari.

'A Porsche 911?'

She flicked her ginger fingers disdainfully. 'Too popular.'

A gleam in his eye told her she had aroused his fighting instincts and to disguise her laughter she turned her back.

'Ah! Now *that*! That is *definitely* me!' She wove her way around several other menacingly virile machines to stand beside a lustrous royal blue convertible, the stylish rear spoiler adding a wicked flip to its tail that thumbed a nose at all who trailed in its wake.

'A Corvette?' His sly delight as he hurried after her seemed to indicate that the reputation of Corvette women was not all that it should be.

'Here, hop in, try it out for size,' he said eagerly, opening the door, ignoring her hesitation as he whipped her fashionable leather document-case and hat out of her hand and virtually bustled her in behind the wheel.

The bucket seat conformed around Claudia's body as if

it had been specially designed for it and the smoothness of the wheel beneath her fingers was such an unexpected pleasure that she didn't even notice that the swivel of her hips as she tucked in her legs had ruffled her skirt up around her thighs, or that the young man leaning on the door was fully appreciative of the distraction.

'It's a Greenwood. The only one of its kind in the country,' he told her smugly. 'And it's actually a bit faster than the Ferrari—not that you'd get much chance to test it around Wellington, unless you're in the Five Hundred.' He watched with interest as she settled more deeply into the blue leather upholstery and studied the impressive dashboard. He leaned across the top of the windscreen and grinned down at her. 'Will that be cash or a cheque, madam?'

Claudia returned his smile. The game was over. She hadn't done anything so light-heartedly foolish in ages. She sighed, running a caressing finger over the smooth curve of the steering-wheel. 'It really is gorgeous, isn't it? It's so...so...'

'Sexy is the word I think you're looking for.'

The young man's spine straightened as if he had been shot, his youthful cockiness deserting him. He stepped hurriedly back from the car, leaving Claudia staring directly into the shock of Morgan Stone's glorious eyes.

'Er—Mr Stone—I was just showing the lady the car—'

'And the lady was taking you for a ride,' Morgan interrupted his stammering with a faintly sardonic smile. 'Shame on you, Claudia, for taking advantage of Carl's youthful inexperience,' he chided, making her blush as if she were guilty of something more than mere frivolity. 'She probably knows a great deal more about cars like this than you do,' he told the chastened young man drily, taking possession of Claudia's hat and the document-case that doubled as a handbag and sending him on his way with a slight tilt of his head.

Claudia hurriedly swung her legs out of the car, only to find that Morgan's stance prevented her from standing up. She sat, skewed on the seat, glaring up at him.

'Well, *do* you think it's sexy?' Morgan asked, instantly making her think of the title of a song sung by Rod Stewart, one of her favourite artists. The answer, to both the mental and spoken question, was undoubtedly *yes* and an odd shiver of apprehension feathered along her nerves. This morning he was dressed with the same sophisticated elegance that he had shown that awful day in Auckland—a dark, double-breasted suit, white cotton shirt and muted olive-green silk tie with a scattered pattern of shell-like white fans. He looked a far cry from the casually dressed man who had firmly established himself as the bane of her life over the past week and Claudia suddenly felt vastly underdressed.

'It's very nice,' murmured Claudia, resenting her enforced submissive position.

'Nice?' The blue eyes narrowed in amusement, fine lines fanning out from the corners. 'That's like calling Fangio a good driver. You obviously have sinfully high standards. What kind of car did Nash drive off the track?'

As always, Claudia felt a jolt when he mentioned Chris's name with that unidentifiable edge that seemed to come into his voice when he referred to her former lover. 'A Boxer Berlinetta.'

'A man with taste.'

'Yes.' She wished she knew what was going on behind that deceptively tranquil expression because his eyes were certainly not calm, they were restless, penetrating, and his remark had an inflexion that didn't seem entirely complimentary. God forbid he should be able to read the confusion in her mind.

'I'm sorry I wasn't here when you arrived. I had an important meeting this morning, hence the formal attire.' He indicated his suit, for all the world as if he had divined the source of part of her discomfort. 'But I see that Carl has kept you amused.'

'He was only doing his job,' she felt bound to say defensively.

'Flirting with the female customers?'

'Isn't that part of the training?' she said tartly.

'True. May I help you up? That skirt must make that low-slung seat rather awkward to get out of without compromising your modesty.'

She would have liked to ignore his proffered hand haughtily but the mockery in his eyes made her all too aware of the truth of his statement. His ease of strength made her freshly conscious of his height and breadth when he pulled her upright. Instead of moving back from the door he had stayed where he was and her body rested full-length against his for a few disturbing seconds before he stepped away.

While she was still trying to decide whether the contact had been accidental or deliberate he handed her her possessions and placed a hand under her elbow, guiding her gently but very firmly across the marble floor towards an unmarked door in the windowless back wall of the showroom.

Expecting to be ushered into an office, Claudia was surprised to find herself blinking once more in the sunshine of a small brick courtyard shaded with a scattered planting of trees interspersed with several casually parked cars.

'I—thought we were going to your office.' So far all their preliminary meetings had been at the HarbourPoint where Claudia had at least had the illusion of being in control.

'It's just across the way.' Morgan indicated the striped awning sheltering a tinted glass door in the brick-fronted building on the other side of the courtyard.

Once there, however, Morgan paused only long enough to leaf through a stack of messages handed over by the sleek blonde behind an equally sleek polished wood reception desk and introduce Claudia to the grey-haired matron who was his personal secretary. She responded to Claudia's polite greeting with a warm smile and a look of frank curiosity that was transferred to her boss at his next statement.

'Claudia and I will be out for at least an hour, Irene.' After a sideways looks at the woman beside him he added softly, 'Or possibly two...'

'Where are you going?' Irene pre-empted Claudia's own startled curiosity.

'None of your business,' Morgan said pleasantly, and the older woman laughed.

'If it's not my business, then it's not business. If you're not back by five shall I send out a search party? You have a dinner engagement this evening.' It was evident that their relationship was tempered by a comfortable disrespect on both sides.

'Don't bother. If I'm not back by five I won't be worth rescuing,' he said drily.

'I thought you said we were meeting here.' Claudia found her voice, faintly hostile and defensive.

'And so we have,' he responded unarguably.

'But—I have all this information that you said you wanted.' She held up her document-case. 'You said we were going to discuss the choices for the celebrity lunches, and the chequered ball...'

Her idea for a ball the night after the race, the black and white theme taken from the colours of the checked flag that would greet the winner past the post, had been a hit with both Morgan and Simon.

'And so we will,' he confirmed, again in the indulgent manner of someone whose own plans were never flouted. 'But there's another priority. One I think you're going to appreciate. Irene—don't bother putting anyone through to the car-phone because I won't answer. No exceptions!'

'Well, if there's a crisis and the whole company comes

crashing down around us—don't blame me!' his secretary
said equably, inviting the sardonic reply,

'Let's get out of here, Claudia, before Irene really starts
to nag.'

A few moments later Claudia was again being dazzled
by the sunlit courtyard, and the car that Morgan was shoe-
horning her into. It was a black left-hand drive convertible,
small, blunt and uncompromisingly masculine from the
steel mesh over the headlights and smooth bulge of the air
intake on the hood to the chrome side-mufflers and roll bar
behind the driver's seat.

'Is this yours?' she asked faintly as he shucked off his
jacket and tossed it behind the driver's seat before sliding
in behind the wheel.

'You mean mine personally, as opposed to being part of
my stock? Yes, it is. I own several cars but the Cobra is
my favourite.' The arrogance of wealth was in the casual
statement of excess as he tossed her a few gratuitous titbits
of information about his favoured vehicle. He flicked a
mocking glance at her taut profile, adding provocatively
when she did not respond, 'I have a taste for the unusual.'

'Are you trying to impress me, by any chance?' she
countered, striving for a caustic amusement when every
instinct was screaming for her to get out of the car and
walk away. The hooded menace of the flared Cobra head
on the marque suddenly seemed all too appropriate to the
car's owner.

'Are you impressed?'

'Incredibly.' Her bored tone denied it.

He turned the key in the ignition and the engine snarled
aggressively, almost drowning out his soft reply.

'Bitch.'

'Well, boys do tend to get rather tedious on the subject
of their expensive toys,' Claudia said, her nails curving into
the smooth leather sides of her document-case as she tried
to concentrate on the conversation rather than the physical

reality. She knew all about boys and their toys. She knew exactly what was going to happen.

And it did.

He was an excellent driver but she was sweating by the time they stopped at the first set of traffic-lights, with sufficient braking force to make the seatbelt tighten between her breasts.

'Still bored, Claudia?'

She stared rigidly out through the windscreen.

'Claudia?'

She didn't answer. She couldn't.

'Claudia?' He swore and reached out and turned her pale face towards him, swearing again when he saw her blank-eyed expression. The hand which had been firm on her jaw gentled to cup her cheek. 'Claudia? I'm sorry. Did I frighten you?'

She blinked, his hard features swimming into focus, his fingers warm against her cold cheek as he held her.

'That was a bloody juvenile thing for me to do, knowing what I do about you. I'm sorry.' Each word was slow and distinct, with a strong emphasis that penetrated her inertia. 'You were there at the track, weren't you, when Nash was killed?'

She blinked again, as if waking from a deep sleep, her eyes darkening as her pupils expanded to their natural daylight size, allowing her to see again, see his rigidly angry expression and know with some relief that it wasn't her he was angry with.

'I—yes.' She never spoke about that day. It was yet another painful memory pushed away out of sight. She shivered. When she didn't add anything else his fingers curled so that his knuckles brushed her rapidly warming skin.

'Do you still have nightmares?'

How did he know? She stared at him, wide-eyed. 'Sometimes. Not often…now.' The last said more firmly as she began to regain her shattered poise, rebuild the image of a woman who was in total control of herself and her destiny.

'Except when idiots like me reawaken them for you,' he said roughly. 'I'm sorry, Claudia.'

She had the feeling that the damned man would keep apologising until he had forced an acknowledgement from her so she shrugged. 'It's quite all right. You just took me by surprise, that's all. I mean, usually I'm OK if I have some indication before that I'm driving with—'

'A speed freak?' He cut across her polite attempt at forgiveness. 'I assure you I'm not usually so cavalier with the road code, especially in city traffic. My ego just eclipsed my better judgement for a few seconds.' He grimaced, aware of having told her that the car could accelerate to a hundred in just under four seconds. 'Is the car a problem for you? Would you rather have a closed sedan? Something less—er—'

'Boastful?' she offered with a stirring of annoyance, ducking her head away from the hand that was still caressing her cheek. Was he now going to treat her as if she were neurotic and feeble-hearted?

'Exposed, I was going to say.' The trace of uncertain humour in his tone gave a boost to her returning confidence. He might be in the driver's seat but he had just given her an indication that she was the one in control. 'Shall we got back and swap cars?'

'No. The Cobra is fine.' She suddenly became aware of the fact that the lights had turned green, and that there was a line of cars trapped behind them. 'As long as you drive it more sedately.'

His eyes flickered at the word. 'Perhaps you'd rather drive?' To her horror he shut down the engine and removed the keys from the ignition, holding them out to her.

She made no move to take them, staring at him in dismay as the car behind them began to toot impatiently. 'Morgan, we're holding up the traffic.'

'Perhaps you'd feel more relaxed if you were the one behind the wheel.' He dangled the keys at her and she hurriedly pushed his hand away.

'No, really, you drive. Morgan, they're tooting at us!' From being pale and clammy she was now flushed with embarrassment.

'Are you sure?' He seemed prepared to sit there all day, ignoring the cars that were pulling out around them. It was almost impossible to credit but he was actually *serious*.

'Yes, I'm sure,' she gritted. 'I wouldn't even know how to drive a car like this.'

He paused in the act of re-inserting the key. 'It's much the same as any high-powered car. What about Nash's Ferrari—didn't you drive that?'

Claudia gave a twisted smile. 'Are you kidding? Chris hated other people driving him, especially women. And he certainly wouldn't let me anywhere near his precious car on my own. If Chris wasn't around I took taxis everywhere.'

'Are you telling me that you didn't have a car of your own—that he wouldn't let you drive—and you let him get away with it?' he said, in tones of such incredulity that if she hadn't already been blushing she would have flushed deeply.

'I didn't need to drive,' she pointed out. 'We moved around so much that my having a car would have been a pretty pointless extravagance anyway. The class of hotel we stayed at always had limo services.' His expression of disapproval still hadn't faded and she added tartly, 'Some people do manage to survive without wheels, you know, especially in large cities with good public transport systems…'

'Usually people who can't afford the luxury. Which I gather wasn't a problem for you while Nash was alive…'

'I just didn't want to drive. OK? Is that a problem for you? Should I apologise or something? Is it an offence to your profession that someone shouldn't care whether they own a car or not? Do you want me to get out and walk? I may as well since it doesn't seem we're going to get anywhere with you in the driver's seat!'

'OK, OK, don't get hysterical, Duchess,' he had the gall to say, his eyes narrowing at the small outburst of temper that had transformed her former dazed inertia into energetic fury. 'See—I'm starting the car.'

'About time,' Claudia fumed, glaring at him as the engine growled impatiently. 'Well?' she demanded. 'What are you waiting for? Plant your foot, for goodness' sake!'

'I'd better wait for the light to go green, first,' he said meekly. 'I wouldn't like to break any more road rules.'

Claudia looked. In the interim the lights had turned back to red and so did she. They were back where they started. She almost exploded with the frustration of trying to keep calm.

'Plant my foot?' The baiting amusement was so overt in his voice that she refused to look at him. 'Not very sedate of you, Claudia.'

She crossed her arms over her chest in a very graphic demonstration of her state of mind.

'You're crushing your hat.'

She lifted her elbows. So she was. The rounded crown was sadly dented. Another fault to be laid at his door. She punched it out, watching him out of the corner of her eye. Morgan had twisted in his seat so that he was half lying against his door. His black hair was ruffled by the summer breeze,and his white shirt pulled tautly across his powerful shoulders. As she surreptitiously studied him he loosened the subdued tie and unbuttoned his collar, a picture of relaxation that highlighted her own nervous tension.

'Hadn't you better keep your eye on the lights? You don't want to miss a second set,' she said waspishly, arranging her hat meticulously on her knees.

'Oh, I don't know. I think it might be worth it.'

She looked at him sharply and was the recipient of a dazzling smile.

'I just learned more about you during one short traffic sequence than in all the previous hours we've spent fencing over ideas in your office,' he drawled.

During several meetings, alone and with Simon, over the past week Morgan had been so formidably businesslike that Claudia had almost shrugged off the unsettling feeling of waiting for the other shoe to drop. Following his unexpected lead, she had pushed aside the dangerous personal antagonism that had threatened to rage out of control and forced herself to view their brief professional partnership as a purely intellectual exercise.

Now, just when she had almost succeeded in believing what her cowardice wanted to be so *was* so, the other shoe—a hobnailed boot by the brutal sound of it—had been dropped with a resounding smash that brought all her doubts rushing back. How could she have allowed herself to imagine that he was anything but the ruthless manipulator he had proved himself in the past?

'I knew it was a good idea to get you out in the fresh air and sunshine,' he continued provocatively. 'And I hope that in the process you've also learned something about me?'

'That you're a bad driver?' she said, hoping to evade whatever uncomfortable observation he had up his sleeve.

He clicked his tongue, unoffended. 'That, whatever appearances might indicate, I don't wish to hurt or frighten you.'

He couldn't have chosen a remark better designed to frighten her. His seriousness, allied with that lazy air of predatory satisfaction, was totally disruptive.

'I see. That's why you've packed Mark off to Italy all of a sudden? Because you were afraid that he might *hurt* me...' she said sarcastically, still smarting over that humiliation.

'Mark packed himself of his own accord. Actually he's been wanting to visit the Ferrari works for some time. Wild horses wouldn't have stopped him accepting that invitation when it finally arrived—and even the omnipotent being you seem to think I am hasn't the clout to influence the personal schedules of car-builders in Milan and Turin. There *is* such a thing as coincidence...'

'Very convenient coincidence,' sneered Claudia, unwilling to underestimate him again.

'What a suspicious little soul you are, Claudia. Missing him already? He's only been gone twenty-four hours...'

'Look—'

'Excuse me, Mr Stone. Do you want me to call a mechanic? I've been parked down the road there and I notice you seem to be having some sort of problem getting your engine going.'

The policeman who was standing at the driver's door seemed torn between officiousness and admiration as he stared down at the car.

To her chagrin Claudia saw that the light facing them was green again, and that neither of them had noticed.

'The problem is with the passenger, not the car,' murmured Morgan wickedly, straightening in his seat as the officer transferred his gaze from the glossy coachwork to Claudia's pink face. 'And my engine is certainly going. In fact it's positively racing!'

'Oh!' The blue-uniformed bastion of male chauvinism grinned understandingly. 'I understand, sir. But I think you'd better get your show on the road. A great car, by the way.'

'Thanks. Incidentally, never call me a mechanic if you see me with a breakdown. I would never live it down with my people. I'm supposed to be a top mechanic myself. Any problem I have I can usually handle myself.'

The policeman grinned even wider, touching his helmet

as he met Claudia's mortified gaze. 'So I see, Mr Stone. Have a good day, sir…ma'am.'

As they shot off with a smooth acceleration designed to please the admiringly envious policeman while allowing for Claudia's fears, she accused furiously, 'What did you say all that for? You know what he's going to think!'

'He was thinking it already. You were blushing so madly when he interrupted us that if this hadn't been a convertible he would have suspected we'd been making love instead of just talking.' He slid the gear-lever forward as he slowed down for a corner, taking in her expression as he checked her side for traffic. 'You're doing it again, you know. Are you thinking of the last time you made love in a car?'

'No, I was not!' she lied even more furiously.

'Don't tell me Chris didn't seek to combine the two great loves of his live on at least *one* occasion.' For the first time there seemed no trace of contempt in his use of her lover's name and, perversely, the teasing familiarity with which he referred to the past somehow removed the pain of remembrance. She had learned to be so defensive about her involvement with Chris that she had repressed all the good memories along with the bad.

'I think we should change the topic of conversation,' Claudia told him primly and he, as usual, refused to be guided by polite suggestion.

'I lost my virginity in a car.'

'How absolutely fascinating,' said Claudia frigidly.

'It was, rather. But extremely uncomfortable. It was a two-seater and the gear-stick got tangled up in my pants. My girlfriend was *supremely* impressed!'

In spite of herself Claudia laughed. And once she'd laughed it was impossible to regain the haughty aloofness she wore as a matter of course when Morgan was around.

'Was that—?' She stopped herself just in time. God forbid that she sound interested in anything about him.

'Mark's mother? Yes, it was. Marina was my first

lover—although I, fortunately, wasn't hers. It was lucky that at least one of us knew what to do!'

Claudia was obscurely shocked. 'You mean, she'd…had other boyfriends?'

Morgan was amused by her attempted delicacy. 'She was eighteen; of course she'd had other boyfriends…but only one lover before me.'

Claudia's head buzzed with confusion at this intimate revelation. In a few brief sentences he had totally up-ended some of her most carefully nurtured prejudices. She hardly noticed that Morgan's gentle handling of the car had acquired an extra zip as they shot past the street façade of the HarbourPoint. 'She was *older* than you?'

'Two years older.' The corner of his mouth dipped. 'Not half the age-difference between you and Mark, but between teenagers an age-gap like that is scarcely significant. What's the matter, Claudia, doesn't that gel with your notion of the selfish, swaggering macho kid seducing a sweet young thing into abandoning her morals?'

'I wouldn't be that judgemental—' began Claudia lamely, conscious that she had thought something along those lines.

'In your position I don't suppose you can afford to throw stones,' he said with cruel perceptiveness, 'but people generally do seem to prefer making unflattering assumptions from the bare facts.'

'Yes…well, you didn't do anything to dress up the bald facts you presented to me,' she pointed out. 'For an articulate man it seems to me you went out of your way to make it sound as if it had been all your fault.'

He shrugged as his hands shifted lazily on the wheel. 'In a way it was. Although Marina may have been sexually more mature than I, I was the more so emotionally. I adjusted far more quickly to the implications of her…pregnancy than she did. I'd have been quite happy to accord her sole responsibility for contraception therefore I couldn't quibble at accepting my share of responsibility for its failure.' His hesitation over the word *pregnancy* would have been unnoticeable to the average listener, but to Claudia it spoke of a sensitivity to which she was acutely attuned.

'Did it ever occur to you—?' She broke off, scarcely believing what she had been about to ask.

Again he seemed to be able to catch her thoughts before she had even voiced them.

'That she had deliberately got herself pregnant in order to marry me? Yes, it occurred to me, especially when she pressured me to accept the financial help of my family, but with the wisdom and hindsight of experience I can say no. She was too devastated by it all for it to have been premeditated. And she didn't really want to be married any more than she wanted to have the baby, but not having it or giving it up for adoption was incompatible with her upbringing…or mine for that matter.'

There was so little bitterness in his words that Claudia wondered whether, for all the evidence to the contrary, he had loved the girl for whom he had altered the whole course of his young life. 'How did she die?'

A tiny pause. 'In a car accident.'

Claudia sucked in a shaky breath at the certain knowledge of the sudden impact of his loss. 'Oh, I'm sorry.'

'So am I. It was such a waste. She was young—only twenty-three—and full of life, just starting back at university on the degree course that she had forfeited when she got pregnant. I wasn't driving—I wasn't even in the car.'

That last, abrupt comment spoke volumes. 'I didn't ask,' she said huskily.

'But you were wondering.'

There was a tension in the hands gripping the wheel that she could not mistake. 'As a matter of fact, I wasn't. You're a very good driver.'

His pale knuckles relaxed. 'You didn't think that ten minutes ago,' he murmured a trifle sardonically.

'There's a big difference between speed and recklessness. Even *I* speed sometimes.'

Her attempt at humour fell flat as he shot her a speculative look. 'So you *do* drive.'

'Of course. I'm not a complete neurotic.'

'Just a sometime one?' His humour reinflated in direct proportion to hers. 'Was Chris reckless when he drove?'

'On the open road, yes. Never when he was working. On the track he was fast but he was cool and calculating; he never broke the rules. When he drove for pleasure he made his own rules—he literally was without fear. He carried his fate around with him, you see. He knew that if he was going to get killed it would be on the track, so off it he considered himself invincible.'

'A tough attitude to live with,' was the only comment. And then, 'Was it he who didn't see any future in your relationship—or you who was frightened of it?'

This time he had gone too far. Claudia recoiled mentally from the consequences of her impulsive confidence, pushing back the silky strands of hair that had whipped across her face as she prepared a deadly, conversation-stopping reply. As she opened her mouth Morgan grunted with satisfaction and pulled into the kerb, neatly slotting himself in behind a car that was pulling out from the solid line of parked vehicles that lined both sides of Oriental Parade.

'What are we doing here? Where are we going?' she demanded belatedly.

'I thought you were never going to ask,' he replied blandly. 'Considering your somewhat savage mistrust of my motives you've been amazingly trusting. In this case your trust is about to be justified. We're going home...'

CHAPTER SIX

'IT'S totally out of the question!'

Claudia stood in the middle of the elegantly furnished apartment, hands on hips, her eyes blazing at the man lounging against the back of the wide cream leather couch.

Morgan studied her calmly. 'Why? It seems like the perfect solution to me. You said you were looking for a place to live. Why not here?' He pushed himself away from the couch and strolled across to the sliding glass door which opened out on to a small balcony. 'It's free, it's private, it has a great view, and Oriental Bay is incredibly convenient to the city—in summer you'll be able to walk to work—I know you like walking because Simon said it was your enthusiasm for exploring the city on foot that led to the hotel's producing a ''sightseers' fitness course'' brochure.' He opened the door and stepped out on the balcony, leaning over the rail. 'Look, you can even see the HarbourPoint from here.'

Claudia didn't move. None of the reasons made a blind bit of difference as far as she was concerned.

'I'm not interested. Can we get back to business now?'

He walked back towards her, the sun streaming in the windows behind him forming a nimbus of light around his white shirt and concealing his expression from her.

'Why, Claudia? You didn't instantly turn your back on Mark's offer to help you find a flat. Consider this reparation for my losing you the opportunity of that one.'

'That was different,' muttered Claudia, summoning the wits which had been scattered the moment Morgan had finished showing her around the top-floor waterfront apartment and told her that it was hers. The fact that he had *told*

99

her rather than offered or asked had got her back up for a start.

'Oh? In what way?'

'It wasn't *his* apartment—' she began defensively.

'And this isn't mine.'

'Your company's, then—'

'Not that, either. Peter is simply a friend who just happens also to work for me,' Morgan cut in mildly. 'He would be very offended at your suggestion that he doesn't own his own home. He's spending the next four months in Germany and the house-sitting arrangement he had with a student fell through just before he left. He doesn't want to risk leaving the place empty and asked if I would do him the favour of finding someone trustworthy to look after the place for him...'

'And you, of course, thought immediately of me!' Claudia said sarcastically. 'Since when have you honoured me with your trust...?'

'Is that how you see my trust, Claudia? As an honour?' he said silkily, approaching closer, and she panicked, backing away until the arm of the couch stopped her.

'I—anyway, I'm looking for a permanent place—' she stammered hastily.

'Then consider this a stepping stone. It'll take the pressure off while you look around.' He picked up a heavy blown-glass *objet d'art* that sat on the sideboard at his elbow and turned it over in his hands, his eyes intent on the way the light was refracting through it as he murmured slyly,

'Remember, with Mark away and the Five Hundred coming up I'll probably be staying at the hotel more often than ever. So if you want to keep up your avoidance of me in your off-duty hours you'll have a better chance here than at the hotel. Here you don't have to treat me with the deference due to a valued client. Here you don't have to pretend. Here the only way I can see you is by your own personal invitation…'

She was being shamelessly manipulated, she knew, but that didn't change the truth of what he said. Suddenly she could see advantages where before only unwelcome complications had loomed. It was on the tip of her tongue to deny that she had been trying to avoid him at all but she sensed to do that would tempt fate indeed.

'I—don't know,' she prevaricated, looking around. It was a lovely apartment, one of only four in the irregularly shaped building a stone's throw from the water's edge. The cliché made her smile. She knew one Stone whose arrogance might benefit from the occasional dunking!

'You *do* want it…so take it!' he said, replacing the glass sculpture with a confident smile that interpreted the softening curl of her mouth as a victory, which she wasn't prepared to give him so easily.

'That's your philosophy in life, is it?' she said tartly.

'As long as you pay for what you take,' he shrugged.

'But you said this apartment was free,' she pointed out sweetly. 'In fact, if I'm house-sitting—providing a service—shouldn't *you* be paying *me*?'

'In cash or in kind?' he countered easily. 'Name your price, Claudia.'

That so closely echoed his bitter offer of two years ago that she was shaken by a stormy conflict of emotion. 'You already paid my price, remember?' she said unwisely, turning away.

He stopped her with a mere touch; a single finger on her coral sleeve that burned through to her bare skin beneath, spinning her around as if he had caught her by the throat.

'I rather thought it was you who had done the paying last time,' he said gravely. 'No amount of compensation can replace a life. Consider this favour I do Peter just part of the debt I owe you.'

'You don't owe me anything,' Claudia said desperately,

wanting to run and hide from the brooding blue gaze. 'The past is just that, the past—over and done with! You've told me how sorry you were. So am I. Let's leave it at that.'

'"Words pay no debts",' he quoted softly. 'Shakespeare had the right of it. What I owe you can't be settled in words, nor with money.' She made the mistake of looking at him then, and he added, eyes glittering with a grim purpose, 'And no, I won't leave it. I *can't*...' The words had the ring almost of a vow and Claudia immediately began to panic again.

'Look, I'm taking the apartment,' she said. 'I'm very grateful and—'

'I don't want your gratitude—'

'Then what *do* you want?' she blurted out angrily. 'Why are you doing this to me? For revenge—?' She bit her lip as his gaze sharpened.

'*Revenge*? Why should I want revenge? What have *you* done to *me* that you think I'd need to seek retribution?'

There was an awful silence during which Claudia was sure her anguished uncertainty was written clearly on her pale face. *Now*. Tell him now, her brain urged. Here is the perfect opportunity to clear the slate. To start again...or finish it forever...

'I—I—' As she struggled for the words that would totally destroy any possibility of respect or friendship or anything else between them, he continued thoughtfully,

'What is it that I *am* doing to you, by the way? Besides providing you with a fine professional opportunity to prove yourself in a new job, of course, and helping you find accommodation in a strange town, and asking for forgiveness for mistakes—past and present. What exactly is it that makes it so difficult for you to accept anything from me...?'

He hadn't moved any closer but suddenly she felt crowded. 'Morgan—'

'Is it this, Claudia...?'

This wasn't just a finger. This time his whole hand restrained her nervous shying, sliding under her unbuttoned jacket and around her slender waist, hooking her startled body into the circle of his arms.

'Isn't this what you're afraid of, Duchess?'

His parted mouth came down on hers, damming the cry of protest in her arched throat, sending a dazzling bolt of fearful excitement shearing through her consciousness. After the first instant of quivering shock it was like being enveloped in a slither of hot, wet silk that bound her, stroked her, wrapping around her senses, entangling her in inescapably erotic knots.

The world went black as she closed her eyes, shutting out the deliciously terrifying sight of Morgan's blue eyes a breath away from hers, blazing with a carnal intensity that was matched by the sensual movements of his mouth. It was a mistake. Now there was nothing to distract her from the pure intoxication of her tactile senses.

With the extent of her vulnerability screaming in her mind she tried to shut him out, but he would have none of it, nipping softly at her lower lip until she allowed him precious access again, dominating her with his lips and teeth and tongue in a way that frightened and exalted her. That battle won, he smoothly adjusted his grip on her torso, his fingers splaying out around her waist to overlap at her back, his thumbs digging into the soft ribbed cotton just below the weight of her breasts, moving back and forth in a sensuous precursor to the caress to come. In spite of her confusion Claudia responded like a flower to the sun, unfolding to the warmth of half-forgotten feelings and sensations that had for too long been associated with the accompanying pain of emptiness and loss.

Unknowingly she rose on to her toes, flexing her spine, faintly arching and twisting her hips, the white piqué skirt flaring across the dark fabric of Morgan's trousers as she sought to assuage the empty ache aroused by his sudden

assault. She felt a thick ridge of flesh compress briefly under her dragging hipbone and then spring bluntly forward
into the hollow cup of her pelvic girdle, realisation of what
it was bursting upon her comprehension too overwhelm-
ingly for her to pretend ignorance. Her eyes flew open. His
were still there, brooding in wait for her, swamping her
field of vision in a hot blue haze, watching her arrive at the
shocking knowledge of what she was doing to him…and
he to her.

'No—' Her tiny breath of denial died on his tongue as
it curled over hers in a gesture that was both intimately
protective and provocatively sensual. She moved her head
and he let her go, but only in order to feast on the frantic
pulse beneath her ear, his mouth cascading gently down the
exposed nerves of her throat to settle moistly in the vulnerable pool of her collarbone, licking at the clamour of
blood under her skin.

'Yes…' His thumbs pressed upward, compressing her
swollen flesh in a sensual parody of the way her hip had
stroked his, then releasing it, only to press again, moving
her breasts rhythmically against the lacy cups of her bra so
that the tips stiffened with the delicately judged friction.

'Morgan…' Her hands clutched at his shirt-front, seeking
to ground herself in the solid reality of his presence, to warn
her dwindling resistance that this wasn't simply a reckless
figment of her sinful imagination.

'Yes…' He wasn't replying to her weak plea, but fer-
vently approving the tremors of delight he could feel rippling through the supple arch of her body. His thighs
moved, urging her unsteady legs softly across the carpet
until her bottom hit the firm rounded arm of the couch. His
languid momentum carried him further as he rode up over
her thighs, straddling them with his, bending her against
the couch and the brace of his hands as his mouth nuzzled
at the white cotton over her breasts.

Claudia found herself blinking at the ceiling, dazed at

the speed and intensity of the conflagration in her senses, her limbs weighted by an unprecedented pleasure. If this was truly happening surely it wouldn't feel so—so… incredibly good…so *right*? And if it was a dream it was the most erotic one she had ever had…

Her hand slid up over his loosened collar to sink into the frosted darkness of his hair at the back of his head, her fingers tightening in instinctive protest among the short, soft strands as she felt his movements momentarily still. Then he was in satisfying motion again, rubbing the hard angles of his face against the stretched cotton in a deliberately explicit gesture of possessiveness that made her say his name again, this time in a whisper of bewildered need.

He uttered a thick growl of satisfaction, dragging up her ribbed top and moving his mouth over the creamy curves exposed by her low-cut bra. Across the bare slope of hill and provocatively perfumed valley he strung a line of luxuriant, biting kisses that melted like hot honey down over her sensitive flesh, drenching her with a sweetness that seeped into the very heart of her being. Now she had both hands in his hair, urging him fiercely to her pleasure, aching for him to touch the lace that he was so assiduously avoiding, the passionate restraint of his tender assault both a joyful revelation and a searing frustration.

Not until she felt the fingers slowly easing up her flank, catching the hem of her skirt and pushing it high over her captured thighs did she feel the trickling return of her former fears.

She murmured, struggling to surface from her sensual stupor, and he soothed her by at last seeking one of the rigid peaks sheltering behind the seams of her bra, taking it between his teeth and biting, firmly. Wanton desire exploded violently in the pleasure centres of her brain, obliterating her returning reason. Her head fell back in erotic shock as in the same moment he shifted the hand under her skirt gently between their bodies and touched the secret V that sheltered her femininity. It was a light, sliding touch, one fingertip barely intruding between the silky compression of her inner thighs, clamped together between his powerful knees, but combined with the stinging tug on her nipple the explicit delicacy of that warm fingertip curling against the clinging film of her panties was every bit as shattering as his full possession would have been.

Claudia uttered a frantic cry, convulsing helplessly, blind and deaf to Morgan's muttered curse as his head jerked up and both arms whipped tightly around her to secure her shuddering length firmly against his. As she continued to be racked by shivering contractions he lifted one thigh, roughly pushing it between hers, seeking to ease the painfully exquisite need that he could see expressed in her tautly stretched body, her wildly flushed face and lustrous golden eyes.

With a greedy fascination he watched as the woman in his arms peaked and gradually quieted. His head pounded with hot-blooded triumph, mingled with a savage sense of possessiveness and almost angry envy of the uninhibited bliss she had stolen from what he had only intended to be a little light-hearted lovemaking.

Any minute now Claudia was going to realise what had happened and it was going to take some very skilful handling on his part to persuade her that her newly revealed vulnerability to him was not something he was going to take ruthless advantage of...even if he was!

Claudia didn't want to lift her head from his chest but she knew she was going to have to face him some time. She couldn't hide her shame forever.

She forced herself to stand stiffly straight within his arms, silently indicating that she no longer needed his support, and slowly raised her chin, mentally cringing at the prospect of meeting his knowing gaze.

But instead of smug or leering satisfaction she found Morgan's expression sombre and curiously gentle. That only made her feel worse. He was probably thunder-struck…disgusted, even. *She* certainly was! She sought desperately for an explanation for her scandalous display and realised there was none. Her flushed face paled, then flushed again. There was no graceful way out of this humiliating embrace, she thought miserably. Whatever she said he was going to think that he had just proved she was every bit the promiscuous tramp he had always suspected her of being!

The silence stretched unbearably. There was no use waiting for him to get her off the hook. It seemed he was content to stand there forever, waiting for her to speak. What could she say that might bring some semblance of normality to this horribly abnormal situation? She scrabbled for a neutral topic, something that might allow her to back off with at least the semblance of her pride intact.

'Er—' She cleared her throat and made a half-hearted shuffle with her shoulders and to her surprise Morgan let her go. She moved an uncertain step away and watched him push his hands into his trouser pockets, bunching out the dark, pleated fabric. Definitely a man waiting for something. Say something, Claudia—*anything*—to demonstrate that you aren't the frenzied madwoman of a few moments ago…

'I—you—are you really a qualified mechanic?' He looked at her incredulously and she continued doggedly, 'I mean, you told that policeman that you fixed cars. Did—did you do the usual apprenticeship…?' Oh, God, this was terrible. She sounded like a prim spinster at a tea-party making polite conversation with a stranger!

His burst of laughter confirmed the absurdity of her choice and she blushed even more fierily as he finally calmed down enough to shake his head.

'Is that a criticism, Duchess? Are you trying to tell me in a roundabout way that my performance just now was disappointingly mechanical?'

Performance? The word implied a detachment on his part that was an insult and his faint emphasis on *disappointingly* made a pointed mockery of any denial she might offer. He knew very well that the last thing she had been was disappointed!

He was still laughing and anger began to replace her crippling embarrassment. But in the next instant he whipped the ground from under her by saying with a warm chuckle, 'I can assure you, Claudia, that the mechanics of what we were doing was the very last thing on my mind. In fact I don't think my brain was engaged at all; I was operating purely on instinct. All I could think was how incredibly delicious you tasted and how eager you were for my touch, how generously responsive you were…'

She knew it! 'I am *not* promiscuous!' she told him raggedly.

'I never said you were,' he said, his face again adopting that dangerously inviting gentleness. He had no right to stand there looking so…cool and untouched when Claudia was a welter of anguished self-disgust.

Well, not precisely cool, she corrected herself. There was a certain indefinable, smouldering heat in those innocently sky-blue eyes. And not entirely untouched, either. His mouth was reddened and faintly swollen, its usual crooked narrow line looking surprisingly lush and sultry, and his closely groomed hair was ruffled unevenly. He took his hands out of his pockets as she frowned suspiciously at him, and she discovered what his gesture had originally been designed to hide when the bunched material relaxed over an explicit tautness.

Too late, she snatched her eyes back to his face.

'And nor, I might add, am I,' he murmured, confirming her discovery with a ruefully frank reference to his continued state of sexual readiness, 'just because I find being with you intensely arousing. What happened naturally happens between men and women. The survival of the entire species depends on it...'

'But I—you—' She was confused by his apparent benevolence. Could it be that he really didn't realise exactly what *had* happened to her alone—had he been too caught up in his own pleasure to realise the extent of hers?

He dashed her faint hope with a smile. 'You just outpaced me a little this time, Claudia. Nothing to look so embarrassed about. I'm very flattered that you trusted me enough to let yourself go.'

This time? Her heart shuddered at the casual tossing down of the flagrant gauntlet of his intent. As to letting it happen—he flattered her by assuming that she had had any control whatsoever over her responses.

'But I don't—I mean I didn't mean...it all was a mistake...' she said frantically. 'I don't usually—I mean, I've never—oh, *God*!' With a moan she covered her embarrassed face with her hands.

'Never gone so far so fast? Or never had an orgasm before?'

'*Morgan*!' She was sure that by now she was pink all over.

'I'm sorry if it embarrasses you to talk about it, Claudia, but not sorry enough to regret what we did. I enjoyed overloading you with pleasure, so much so that I think it could become very quickly addictive...'

She peeped out between her fingers to see if he was teasing and almost groaned out loud at the expression on his face. *Now* he was looking smug and self-satisfied. And, instead of shaming her as she thought it would, the swaggering of his male ego made her feel shockingly aware of the depths of her own sensuality.

He took her wrists and pulled her hands away from her face. 'There's no point in trying to hide any longer from the attraction between us, Claudia,' he told her gravely. 'It's just been proven beyond a doubt. You want me. I want you. Sexually we're exquisitely compatible. That accepted we should discuss the other possibilities available in our relationship...'

Claudia stopped trying to pull her wrists away, subduing a traitorous pang of disappointment as her eyes flicked momentarily down below his waist and skated nervously away. 'You mean you don't—' She broke off and he took pity on her confusion.

'Want to take you into the bedroom right now and confirm that compatibility to both our satisfaction? You don't know how badly.' He rolled his shoulders and shuddered slightly in a graphic attempt to shake off the tension in his big body. 'But I can wait. I didn't bring you here to seduce you. At least not to the point where you could later claim that I swept you off your feet without allowing you to weigh the consequences of your actions. I know that you consider yourself a cautious woman. For the moment I'm willing to respect that caution. Hungry?'

'What?'

'It's lunchtime.' He cocked her a wicked grin. 'Doesn't time fly when you're having fun?'

She managed a very shaky smile. 'If that was fun why do I feel so battered and bruised?'

'I could give you a very indecent answer to that but instead I'll undertake to feed you lunch while we talk about the contents of that briefcase you brandished at me earlier.'

'I—I'll need to freshen up,' said Claudia, disconcerted by his cheerful change of subject and thinking that if they were going to a public restaurant it would be better for her reputation if she didn't look as if she had just climbed out of bed with her escort.

But when she emerged from the bathroom it was to find Morgan setting the small table on the sunny balcony with food from a woven hamper that lay open at his feet.

'Where did that come from?' she demanded suspiciously,

having been shown around an empty kitchen earlier. No takeaway delicatessen delivered that fast!

'The boot of my car.'

'Do you always carry around emergency hampers?' She approached warily to check the mouth-watering ingredients he was placing on the white tablecloth. 'HarbourPoint deluxe hampers at that!' She recognised the labels from the hotel brochure.

'Only when I'm attempting to persuade a highly discerning lady to like me,' he said, waiting until she was seated on one of the wrought-iron chairs before he sat himself.

'Is it really necessary that I like you?' said Claudia stiffly, not sure how to view the fresh evidence that he had had far more planned for this day than he initially let on.

'Essential,' he said simply. 'No matter how sublime the sex, I can't make love to a woman who doesn't appreciate my mind as well as my body. You'd never respect me afterwards.

'Now, stop trying to provoke me and eat. And tell me, have you decided on anyone in particular to design the invitations for the ball? I know of a very talented young graphic artist you might like to consider. And what would you say to one of the world's leading racing drivers and the head of a famous champagne house as celebrity speakers for starters?'

CHAPTER SEVEN

MORGAN poured the last of the bubbling wine into her long-stemmed glass and Claudia twirled it between her fingers, wondering how much of the bottle she had drunk but too relaxed to care. She knew by now that Morgan had no need to seduce a woman with alcohol. He did quite well without any artificial aids!

Her attitude was very different from what it had been two weeks ago, when they had sat together on the balcony of the Oriental Bay apartment she had eyed the wine that Morgan had produced from a chilled compartment of his hamper with suspicion and disfavour.

Both then and since that suspicion had proved unfounded.

Then, he had deftly eased her over the barrier of her mortification by plunging into a lively debate over the ideas that she had produced for his approval, subtly challenging her on a number of points so that she was forced to concentrate on her arguments rather than the intimate submission that he had just extracted from her.

Even so, she hadn't quite been able to conquer the flustered leap of her heart when her hand had inadvertently brushed his while pointing out a paragraph on her sheaf of papers, or when she had looked up to catch him studying her with a narrow-eyed speculation that she knew had nothing to do with the subject in hand.

Today, he had used that same earnest concentration on detail successfully to take her mind off the fact that this time the balcony was his and the lunch prepared, not by the hotel kitchen, but by his housekeeper.

The meal had been light and delicious, the panoramic

112

view from his clifftop home glorious and business satisfactorily disposed of in a thoroughly professional fashion. In fact, Claudia was feeling confident enough to feel that she could handle almost anything at the moment—even Morgan Stone.

The promotion centred around the race was shaping up nicely, a fact which, she was willing to admit, had a lot to do with Morgan's persistent involvement. Although he was ruthlessly efficient in his business dealings, demanding a high standard of performance from those who worked with and for him, he was equally demanding of himself. In her first-hand observance of his business acumen Claudia had come to see that part of the strength of his company was his own dedication to excellence coupled with a personal charisma that evoked the loyalty of his employees even when they were at loggerheads with him.

Only on two occasions had she been given a glimpse of the dogmatic autocrat that Mark had so resented as a teenager. Both times had been at his office when Morgan had lost his temper over what Claudia had thought were relatively trivial matters but which he seemed to see as an intolerable attempt to pre-empt his authority.

She had got the strong impression that Morgan actually *enjoyed* the shouting and pacing and banging things around on his desk like a bad-tempered boy. Certainly after both incidents he had appeared cheerfully refreshed and invigorated, as if his outburst had shed some of the internal tension that seemed part and parcel of his complex personality. And, from the wry grin she had received from the first chastened victim as he had slunk out of the door, she thought the employees who knew him well had learned to take the odd tantrum in their stride.

She, too, had learned a valuable lesson. If you stood up to Morgan you had a far better chance of getting him to listen to you than if you tried to appease him by making excuses, however justified.

Intrigued as she was by these insights into his character, Claudia had stuck firmly to her resolution not to allow her personal curiosity dangerous rein. She had never invited him back to her new apartment—not even to the small housewarming she had held—and she never accepted an invitation from him without first satisfying herself that it was solely business-related.

Still, that criterion had proved amazingly flexible and in this past fortnight Morgan had managed to produce an impeccable reason for her company almost every second day. In the process he had contrived to introduce her to a considerable number of influential Wellingtonians who would be useful contacts, not only for the current project, but for future ones as well. He had even managed to get her invited to two embassy cocktail parties which she would have been a fool to refuse, even if this had meant accepting Morgan as her escort. There she had encountered a Morgan she had never seen before—urbane, almost courtly in the politeness that sheathed his normally blunt self, and on first-name terms with many of the high-level political movers and shakers they encountered.

Shortly afterwards Simon had complimented her on her cleverness in gaining such a swift entrée to the cream of Wellington society and on the second Friday of what Claudia wryly thought of as her unholy alliance he had passed on the information that head office was so impressed with her plans that it wanted to increase the hotel's involvement by sponsoring one of the cars, if possible.

That, of course, had required yet another discussion with Morgan but he had been unable to fit it into his schedule and had suggested the next day. Claudia had been too pleased with the prospect of a new feather in her cap to balk when he had added that his weekends were normally inviolate but that, providing he didn't have to come into the business district, he was willing to compromise. He had all the extensive race files at home on his personal computer, including those individuals still seeking whole or partial sponsorship, and she was welcome to take advantage of them.

Nervously aware that she was stretching her self-imposed rules to suit the dictates of her disobedient curiosity, Claudia had agreed, but had borrowed one of the hotel cars so that she had the security of knowing that she could leave whenever she wanted.

'Shall I crack open another bottle?'

Claudia surfaced from her meandering thoughts and realised that her glass was empty again.

'We're not celebrating anything are we?'

It was a leading question, which Morgan wisely declined to follow to its tempting conclusion. He raised his glass to her.

'Only the prospect of another long, slothful summer weekend. Would you believe I used to work all the hours God made? That was before I realised that I was slowly petrifying in the ivory tower of my own self-importance. I was losing touch with the simple pleasures of life. I was growing old while still trapped in the selfish ambitions of my youth—to have enough money and power to do whatever the hell I wanted. I just never stopped long enough to figure out exactly what it was I *did* want so desperately.'

'You still seem to be fairly confident of your own self-importance,' Claudia was unable to resist commenting, although the acerbic tone was tempered by her hesitant question, 'And when you did figure it out—what was it?'

He smiled at her ruefully. 'A place where I feel at home, someone to feel at home with. I suppose you might say, to be loved for myself. Trite, but true.' He looked down into his glass as he continued, his smile withering on the crooked vine of his mouth.

'Of course, if you consider that the self that you are is more worthy of hatred and contempt than of love, it's very difficult to persuade yourself that it's even worth trying to change for the better. I'm not a religious man but deep down I do believe that you reap what you sow, particularly where human relationships are concerned. I also believe that pride goes before a fall, and mine was monumental in both cases.'

The bitter note of ironic self-mockery in his voice pierced her compassionate heart to the quick and she knew suddenly, with apalling certainty, what he was trying to tell her. *She* was the cause of his dramatic change of attitude and lifestyle over the past few years. By blindly striking out at him in her pain she had changed something fundamental in him, at once and forever. Her random act of emotional vandalism had caused him to build a whole new image of himself around a lie.

He saw the horrified knowledge dawn in her eyes and interpreted it as something else.

'You have every right to look disbelieving, Claudia, but I assure you that I'm a completely different man from the one I was two years ago. OK, sometime I lapse,' he corrected himself, his determination to be relentlessly honest painfully visible. 'I'm human—but in general I've conquered the personal demons that had me ride roughshod over other people's dreams. I know you probably thought that I callously shrugged off what happened that day, that I never even bothered to think about you again. But I did. I do. I stayed out of your life and kept Mark out too because I believed that was what you wanted, that that was the least painful alternative for you. But if you had ever been in trouble I would have known—would have helped you. But you didn't even grant me that small penance. You managed very well for yourself.'

'How—how would you have known I needed help?' Claudia asked shakily, her skin crawling with renewed guilt.

'I had a friend in Auckland check up on you occasionally. Nothing intrusive—just the bare bones,' he assured her quickly, seeing the sudden distaste in her eyes. 'To see that you weren't in any dire straits—whether you had a job and if you seemed happy.'

The knowledge that he had been watching over her all this time, however casually and intermittently, gave her strange chills. While he had been facing his demons, she had been hiding from hers. She was still hiding.

'Are you sure you don't want some more wine?' he asked, and she realised that she had raised her empty glass to her lips to conceal their trembling.

'Oh, no—no, thank you. Er—perhaps some coffee.' She had used the computer earlier and with Morgan's help chosen an up-and-coming New Zealand-born driver for the hotel to sponsor. Now what she needed was something to counter the volatile compound of guilt and alcohol that mingled in her veins.

Morgan collected their empty plates and excused himself to carry them back into the terracotta-tiled coolness of the interior of the house. Claudia narrowed her eyes against the sun slanting in over the glittering waters of the harbour, and tried to let the sheer beauty of the view calm her unquiet spirit.

Morgan's whitewashed concrete house, a tribute to modern engineering, seemed to grow out from the very side of the cliff, the high-sided balcony on which they sat curving out over a breathtakingly sheer drop to the winding tarmac of Marine Drive below.

Leaning on the rough-cast top of the balcony, Claudia tilted her head to let the warm sunlight wash over her face and bare arms. She had put on a soft cardigan-jacket when she had set out in the overcast morning but was glad now that she had worn a yellow dress with tiny, loose cap-sleeves underneath. The smoothly underturned ends of her blow-dried hair flirted in and out of the little stand-up collar as a breeze that was a far cry from Wellington's reputedly fierce windiness drifted gently in off the sea.

From here she had a perfect view of the irregular sweep of small bays that scalloped the eastern shores of the harbour. Way down to the left she could see the narrow wooden tongue of the wharf at Eastbourne poking cheekily out into the sea, a ferry wallowing squatly at its side. And across in the western haze lay the compact building blocks of the central city, crouched beneath the hills that rose sharply behind it, creating the steep inner-city suburbs that had astonished Claudia when she had first had cause to visit one or two apparently vertical streets and note the property-owners' hair-raising answers to providing accessible drive-ways. She smiled at the memory.

'You see—a little sloth is good for us all. You look very contented out here in the sun.' Morgan's return with the coffee-tray took her off-guard, but there was no trace of his sombre mood of a few minutes ago as he relaxed opposite and began to pour the coffee. In black polo-shirt and white designer jeans he looked very Continental. 'Aren't you glad you came? We get on well together, don't we? There's hardly been a single cross word between us in the past two weeks.'

'But that's because—' Claudia stopped and he lounged more comfortably in his chair.

'Because?' he invited lazily, his blue eyes almost the same colour as the shifting, sun-lit sea behind him.

'Because you've been putting yourself out to be...co-operative,' she said grudgingly.

'Co-operative?' His quizzical smile flicked at her hesitant choice of words.

'Pleasant,' she clarified with even greater reluctance, concious that that twinkle in his eye was a great deal more attractive than it should be.

'Only pleasant? I must be slipping,' he murmured. 'I thought I was being thoroughly charming.'

'I've had a lot of practice at seeing through charming

fakes,' said Claudia, almost burning her tongue on her coffee before she remembered she usually took milk.

'Do you mean when you were with Nash? I guess that in any situation like his there are an inevitable number of hangers-on, hoping some of the glamour will rub off...'

At least he was no longer classing *her* as one of the groupies!

'Chris liked to have lots of people around him. He loved the crowds and the parties.'

'But you didn't,' he guessed shrewdly.

'I didn't say that,' she said, her sensitivity quick to sense criticism where there was none. 'I was young and in love with a famous man. I liked to have fun, to meet new people. We could go anywhere in the world and be swamped with invitations—'

'Was that what you fell in love with—the glory rather than the substance of the man?'

'Actually when I fell in love with him I didn't know he was famous,' she said tartly. 'He was recuperating from an accident and hiding out from the Press. He came to stay at the country inn my parents owned. He was there for three weeks.'

'And when he left?'

She lifted her sharp chin in a mixture of bravado and defiance. 'I left with him.'

And in spite of subsequent events she had never regretted it. If she had stayed within the narrow, blinkered world that her parents inhabited she would never have discovered the true richness of living. Looking back, her childhood had been amazingly arid. It seemed that she had spent all her youth desperately seeking the approval of parents who believed that to praise was to encourage sinful vanity. They had rigidly adhered to the principle that sparing the rod spoiled the child and, as an only child, Claudia had been constantly monitored and pressured to conform to their traditional concept of female modesty and subservience.

Dutiful obedience was the only proof of love that they recognised or required and Claudia was taught.

Chris had burst like a dazzling revelation into that joyless
existence, embodying all the secret yearnings of her im-
prisoned young heart. For him love had been easy—bright
with laughter, warmth and golden pleasure and wonderfully
liberating to Claudia's strait-jacketed emotions.

'You still didn't realise who he was?'

'Of course I did. He didn't mislead me, if that's what
you're implying,' Claudia said. 'He told me who he was,
what he did for a living, what it would be like—'

'It must have sounded exciting. But still, the reality must
have been a bit of a shock—especially for an over-protected
country girl.'

It annoyed her that he so swiftly analysed her home life,
laying its deficiencies bare in just a few well-chosen words.
'I adjusted,' she said stubbornly. 'It wasn't just a fling, you
know, to relieve the boredom of his convalescence. He
didn't have to ask me to go with him. He loved me.'

'You're very loyal, aren't you, Claudia?' he murmured,
the steam from his cup momentarily obscuring the expression in his eyes. 'Was he really such a shining paragon of
manhood? Is that the kind of woman you are, one who
needs to hero-worship her man?'

'No, of course not,' Claudia responded hotly, 'but you
seem to be trying to imply that Chris somehow took unfair
advantage of me. I *wanted* to go with him. I was twenty
years old and I might have been innocent and over-
protected in some ways, but intellectually I was probably
more mature than most girls my age. I knew what I was
doing—that there would be no going back.

'In fact, in some ways I felt older than Chris,' she admitted revealingly. 'He'd always lived such a charmed life.
He never really knew what it was like to lose at anything.
And he was always so…optimistic about life, so open about
his feelings…so—boyishly trusting that everything would

turn out all right in the end…as if life were just a great game to be enjoyed. He had to be like that, I suppose, or he'd never have survived the incredible stresses of motor racing, but it could be quite irritating sometimes, when I wanted him to take something seriously and he'd just grin and tell me not to worry, that everything would be OK.'

'Do you ever wonder whether you might have been outgrowing him by the time he died?' said Morgan quietly.

'No, of *course* not! I was going to marry him!' she blurted out heedlessly, the fervency of her denial repressing the doubts that still lingered inside her.

'There was never any mention of marriage in the papers.'

She couldn't tell from his expression whether he believed her or not and all of a sudden it was important he did.

'It was a secret…Chris had arranged for us to go to Las Vegas the day after his race. No one knew about it. We were going to announce it afterwards. He liked doing that—putting one over on the Press, springing surprises on his friends. But instead of a marriage that week there was a funeral…'

She had felt guilty about that, too; the feeling that his death had somehow opened a cage door. Previously, she had fended off Chris's confidently light-hearted proposals, uneasy with the knowledge that they seemed to be spending less and less time together as his driving successes mounted. With his usual quick-fire optimism Chris had decided that her problem was a lack of security that their marriage would solve but Claudia had been less certain. Two or three years before she would have jumped at his offer but with more worldly experience under her belt she had been quietly beginning to question whether the love that she bore him was strong enough to survive a lifetime of public scrutiny and private stress over his risk-laden choice of career, one that she knew he would never voluntarily give up.

Her pregnancy had pre-empted her vague thoughts of

leaving and she had allowed Chris's genuine joy at the prospect of their child to overwhelm her misgivings. Whatever his other failings she knew that he would love his child with all the warmth of his volatile nature. He might be a bit irresponsible as a day-to-day parent but no child of his would ever have cause to feel like a burden or a duty. Claudia had felt that she owed it to their baby to give it the early security of a real family, to at least give the marriage a fighting chance…

'No wonder you felt the need to escape the media circus that followed. You must have been feeling very vulnerable…'

A muscle jumped in Morgan's cheek and she realised wretchedly that he was probably reinterpreting her seemingly promiscuous plunge into another man's arms so soon after her lover's death in an entirely new and erroneously compassionate light.

Tell him.

'Morgan, I—'

'Did you ever think of perhaps going back to your parents?' he cut across her faltering beginning.

She unknowingly flinched at the suggestion. 'My parents were very…insular people, very strict in their principles. Decent people don't show affection or touch each other in front of others, you see—even if they're married or members of the same family. In fact they were so humiliated by my notorious fall from grace that they couldn't hold up their heads in the community they'd lived all their lives in. They sold the hotel not long after I left and moved to Australia. I haven't spoken to them in years.'

'What parents put their children through in the name of pride,' Morgan murmured and she knew that he was thinking of his own experiences—first as a son and then from the diametrically opposed perspective of beleaguered fatherhood. From what he had let drop about his business she knew that he had never fully reconciled with his own parents after his enforced teenage marriage. What he had achieved he had done so without the inheritance that his youthful pride had rejected as a bribe. When his parents had died their entire estate had been put in trust for Mark.

'And yet you encouraged Mark to open the lines of communication with *me*...so you must believe in the importance of family relationships...' he said softly.

'I didn't think you believed me about that,' Claudia remembered grimly.

He bluntly conceded her point. 'I didn't—at the time. Mark told me later that it was your chipping away at his stubbornness that wore him down into agreeing to see me.'

His voice was low with impatience. He was far less interested in the known facts of his own past than in the mysteries of hers. Her reactions to him were so erratic— tacitly inviting and yet overtly rejecting—that he knew there must be some powerful psychological inhibitor in operation.

Claudia seemed to have a subconscious fascination with the forbidden, perhaps as a result of those formative years in which an impulsive child had been drilled to maintain a prematurely adult self-control. But she was also intelligent and self-aware. The prospect of being out of control, sexually or emotionally, was probably as threatening as it was irresistibly exciting.

At least he *hoped* it was going to prove irresistible!

The great temptation was to use her potent sexual awareness of him to bludgeon rather than seduce, to force her to the point where she would either admit to her fears or succumb to him in spite of then, thus neutralising their threat.

As temptations went the idea held a savage allure. It also had the potential to backfire to devastating effect.

'Have you tried to contact your parents recently?'

'Since I became respectable, you mean?' Claudia murmured cynically, wondering what on earth was going on behind that cloudless blue gaze to cause him to look broodingly male, as sultry as a summer storm about to break out of a clear sky. Even his question had been uttered in a husky growl, like the distant rumble of warning thunder, she thought nervously.

'I'll never be that as far as they're concerned. I…I wrote to them about—when I knew I was pregnant.' She immediately hated herself for the feeble prevarication. 'They sent my opened letter back in a plain envelope. That's all—no note, no message. A fairly explicit rejection, I thought.' Her twisted smile belied the uncaring shrug. 'I suppose an illegitimate baby was no less than they expected of me. Maybe they were afraid that if they gave me the slightest sign of encouragement I might turn up on their doorstep one day with my tainted child in tow…' She tailed off. Even though her childhood had been less than idyllic, it hurt to think that to her parents she no longer existed.

'It was their loss, Claudia. You baby would have been a beautiful child. As you would have been a fine mother.'

The simple comments tore at her heart. Tears stung her eyes and she tried to pretend it was the sun. She looked down at the fingers clenched in her lap and didn't see him stand up and come around the table. Not until he crouched by her chair, his hands sliding warmly over her cold ones, did she realise what she had done. She had invited him this close with her appalling weakness!

'You don't know that—' She tried to pull her hands away but he wouldn't let her. 'It was all a horrible mistake, anyway. You were right when you said that it was a blessing that I lost him—'

'I never said that,' he denied quietly, his thumbs moving gently over her tense white knuckles. 'And you didn't *lose* your son. That implies carelessness and I know you're not that—'

'It was sheer carelessness to get pregnant in the first place,' she said, the tears finally spilling over as she stiffly rejected his comfort, still refusing to look at his face, upturned to hers. Not for two years, she thought with a wrench, had she been so recklessly emotional as to cry in front of someone else. That time it had been him, too...

'Was it? Who was taking care of contraception—him or you?'

Now Claudia was flushed among her tears. He thought he was asking about his son—whether it was *Mark* who had been irresponsible. Hadn't she caused him torment enough?

'Me. And I didn't forget. Not once. It was just one of those things.' The irony of her phrasing hit her as she realised that those were the very words that the doctor had used to console her after her baby's death.

'I didn't want to get pregnant, I didn't even want a baby,' she said starkly. There! Perhaps that would be enough to put him off, stop him tormenting her with his compassion...

'Then it certainly wasn't carelessness. It was a miracle. The miracle of conception. You might not have wanted a baby, Claudia, but you wanted *your* baby, didn't you...?'

She thought the moistness on the back of her hands was the tears that had escaped her vigilance, but it was his mouth. She stared at his dark head, bent over her lap, and watched, shocked, as he drew her hands aside and kissed the gentle curve of her stomach just below the slim white belt that separated the narrow yellow skirt from the buttoned bodice of her dress.

'Don't—'

She could feel the heat of his mouth smouldering through the thin fabric and her hands clenched protestingly around his. He raised his head and moved their entwined fingers to stroke where he had kissed.

'You were wretchedly ill all through your pregnancy—Mark did tell me that much—and you had a terrifying experience of childbirth. Did the doctor tell you that you might have similar problems with future pregnancies? Was there any permanent damage?'

'I—no. He—he said that…that my health had been stressed even before I got pregnant—that otherwise I was—was quite normal…and that I shouldn't have any trouble conceiving again if I wanted to…' She couldn't concentrate on her words, not when he was looking at her with that peculiar gravity, his knuckles brushing gently back and forth over her dress, his lids sinking sensuously down over his eyes as she stumbled over the word that suddenly seemed indecently tangled on her tongue.

'And do you want to? Or are you frightened by the bad memories…afraid to risk ever getting pregnant again?'

Why had he said *risk* in that slightly disparaging way, as if he expected her to cringe at the prospect? Did he think she was that neurotic? She hesitated, sensing some kind of trap, but not being able to distinguish where it lay.

'Would you like another baby, Claudia?' he persisted softly, almost tauntingly. His hand stopped guiding hers in its provocative stroking, pressing instead into the taut resilience of her belly, the masculine-enwrapped femininity fisted over her womb. 'Another son or daughter.'

'I—' She licked her dry lips and whispered helplessly, 'Some day, I suppose. I'm not…I mean, I don't—it wouldn't be the same—'

'Of course it wouldn't,' he agreed quietly. 'This time you would plan carefully for your pregnancy. Make sure that you were properly healthy before you conceived, prepared both mentally and physically, financially and emotionally secure.'

'I—yes—I suppose, yes, I would—' She felt as if she was being lured along a secret path, whose intriguing twists and turns obscured its destination. The hot sun poured down on her head. Morgan, on his knees facing her, was in the shadow cast by her figure, and the expression in his eyes… She went very still.

'It wouldn't be a replacement, but, if you had another baby whose father was from the same genetic background as the father of your son, the child would probably grow up to share many of the physical characteristics that your son would have had...'

She was suffering from heat-stroke. He couldn't *possibly* be suggesting what she thought he was suggesting in that deep, slow, calm voice! Her lashes spiky with tears, her eyes golden with shock, she listened to him utter the shattering proposition, 'I told you I owed you a debt, Claudia, and that it couldn't be paid in words. As I see it, the only way for me to truly heal the breach between us and redeem my honour is to repay exactly what I deprived you of: a life for a life.

'I can't bring your son back, but I could give you another. Only this time I wouldn't be grandfather but father to your child. And, if you're as honest as I'm trying to be, I think you'll admit that the act of making our baby would be an immensely pleasurable and deeply sensual experience for both of us...'

CHAPTER EIGHT

CLAUDIA opened her eyes.

'W-what happened?'

'I'm not sure, but it looked to me like a good old-fashioned swoon.'

Claudia struggled to sit up among the sinkingly soft cushions of the brick-coloured sofa, only vaguely recognising the white room with the terracotta floor and Turkish rugs as being somewhere in the cool depths of Morgan's clifftop house. Surely it had all been a dream; an impossible, improbable dream... She pushed a shaky hand through her hair and looked at the man sitting patiently beside her, his hip level with hers.

'I—how did I get here?' she murmured with confusion. She didn't remember any of the warning dizziness that usually presaged a faint.

'I carried you.' He held a chilled glass to her lips.

Water. She sipped it gratefully, moistening her dry lips. She tucked her hair behind her ears and lowered her hand to her throat, where she discovered her collar and several buttons undone and a necklace of tiny wet droplets across her exposed collarbone. Her belt had also been removed, she noticed. She leaned back against the cushions that were piled behind her shoulders, nervously fingering an empty buttonhole.

'Was I out for long?'

'Not long enough for me to ravish you,' he said drily, his perception as acute as ever as he replaced the glass on a squat wooden table beside the couch. 'That bodice is quite tight and I thought it was a good idea to ease the constriction over your chest and cool you down with a few splashes of water.'

There was no anger in his expression but there was no gleam of mocking amusement, either, and she was shocked to realise how much she missed it. She deserved the setdown. She had insulted both his honour and his manhood with her momentary suspicion that he might have taken advantage of her helplessness.

'Thank you,' she murmured awkwardly, not knowing quite how to apologise. She wanted to do up her dress again, but her wicked imagination now turned even the modest act of doing up the buttons into a subtly provocative performance that would draw attention to her womanly curves. Instead she merely dabbed at the dampness on her throat with her unsteady fingers.

'My pleasure.' He reached into his jeans and produced a clean, pressed handkerchief. 'Allow me.'

His eyes were lowered, his lashes concealing his expression as he gently mopped away the beading of water that she had smeared into a wet slick across her upper chest. His touch was gentle, the blunt features and square jaw tight with absorption as he concentrated on his simple task.

He was very thorough, Claudia thought breathlessly as the moments ticked endlessly by. He had to part the edges of her dress a little more to catch the drops that had succumbed to the force of gravity, holding first one side and then the other out of the way as his hand slipped under the gaping fabric and patted the soft cotton over her bare skin.

It seemed to take him a long time to dry her to his complete satisfaction but Claudia didn't protest, staring resolutely at the hollow at the base of his throat, aware of the hush around them, the soft rasp of their breathing.

His hand finally stilled against her, the handkerchief tucked into the exposed hollow between her breasts where the tiny white bow that concealed the front catch of her bra just peeked above the first fastened button. She felt a tiny tug and that button, too, fell open. Her eyes flew to his face.

He was waiting for her, his smile blazing with sensuous challenge as he flicked open another button, and another.

'*Now* you can plead ravishment…'

He plunged his hands around her waist under the thin fabric, raking the bodice wide open. But instead of bending over her submissive figure he lifted her sharply up against him, his fingers tightly constricting around the base of her ribcage as he positioned her mouth under his.

Her gasp was absorbed by the swift, rough thrust of his tongue and a low growl greeted her instinctive impulse to ease the pressure around her waist by gripping his shoulders. Once there, gravity was again a powerfully seductive force as her hands slid helplessly down over the straining muscles of his back, her fingers digging in for purchase as she used his steely strength to arch herself against him.

'*Yes…*' The hiss of triumphant satisfaction sizzled in the dark cavern of her mouth as he devoured her ungoverned response, twisting so that he pulled her half across his knees. One hand unwrapped itself from her waist to splay across her breasts, his thumb and fingertip stretching possessively from peak to lacy peak. Held tightly against his hardness and consumed by his softness, Claudia gloried in the erotic contrasts of his maleness, the brutal strength that was tempered by the heat of passion, the thickening need that bespoke his ability both to lose control and to wield it to exquisite effect.

When his mouth broke away from hers her head fell back with a shuddering sigh.

'I take it this means you've decided that you like being ravished,' he said thickly.

She lifted her head. She had made no conscious decisions, she had just flowed with the desires of the moment. 'I—'

The hand on her breast pressed lightly against their weight. 'All you need to answer is yes.'

'W-what was the question?' A breath of caution rippled across her dreamy pool of sensual delight.

'You know what it was…'

'I—you weren't serious!' Her whispered protest was without conviction. The grave intensity in his stunning blue eyes was terrifying.

'Wasn't I?' he asked steadily, his hand moving to settle firmly over her left breast, and the hot, uneven thump of her heart. 'Then why did you swoon?'

Swoon. It sounded so weak and ineffectual, so Victorian for the modern career woman she strove to be.

'I fainted, that's all,' she said more firmly. 'The wine and the sun—'

'And the shock. You shock easily, don't you, Claudia, for all your worldly experience…?' He studied her pale mouth, and the flush on her cheeks, her wide brown eyes shadowed with deep secrets. He bent over her to murmur, 'Is the idea of having my baby really so shocking?'

Utterly. It was indecent. Wicked of her even to contemplate it. Wicked of him to make her want it. His mouth was a kiss away from hers. She turned her head aside, her throat arching in resistance to his enticing invitation.

'Any woman would be shocked to be, to be—'

'Desired?'

'What you're talking about isn't desire—' she began raggedly.

'True. *This* is desire.' His other arm tightened around her waist, pressing her firmly down in his lap as he shifted his thighs, the small undulation of his hips imprinting the firm outline of his masculinity against her soft bottom.

'So don't think that I'm offering to make love to you out of mere altruism,' he warned softly, his breath warm and sweet in her burning ear. 'I want you, Claudia—badly enough to try to stack the deck in my favour with every incentive I can think of. I know you want me, too—' his thumb scraped gently across the stiffened peak of her breast to prove his point '—but you think the wrongs of the past too important to ignore. This way you don't have to feel guilty about betraying your past by taking me for your lover. You can have it all: me *and* your revenge—'

'You don't have to do this,' she said desperately. 'I don't want revenge. It wasn't your *fault*! You...you can't want a baby with me—'

'Why can't I?' Her much agonised confession was ruthlessly shouldered aside as Morgan stubbornly pursued his own ends. 'Is it only women who are allowed to yearn for children? Last time around I was working so hard that I missed out on most of Mark's childhood. I was so busy proving what a successful businessman I was that I was virtually an absentee parent. I didn't put enough effort into being the kind of ordinary, everyday father a child can relate to. I know that I'll be a far better father this time...'

His confident use of the present tense edged her on to the verge of panic. But the word 'yearn' made Claudia's tender heart stagger.

'But—Mark—'

'Ah, yes, Mark.' His mouth firmed into a grim line. 'The magic banner you brandish whenever you want to fend me off. Let's talk about Mark. Are you worried I'm exhibiting some obscure form of sexual deviance by lusting after my son's former mistress?'

His words were crudely effective but Claudia refused to flinch. 'Are you?'

A glint of grim humour smouldered in the dazzling blue. 'Lusting after you? Certainly. But you and I know there's a great deal more than that between us. A man doesn't offer a baby to every object of his desire. Perhaps it's not my motives so much as my potency you're afraid to trust?'

'I can hardly doubt that, can I?'

Again that wicked undulation of his hips which sent heat coursing through her veins and flattering her skin. 'True.'

'I *meant* considering that you had Mark.' She tried to quell him with a haughty look, confused by the teasing that had come hard on the heels of his ardent seriousness.

'That was a long time ago, but I have no reason to think that the years of abstinence have diminished my fertility,' he responded with suspicious gravity.

'Abstinence!' The glowing gold flecks in Claudia's eyes expressed her fierce scorn of that idea.

'I meant from having children,' he said meekly. 'I've always used condoms when I slept with other women, Claudia. I wasn't going to risk another accidental pregnancy.' His thick, dark lashes suddenly veiled the searing blue gaze as it sank to the rapid rise and fall of her semi-exposed breasts. 'I'm looking forward to the novelty of being naked inside you. I'm curious as to how it will feel. I'm sure it will be a very intense experience for both of us. Are you, or have you recently been, on the Pill?'

Still stunned by the graphic description of his sexual eagerness, she responded with automatic truthfulness. 'No, but—'

'Good. Then there's no inhibition to your own fertility. Does that mean that it's been a fairly long time for you, too, Claudia?'

'A long time?' she repeated his gentle enquiry blankly.

'Since you allowed a man to—' His words were dammed by her flying fingers as her hand shot up to prevent him uttering the rest of the shatteringly indecent comment. He kissed her smothering palm, his sinful tongue darting out to trace the sensitive creases as his eyes mocked her over his fleshly gag.

She hurriedly withdrew her tingling hand but he still held her flustered gaze captive with his triumphant one.

'You can stop me saying it but we're both thinking about it, aren't we? It's very erotic, the thought of you and me nude together, without any artificial barriers between us, creating something beautiful out of our joining, something sweet and precious…'

Claudia could feel her body melting into the masculine strength that surrounded her, enchanted by the spell of his sensual poetry. Perhaps, if his need and desire were so great, she could make private peace with her unquiet conscience by giving him what he wanted, and in the process steal a little happiness from under the very nose of wretched fate…

'Actually, I find the thought of your pregnancy extremely erotic, too,' he murmured, lowering his head to kiss the warm swell of her breast above her bra. 'I like the idea of making love to you while my baby ripens inside you, of exploring your new sensitivities, of watching your body change and grow as it prepares to welcome a new life into the world…a new beginning…'

She stiffened, as she realised what he was suggesting. 'You mean, you'd expect…? But, I thought…'

'Very soon you're going to run out of those all-purpose buts, and then where will you be?' Morgan commented drily. 'I suppose that, as usual, you assume the very worst of me. What did you think I meant? A one-night stand of guaranteed hot-and-fertile sex at the receptive peak of your hormonal cycle? A brief affair to be broken off the instant that conception is confirmed?'

Claudia flushed miserably and squirmed, but he would not let her escape either his grasp or his censure.

'Damn you, Duchess, if I had intended to be merely a sperm donor I would have suggested artificial insemination,' he said roughly. 'I'm not going to get you pregnant and then cut and run like some irresponsible kid! Naturally I'll look after you during your pregnancy…given your medical history you'll need the extra security of my support and involvement. And, well…' the smooth descent from crisp command into slow drawl alerted her to the probability of fresh outrage '…it's an accepted fact that many pregnant women experience a sudden increase in their sex drive. In the best interests of your general health and well-being I would make sure that *all* your cravings were satisfied…'

She felt waves of heat wash over her. 'How—how very self-sacrificing of you,' she managed, in a trembling voice that failed miserably to be sarcastic.

'Isn't it?' he purred, his hands beginning to move against her again in a very disturbing way. 'How can you possibly deny a man on such a noble quest?'

Oh, God. Claudia knew that the only way to fight the fierce desire flooding through her mind and body was to have him battling on her side. She closed her eyes, and said a silent goodbye to the glorious, sensual gloating of his touch.

'Morgan…?'

'Don't worry, Duchess. Don't worry about anything. Let me take care of you and our baby…I promise to make it good for you…'

'The baby—'

'Will be as perfect as we can make it. And if that's not absolutely perfect, well, we'll love her anyway, as the most innocent part of ourselves…'

Oh, God. Why did he have to be so damned *fine*! Tears welled up behind her closed eyes as she contemplated what she was about to lose. 'No! No, I mean the *other* baby. *My* baby. My son.' She was very careful to stress the exclusivity of her possession. 'I saw him…afterwards…I asked and they showed him to me—'

She felt him still, sensed the new physical tension that entered his limbs. 'Oh?'

It was a very careful, very neutral response, thought Claudia bitterly as she opened her eyes. His hard features were quiet, composed, and very, very wary. He did well to fear the trend of the conversation.

'He had dark hair and…and—I don't know what colour his eyes were…I never saw them open.' That had troubled her, haunted her for a long time. She stumbled on, 'There was a funeral service—'

The tension in the arms holding her tightened, his eyes still locked with hers. 'And you were alone—I'm sorry—'

'And a christening,' she cut him off quickly, before he could undermine her courage with his sympathy. 'I had him christened first—so that he could be buried with a name, not just as a…a thing…but as a person, who belonged to somebody.'

'Claudia—'

She shook her head. 'Do you want to know what I called him?' she went on relentlessly.

Some of the tension drained out of him. 'If you want to tell me.'

He thought it was going to be as simple as a name. She almost hated him at that moment for his unwitting ignorance.

'Christopher!' she said fiercely. 'I called him Chris!'

'A fine name for a boy,' he said calmly, and she couldn't believe that an intelligent man could be so wilfully stupid.

'Chris! After his *father*.' She could no longer hold his steady gaze. She looked down at her hands pushing against his rock-solid chest, trying to prise her out of the hideously inappropriate intimacy of his embrace. 'Christopher Nash Lawson!'

There was no immediate response and Claudia couldn't help darting a look at his face, as unreadably still as the rest of him. Why, oh, why wasn't he letting her go, shoving her away in disgust?

'Mark and I weren't even lovers!' she cried angrily, fisting her hands as she struggled futilely against his implacable calmness. 'Dammit, don't you *understand*?'

'I understand perfectly. You're telling me that Mark wasn't the father of your baby.'

Now it was her turn to still. Something in the way he said it, the easy self-control that was in marked contrast to the blast of hot-tempered condemnation she had expected, the sheer lack of hostility when he had every right to feel bitterly betrayed…

'You *knew*!' Her fists fell weakly into her lap as the instinctive certainty overwhelmed her. 'All along, you *knew*…!'

'Not all along,' he confirmed bluntly. 'Not until several months afterwards, in fact. I went back to see you—or at least I revisited your home and found out that you'd moved. Your neighbour was very informative, though, very sorry for all that you had gone through…losing your baby so late…at *seven* months.'

Only now, when it was too late for her to remove herself to a safe distance, did he relinquish his binding grip, instead massaging his flattened palms up and down her arms, as if he could feel the inner chill that sapped her will and the energy to move her limbs.

'You knew…' It was still sinking in, her thoughts a frozen mass of confusion as the implications of his confession gradually began to percolate into her mind. He knew that his son wasn't the father of the child she lost. But…that didn't make sense!

'How…how much do you know?'

'Everything.'

It was hard to take. 'You *couldn't* have known…all the things you've said—' Her voice was as broken as her thoughts. 'And just now, before I fainted—what you said about the father's genes—'

'I knew that if I gave you enough openings you were eventually bound to trust me with the truth,' he said simply.

'You mean—you said all those things *deliberately*?' she demanded wildly, trying to remember everything that she had ever said to him. And all the time that she had been evading the consequences of her actions, had been fending him off with lies and half-truths, he had *known*!

Shame engulfed her, then defensive anger. 'You were trying to trap me!' she accused rawly.

'How can the truth be a trap, Claudia?' he murmured, his hands still generating the warmth of friction against her clammy skin. 'You know that you wanted to tell me…I didn't force it out of you.'

The knowledge that he was right didn't resolve the violent conflict inside her. All that mental torment—for *nothing*!

'You could have told me!' she choked.

'It was your story to tell, Duchess, not mine.' His sombre smile was like salt in the wound.

'And what if I had never told you?' she challenged.

'Well, then, I would have respected your silence.'

To her horror she believed him. 'And all that about having your baby?' she asked hoarsely. 'That was just a way to…to make me tell you…?'

'I don't make promises I don't intend to keep.' Morgan picked up one nerveless hand from her lap and held it briefly against his mouth before drawing it to his chest. She suddenly realised that her bodice was still gaping and her other hand came up to clutch it closed. 'As far as I'm concerned nothing is different. *I* haven't changed my mind. Have you?'

'You must hate me…' she whispered. She knew that *she* would, if their situations were reversed.

'I had hurt you and you retaliated in the only way available to you at the time,' he told her, with a gentle understanding that lanced old wounds. 'Of course I was angry— I was gut-wrenchingly furious at first, which was one of the reasons why I decided to keep track of you, but I've had two years to come to terms with it and, since I met you again, I've realised that that impulsive lie was probably as painful for you as it was for me. After all, whatever the baby's parentage, I *did* cause you to fall and lose him…'

Her lips formed a hushed O of dismay as the significance of the last sentence hit her squarely in the chest, congesting it with thickening horror as he continued, 'You don't find it easy to inflict pain on others, do you, Duchess, even when you think it's justified? Why don't you let me show you how much easier it's going to be for you to inflict pleasure…?'

And he showed her, by leaning forward and covering her parted mouth with his own, feeding her with the strength of his desire.

Under his kiss she acknowledged that her courage had already exceeded its limits. She couldn't bear the thought of now confessing an even greater betrayal of her honour. She desperately wanted to accept his assurance that he knew everything, even though it was now achingly obvious that he didn't.

Her wonderful reprieve was only temporary, but suddenly she no longer cared. Let the future take care of itself. She wasn't going to risk having to wait another two years before his anger abated enough for Morgan to accept her in his arms again, if he ever could. She needed him *now*, right this moment. She needed the passion that could heal her, the desire that she could use to express her silent remorse, her unspoken love…

He slid her off his lap, turning into her as she half lay, half sat on the couch beside him. The hand that had been guarding her disarray reached for him, burrowing under his shirt until he impatiently pulled it over his head, ruffling the dark hair on his head and leaving her awed at the first sight of his bareness. He was broad and strong, a light tan sculpting the rippling muscles which were exposed by his smooth, almost hairless chest. She touched him, tentatively, on the hard ridge of bone centred between the flat, male nipples.

'Disappointed?'

Her startled eyes flew to his steamy gaze. 'Some women equate masculinity with a hairy chest. I assure you, I'm not less of a man for my lack.'

It stunned her that he could believe that he needed to reassure her of the fact.

'I know.' Her hand flattened and he let out a hiss of breath, the ridging of his flat belly above the leather-belted trousers clenching in a ripple that vibrated up under his skin to tease her fingertips.

'Now it's my turn.' He peeled back the edges of her dress, this time pushing it off her shoulders and gently pulling her arms free of the sleeves.

She watched his face, the sultry fascination that drew his features tight as he reached for the decorative bow between the lacy cups of her bra and smoothly curved his fingers around the plastic clip.

'You've done this before,' she said, unable to help the breathy expression of her nervousness. She had always needed two hands to undo the secure catch but he was revealing a single-handed skill.

'But never with such delicious anticipation,' he said with a glibness that might have offended her if she hadn't been watching the smouldering intentness of his gaze, the quivering flare of his nostrils as he scented the faint natural perfume of her body and drew it inside himself. The tiny snick of the catch sounded thunderingly loud to her ears and she closed her eyes, the better to concentrate on the joy of his first caress.

Nothing happened and, aching for his touch but too shy to articulate her need, she lifted heavy lids to find him studying her face with savage masculine pleasure. Satisfied that he had her fullest attention, he very slowly eased away the intricate lace, taking care not to touch her, never taking his eyes off hers. Only when the fragile straps had slid down her arms did he lower his eyes again. For a breathless moment there was utter silence.

'I can see your heart beating,' he said huskily, still not touching her, and she looked down at herself and saw that it was true: the rigid peak of her left breast was visibly pulsing in time with the quickened internal rhythm inside her chest. The creamy flesh around it seemed to quiver with each tiny rise and fall, a delicate but explicit invitation that made her blush to see it. It seemed so terribly brazen, a bold flaunting of her physical desire for him, that her blush spread inexorably down over every inch of exposed skin, tautening her breasts even further with the warm, tingling excitement of sensual awareness.

Morgan smiled, intent on his prize, and his voice was thick with velvety promise as he cupped his hand around the flushed offering. 'So when I taste you I shall literally have your heart in my mouth.' He bent his head, so slowly that Claudia bit her lip to stop herself crying out in frustration.

At last she felt the hot, silky moistness surrounding and absorbing her aching flesh as he suckled her with exquisite finesse, and this time she did cry out, only to suffer the agony of having him lift his head.

'Am I hurting you?'

Her hand sank into his crisp, short hair, tugging him back. 'No…yes…please—don't stop…'

His smile smouldered across her senses, his eyes burning in their vivid intensity. 'I'm yours to command, Duchess.' The hand lifting her breast tightened possessively. 'All you have to do is tell me what you want and I'll do it for you. Your pleasure is my fitting reward…'

His dark head bent over her again and she arched into the sweet-savage pull of his clever mouth, knowing that she didn't have to tell him what she wanted, he knew—he would always know, seemed to sense her desires even before she did…

His lavish praise of her breasts went on and on until she was drenched in the promised pleasure and needing more, much more; she ran her hands across the broad striation of muscle on his curved back, her fingernails digging into the compact flesh in a piercingly articulate demand that brought a gloriously swift response.

With a few quick, economical twists and turns, Morgan stripped the rumpled sundress off her hips and disposed of his jeans with an expressive groan as, in his haste, the heavy fabric scraped across his heated arousal. He took longer to remove the white cotton panties she wore, seemingly fascinated by the demure contrast to her sexy bra, and enjoying the involuntary movements of her hips as he languidly caressed her last covering down her trembling thighs. She almost died of shocked delight when he brushed a deft kiss across the soft triangle of curls so dark against the pearly sheen of her inner thighs but the brief intimacy was withdrawn immediately as he shed his own modest white briefs.

His lack of haste allowed Claudia to study covertly the full power and beauty of his virility and when she realised that he had caught her sidelong glances of flatteringly wide-eyed appraisal she instinctively attempted to protect her own body from his frank gaze. The differences between male and female apart, his physique was nearly perfect whereas Claudia's body had borne a child and she was suddenly aware of imperfections that had not mattered a few moments ago, in the throes of mindless abandonment.

He froze, one knee pressing down beside her supine body, the other foot still planted on the tiled floor.

'Am I pleasing to you, Claudia?' he murmured, making no attempt similarly to hide the blatancy of his desire. 'I hope so, because you're very, very appealing to me...especially like that, your lovely full breasts peeping at me through your fingers and the soft rounded thigh drawn up to shelter the hot dewy silk I'm aching to feel

around me…' He shuddered lightly, throwing his head back
as his whole body flexed with the acuteness of his need.
He was proud of his passion, engendering a similar pride
in Claudia as he looked down at her and asked bluntly,
'Can you ease that ache for me, Claudia? Will you touch
me and taste me and pleasure me in the way that I need to
be to feel completed?'

As he intended to complete her? Claudia's uncertainty
vanished; his honesty, verging on the crude and yet also
poetically erotic, was just what she needed to reassure her
of her desirability. How could she refuse him anything that
he asked of her? His passion, his tender consideration, his
magnificent male vulnerability conquered all her inhibi-
tions.

He must have read her answer in her eyes, in the graceful
falling away of her protective limbs, for he was coming
back to her, folding himself down over her restlessly shifting body, again with that slow, sensual appreciation that
was both infuriating and inflaming, caging her eagerness
with his incredible self-control until they were melted, skin
to skin, full-length on the resilient softness of the cushioned
couch. Even then he paused.

'Are you comfortable? Or would you rather move to the
bedroom…?'

'I wish you'd stop asking so many questions,' Claudia
murmured, a bubble of sheer joy making her voice ragged
with laughter as she revelled in the intoxicating savour of
his salty, satin-rough skin and the heady aroma of his masculine arousal.

'I can't help it.' His caressing amusement encouraged
her mischievous delight in the the silken splendour he was
unravelling for her dazzled senses. 'I'm a very articulate
lover and making love with you has turned me into an
unashamed sybarite. I want to indulge in all the sensual
vices with you in such luxury and comfort that you'll want
it to go on forever, and ever…'

He was as good as his word. Claudia knew that, whatever else she might be able to force herself to forget, the timeless beauty of his fiery passion would always be part of her. He praised, he urged, he groaned, he poured out the pleasure that he had promised her with an endless, inspiring energy that never faltered. He was violent and aggressive, tender and gentle, never content for her to be passively receptive but fiercely demanding of her totally wanton and greedily eager response.

His passionate prowess made a liar of him when, at one point, they tumbled heedlessly off the wide, luxurious couch and he scarcely missed a beat, taking her on the hard floor, the rough weave of a thin woven rug barely protecting her from the cool shock of hard terracotta as he cupped her bottom and roughly parted her legs to plunge tightly into her, a thick moan of sexual gratification wrenching from his throat as he drove himself, and Claudia, to new extremes of pleasure.

Afterwards he carried her remorsefully into his sunny bedroom and laid her on the soft white polished-cotton spread of his huge bed where he proceeded to render his apologies with an exquisite, unselfish delicacy. While she lay, still dazed with delicious exhaustion, he sat and placed his hand over her shivering belly and said boldly, 'I wonder if my baby is in here already, experiencing the first spark of joyous life?'

If Claudia hadn't already been flushed all over she would have blushed at his gloating eagerness. He was certainly taking no chances. He was making sure that his intentions were clearly understood and accepted.

'I doubt it, certainly not so soon,' she said repressively, pushing away her doubts.

'A few moments is all it takes,' he smiled, his fingers tracing around her sensitive navel.

'Conception isn't instantaneous, you know,' she said,

trying to sound blasé. 'Anyway, it isn't really the best time for me right now—to conceive, I mean.'

His amazing eyes were deep blue with slumbrous satisfaction. 'I know you didn't mean to make love. It was very much the best time for that, wasn't it, Duchess? And now you've had the pleasure I hope you're not going to try and renege on the responsibility that you owe to me...' The finger rimming her navel slipped inside, making her stomach muscles flutter.

'Owe you?' Claudia could hardly concentrate on the words, her body attuned to his fingertip control.

'An old debt. All that money of mine that you frittered away two years ago. The money with which I bought off my obligation to my grandchild's mother...'

'Oh, that money,' murmured Claudia hazily. The soft pad of his finger withdrew and slipped inside again. 'I...I'll pay you back...' she offered, his silky taunt causing a nibble of guilt to eat at the fringes of her consciousness. She didn't know if he truly believed that she had used the money as frivolously as she had pretended but there was no denying she had allowed him to 'buy her off' under false pretences that still stood.

'Of course you will—in the most intimate and appropriate way imaginable.' His determined words were interspersed with soft kisses strung the length of her torso until Claudia felt the moist shock of his tongue replacing his finger in the small knotted recess in her belly. 'This baby will be our mutual gift of reparation. Accept it gratefully, as I am, in settlement of all outstanding debts between us....'

CHAPTER NINE

'SO WHAT practical plans have you made? What do you intend to do about your career when the baby's born? Juggle with a string of babysitters? Daycare? Or do you want me to pay for a live-in child-minder?'

Claudia gritted her teeth and shovelled the bacon and eggs that she had cooked on to Morgan's plate, striving for a lightness that she didn't feel.

'What is this, an interrogation?'

She turned back to the bench to pick up his coffee and pluck the toast from the toaster. She gave both pieces to Morgan and put in another slice for herself, not because she was hungry but because she needed an excuse to stay out of the hot seat across the table from that penetrating blue gaze.

She had no intention of letting him harass her into admitting that she didn't have any long-term plans. Such practicalities hadn't even entered her mind a week ago when she had succumbed to 'his persuasive seduction and now sheer terror at what the future might hold made her resolutely refuse to dwell on it. Her only thought then had been, if he could promise to love her baby, then perhaps was there a chance that he could also learn to love the baby's mother…?

A foolish fantasy. He might care for her, but although guilt and desire were a potent mix they didn't add up to love. As frank as he was about everything else, if he loved her Morgan would have told her so. But a vital ingredient was missing from their relationship. Trust. On his side it was misplaced, and on hers deliberately withheld. As a lover he was exciting, passionate, tender, but she never let herself forget that he had been a brutally ambitious, impossibly demanding autocrat for many more years than he had been the compassionate and easygoing man he was emulating now. The cynical, ruthlessly manipulative side of him would never be entirely repressed; it was too ingrained, surfacing automatically whenever he felt thwarted…or betrayed. He was quite capable of reverting, especially if he found out that his newly acquired persona had allowed him to be played for a fool.

Weighing up the risks, she had decided the pain of losing him was better postponed until she had hoarded up enough happiness to last her over the emotional winter that was sure to follow.

At least if she had his baby Claudia would always have a permanent link with him, an added dimension to her love that would give her life a richness of variety and purpose that had been lacking before. Morgan might deny her but he would never be able to bring himself to deny his child, whatever he felt about its mother. It was selfish, it was probably immoral but she was going to do it anyway. She was going to cheat fate.

'Just understandable interest. You are a cross-patch in the mornings, aren't you?' Morgan replied mildly as he attacked his breakfast. With his shirt unbuttoned and his chin unshaven he looked sensuously rumpled and regrettably sexy while Claudia, already carefully dressed in her hotel uniform, felt uncomfortably formal in her own kitchen.

'Is that why you haven't let me stay the night before now? Afraid I'd be disillusioned in the morning?'

No, afraid that he would become even more deeply embedded in her heart than he was already. Afraid that in the languid aftermath of sleepy passion she might reveal more than was healthy for her. As long as she withheld the totality of her need Claudia felt reasonably safe. If she was independent and slightly aloof then she kept him off-balance, and had a better chance of sustaining the interest of a man who thrived on challenge.

Last night he had fallen asleep in her arms after making love to her for hours and she had made the mistake of thinking that she could lie awake for a while, just holding him, enjoying a brief pretence of ownership of the hard body that was relaxed and vulnerable in sleep.

Of course, she had fallen asleep too and paid the price for it when she had woken just before dawn to the skilled caress of his hands and mouth and seen the sensual triumph in his expression. She had roused instinctively to his touch and been helpless to prevent her swift response, even as she realised the reason for his flagrant complacency. In staying he had broken her unspoken rule and, judging from his arrogant self-satisfaction when they finally rose, he had done it deliberately—shown her that there were no rules to this relationship but what she was prepared to speak out loud, and thus provide him with the opportunity to challenge.

'*You* may be able to take your time wandering in to work in the mornings, but you forget that *I'm* only an employee,' she said pointedly, still unwilling to concede his sly victory. 'Mornings are usually a rush for me. I don't have time to…to…'

'Enjoy a leisurely wake-up call? That's why I woke you before your alarm went off.' His grin was boldly unrepentant as he made short work of the bacon and eggs. 'Didn't you notice bells going off at a critical moment or does my lovemaking always ring peals over your head? I thought I had everything very nicely timed. In fact, if you don't sit down and relax for a few minutes you're going to be *early* for work. Don't worry about the dishes, I'll clean up. Aren't you going to have more than a piece of toast?' he added reprovingly as she reluctantly took his advice.

Now he was trying to manage her diet as well as her sleeping habits. Claudia's folly rose up to haunt her. Did she really want to give this dominating man house-room in her life despite the agonies he caused her? Unfortunately the answer was *yes*!

'It's all I ever have in the morning.'

'But now you're going to need to supplement your normal diet. You should be having cereal and milk and maybe some fresh fruit.'

'I have a perfectly balanced diet, thank you,' she said tartly. 'Besides, I'm not pregnant yet.'

'How do you know?'

She could feel herself blushing and concentrated fiercely on spreading marmalade on her toast. 'The usual way.'

There was a small, crackling silence. 'This morning?'

She knew that if she put the piece of toast she was toying with into her mouth she would choke.

'Yes.' She took a sip of coffee instead and burnt her mouth. She didn't know whether she was pleased or sorry that pregnancy wasn't even a possibility yet. Now, if he wanted to back out, she had given him the perfect opportunity!

'You should have said something…were you feeling uncomfortable? For God's sake, Claudia, I'm not an insatiable sex fiend, you know, you can refuse me whenever you want to…'

His voice was such an aggressive mixture of awkwardness and annoyance that she was jolted to look at him and as she did so his hard face began to tinge with unmistakable colour. Claudia's own embarrassment was forgotten as she realised that *he* was the one blushing for a change! Her fears that his first reaction would be relief subsided in a fierce surge of joy.

'I'm so glad to hear it,' she said, watching his colour deepen.

'You could have said you had a headache or something if you didn't feel like making love,' he muttered, clearly on the unaccustomed defensive.

Revelling in the moment, she raised her eyebrows and made the mistake of saying haughtily, 'Euphemisms, Morgan? I didn't think you were the kind of person who liked to have the bald facts cloaked in polite phrases.'

'I don't, but I thought you might. So why didn't you just tell me that you had your period and didn't want to make love?'

On the verge of taking another sip of the cooling coffee, she almost choked. Damn him for being so impossibly blunt! 'I didn't know until I had my shower.'

Another mistake. His high colour faded, a shiver of sensuous curiosity entered his eyes. 'And because you *did* want to make love...my instincts didn't fail me there, did they? So what is this about? Are you trying to find out my feelings on the subject? Are you expecting me to tell you that I won't be around until you make yourself sexually available again?'

'Morgan—'

'Because if you are, Claudia, you're being very insulting, to me and to yourself. I told you at the outset that this wasn't going to be a calendar-driven affair. Whatever time of the month it is makes no difference to me. If you don't want us to make love for the next few days we can still spend time together, and still enjoy a pleasurable degree of physical closeness...'

Somehow she didn't think he was talking about just holding hands. Stricken with a feverish shyness, Claudia stumbled into speech. 'I didn't mean to—'

'Good.' He picked up his cup with an irritating smugness. 'That's settled, then.' He took a taste and grimaced. 'Is this coffee instant?'

He looked down his wrinkled nose at it and his endearing expression of woe was such that she had to fight the urge to lean across and kiss him.

'If you don't like it you know what you can do. You're

quite welcome to *uninvite* yourself to breakfast!' she crisped instead.

'I shall obviously have to buy you a percolator and show you how to make real coffee,' he said, looking amused by her pettishness.

'If I think it's worth having a percolator I'll buy my own,' she told him, her brown eyes snapping.

'Then I'll have to make sure you think it's worth it,' he murmured creamily. 'Why are we arguing over these minor details, Claudia? Did you think it would take my mind off the major ones? Like what you're going to do when you finally *do* get pregnant?'

Finally. He made it sound as if it was a difficult assignment that was going to take a long time. For a fleeting instant the evil thought flitted across her mind that, if she was very, very careful, she could stretch her time with him into months and months...

Shocked that such wickedness would even occur to her, Claudia punished her hopelessly compromised honour by taunting herself with the impossible.

'Why, give up my job and move in with you until the baby's born, of course,' she told him brazenly. 'You did offer to provide me with any support I needed and since I'm going to be bearing the entire physical burden of carrying your child it's only fair that you do your part by carrying the entire financial burden. After all, it seems the most practical thing to do.'

Her mockery fell flat. Morgan didn't blanch at the prospect of the invasion of his privacy, as she had fully expected him to do.

'I agree.'

'You agree?' For a moment the succinct answer confused her. Then it hit her. 'You *agree*?'

'I think it's an excellent idea.' His low, measured tone was in stark contrast to her startled squeak. He leaned back in his chair, the edges of his shirt falling away from the strongly muscled chest, a wild distraction to her senses that she desperately tried, and failed, to ignore.

Last night—and this morning—those muscles had been savagely sculpted under their smooth covering of skin as he moved around her, over her, in her, the male torso bunching and releasing with each driving thrust, flesh oiled with the sweat of his heated arousal, rigid and slippery to her questing touch. In repose the muscles flexed slowly, and with each steady rise and fall of his chest Claudia remembered the way that the air shuddered unsteadily in his lungs when he was deep in the grip of intense passion, his elegantly erotic murmurings degenerating into thick, involuntary grunts of uncontrollable pleasure as he approached his peak, instinctively trying to withhold his frenzied release until she could join him. And when he reached it the shout of raw, articulate triumph that accompanied his violent convulsions: her name…always her name, an acknowledgment of the extent, and the limits, of her power over Morgan. In bed there was no future and no past…no fear of failure, of betrayal, of pain…

'But why wait until you're pregnant?' he continued when she merely stood, staring abstractly at him amid the traitorous turmoil of her thoughts. 'Why not move in now?'

'Move in?' she parroted in shrill disbelief as she was jolted out of her distraction. 'With *you*? You mean—*live* with you?'

She sounded so incredulous that his unshaven jaw shifted, manoeuvring his mouth into a thinly uncompromising line as he hammered out his usual impeccable logic.

'Why not? It seems even more practical than your idea. Not only does it solve the problem of—er—immediate accessibility at critical points during your cycle, but it will also give you time to settle in and establish a comfortable routine before your hormones start rampaging. If you lived with me you wouldn't have to worry about paying rent or buying groceries, or the drudgery of housework…you wouldn't even have to work at all.

'Think of the advantages. Your job is quite a stressful and demanding one. Sure, you enjoy it, but it requires a consistently high level of energy and enthusiasm that puts you under considerable pressure to perform. I've seen you at work. You're meticulous to a fault. You forget to eat when you're busy and your mind is always leaping ahead to anticipate the next problem. I've been there and, believe me, the rewards of constantly outperforming yourself are not all they're cracked up to be. If you gave it up you'd much improve your chances of early conception. I'd make sure you had all the material comforts and the independence of an assured income. You'd be eating regular, healthy, home-cooked meals and getting plenty of rest and relaxation…'

Twenty minutes later Claudia stood staring at the apartment door that had just closed behind him with a smug click, holding her hand against her pounding chest and feeling as though she had swallowed a whirlwind.

The air buffeted in and out of her lungs as she struggled to comprehend what she had just allowed to happen.

She had been so *sure* that he was bluffing!

The fist of hot, red rage that had bunched in her throat when she first realised that he was offering to *pay* her for her exclusive services as a live-in mistress had choked off her outburst of fury just long enough for her see the glaring obviousness of the trap.

Losing her temper was precisely what the arrogant beast wanted! He *expected* her to turn down his insulting offer, just as she had fully expected him to turn down her meretricious demand. His revenge was a double-bluff, designed to goad her into a reckless response that would tell him what she was really feeling.

Instead pride had stiffened her spine, tamped down her bristling fury and called his stupid bluff.

But he hadn't thrown in his hand. Oh, no—he had raised the stakes still further and she, like a foolishly addicted gambler, had defiantly accepted the bet. If he wanted to pay for a love that was freely given, then that was his mistake!

Claudia forced herself to finish getting ready for work, her hands shaking so much that it took three tries to get her lipstick on. She must be mad, she told her pale reflection in the mirror. She must have the survival instincts of a lemming! Falling in love with Morgan Stone was bad enough, but lying to him and agreeing to have his child and moving in with him to live the lie every day was sheer insanity. What on earth did she think she was doing?

The same question was demanded of her a few hours later, by a stunned Simon Moore as he fingered her hastily typed resignation.

'But Claudia, I thought you were happy here!' he uttered in amazement. 'What about the Sports Five Hundred. The whole thing is just about to come together and most of the credit is yours. It's been your baby from the start!'

Claudia winced at the unconscious aptness of his phrasing. 'I have a month's notice to work out according to my contract,' she pointed out huskily, 'so I'll still be here during and for a few days after the race…unless you find someone to replace me sooner…'

Simon frowned, tapping an impatient hand on his desk. 'It's more likely to take longer—and that's fact, not flattery. You still haven't told me why.'

'It's—it's a personal matter,' said Claudia uncomfortably, conscious that he had every right to feel let down by her sudden decision to abandon her blossoming career. 'I really have enjoyed working here…it's just that, well, there are other things happening in my life right now that I want to concentrate on…'

'Have you won a lottery or come into some kind inheritance…' He paused delicately.

'Oh, no, nothing like that.' It was cowardly but she was

reluctant to tell Simon about something she could hardly believe herself, even though she knew he would find out soon enough—as would the whole world!

Morgan had phoned her soon after she had arrived at work, not to whisper the lover-like reassurances that her aching heart craved, but to inform her that he had decided to forestall the inevitable wild speculation over her move into his home by ringing a journalist friend and giving him the 'scoop' on their new relationship.

She was dumbfounded to realise that he was telling her this after the fact. 'But I didn't agree—'

'You said you'd leave the details to me,' he interrupted smoothly. 'However much we might like to ignore it, I'm news. Being frank at the outset will short-circuit the gossip. You know yourself that the more you try to avoid the Press, the more interested they become. If we show we've got nothing to hide then they'll probably settle for a routine raid on their background files to support the story instead of trying to dig up any new angles.'

Crushed by the avalanche of strategic logic, Claudia floundered. 'But—'

'What's the matter? Frightened you might not be able to back out now it's official?' he asked, his voice silky with provocation. 'You could, but not gracefully, I'm afraid. The Press would have a field day if you moved out on me before you'd even moved it! They'd insist on ferreting out the reason and you know what reporters are like when they sniff a scandal…'

How dared he refer to her painful past with such cheerful insouciance? 'Is that all you have to tell me?' she asked stiffly, resisting the temptation to fling the telephone across the room.

He didn't sound afraid at all. He sounded insufferably pleased with himself while she felt buffeted and bullied. She was doing exactly what she wanted desperately to do so why this inexplicable desire to burst into tears?

'Yes,' he lied with flagrant aplomb. 'Except for the fact that I've also arranged for a removal company to help you shift your things this evening. It shouldn't take long, given that you've hardly had time to acquire any furniture of your own. I'd collect you myself but I have a late meeting so I'll have a car delivered to the apartment so that you can drive yourself to the house. I'll see you at home at about eight for dinner—call my housekeeper and let her know if you have any preferences. All right?'

He was too quick for her. He hung up before she had a chance to slam the receiver down on him. He certainly wasn't leaving anything to chance, or giving her much time for first, let alone second thoughts! Everything was happening so fast. Claudia had an awful sense of fate rushing at breakneck speed towards her instead of meekly waiting for her to take her chosen path.

'I'll probably do a bit of freelance PR work if there's any available,' Claudia added hastily now as Simon continued to regard her with a deeply concerned frown.

That had been Morgan's idea, too, as he had taken advantage of the stunned silence that had followed his bombshell in the kitchen. He had murmured that, of course, if living with him turned out to be *too* restful and unexciting, then she was welcome to experiment with his fearsome array of computer technology and set up a home office for herself. The smouldering gleam in his eye when he had said it implied that excitement would be the very last thing her life with him would lack. Given the upheavals of the past few weeks, she could well believe it!

Simon's mouth compressed. 'I can't promise anything, Claudia. You know we handle most of our business in-house.'

'Oh, I wasn't suggesting that.' She flushed awkwardly at the subtle reproof. 'I mean, if you wouldn't mind giving me a reference...'

He had agreed, not without some reservations for which

Claudia couldn't blame him. Discretion was Simon's watchword but she knew that if she told him that her new career was to be Morgan Stone's live-in mistress he would probably feel obligated to warn her of her extreme folly. She didn't need a lecture on the subject; she was already intimately acquainted with it.

The fact that she knew no one in Wellington intimately enough to discuss her feelings with made her feel isolated and yet also, in a strange way, safe. Her aloneness insulated her from the personal consequences of her actions for there was no one else to consider but herself, no one to be hurt that she chose to follow her heart, rather than the dictates of common sense and conscience. Certainly she would have to put up with being in the public eye again for a while, and suffer the sidelong glances and gossip of colleagues while she worked out her notice, but she could cope with that as long as she knew that there was Morgan to go home to at night…

And to go home in she had her shiny new toy!

She had quite forgotten Morgan's mention of a car and when the ornately enamelled Morgan key-ring was hand-delivered to her door that same evening Claudia forced herself to wait until the removal men had left with the final box of her miscellaneous possessions and she had packed up the last of her clothes before she went downstairs to see what kind of car he had lent her.

Instead of the modest compact she had anticipated, there, parked on the street and already drawing interest from evening strollers along the waterfront, was the very same royal blue Greenwood Corvette that Claudia had admired on her first visit to his showroom.

At first she thought that she was suffering delusions of grandeur, and she sat gingerly in the driver's seat for several minutes before she looked in the glove compartment for the letter that the employee who had delivered the car had said was there. Sure enough, there was an envelope with the elegant Morgan and Son logo embossed on the flap and her name printed on the front in a very definite, slashing hand.

If she hadn't been in love with Morgan already she would have fallen irrevocably when she read the provocative note that was wrapped around the ownership papers. Her pride might have balked at the outrageous extravagance of his gift but her heart melted at the words that told her that price hadn't entered the equation. The choice had been a piece of whimsy she was helpless to deny him. He wrote simply.

Whenever I look at this car now, I think of you. I can't imagine anyone else owning it and it's playing havoc with my concentration. A sexy car, for a very sexy lady. Enjoy.

She did. Shamelessly.

At first tentative and uncertain, she was determined to overcome her fear and she soon got the hang of handling such a powerful car, zipping back and forth along Marine Drive every day, discovering for herself the extraordinarily seductive allure of driving a superbly crafted machine. Behind the wheel she gained her first real understanding of the obsession that had consumed Chris, although a ticket for speeding on her fourth outing curbed any desire for recklessness. She saved that for her behaviour off the road!

In fact, her first few weeks of adjusting to being publicly viewed as Morgan Stone's resident woman proved less difficult than she had feared. Envy rather than condemnation seemed the general response. For one thing, to Morgan's amusement and Claudia's chagrin, her exotic car drew more Press attention than the personal aspects of their relationship. The most provocative piece of speculation was a risible suggestion that Morgan had provided Claudia with the Corvette so that she could drive it in the Sports Five Hundred. Reading that particular rumour had wiped the smug smile off Morgan's face and he had scotched it with his friendly sources with considerably less than his usual good humour.

For those few weeks she lived safe within a fragile bubble of perfect happiness, cherishing each unfolding day as a gift more precious and unique than any other that Morgan had bestowed upon her. She was hectically busy in her job as the date of the race neared and secretly resented every moment that nine-to-five reality stole from her beautiful fantasy life with Morgan. It couldn't go on forever, of course, this defiantly carefree existence, and one afternoon, arriving home much earlier than usual because she wanted to make use of Morgan's sophisticated desk-top publishing program to produce what would probably be her last publicity layout for the hotel, Claudia's glorious bubble burst.

Entering the master bedroom she shared with Morgan, she shed her jacket and began to unbutton her blouse, her mouth curving sensuously as she debated which dress she might welcome Morgan home in. Since he worked more flexible hours than she did, he was usually home first, and she looked forward to the prospect of surprising him. The element of surprise, she felt, would be an important factor in retaining his interest once the novelty of their relationship wore off.

At that moment Mark walked out of the *en-suite* bathroom and Claudia froze, the blood running up into her face at the look of stunned condemnation on his handsome face.

'They told me, but I didn't believe it,' he said jerkily, in hoarse tones of shock. 'I really thought it was just someone's stupid idea of a tasteless joke. But it's true, isn't it? You're living here. You're sleeping with him…'

'I—' Claudia moved her hands helplessly. He had obviously drawn his own conclusions from the half-open wardrobe and the cosy clutter of cosmetics next to his father's cologne and shaving kit on the bathroom shelf.

'I didn't realise you were going to be back so soon,' she

said inanely. 'M— Your father said you were going to spend another few weeks in Europe on holiday…'

'You mean this is only a temporary thing? Were you going to move out before I came back so I wouldn't know what was going on?' he asked brutally.

'*No*!' With a wave of horror she realised she hadn't even thought about the complications that would ensue when Mark returned. In her blind grab at happiness she had allowed herself to forget he even existed. 'We—I—I've only been here a few weeks… It sort of just…*happened*,' she explained, her shaking hands trying frantically to rebutton her blouse.

'Nothing ever *just happens* as far as my father is concerned,' Mark cracked out, looking suddenly older than his years and very much a product of his genes. 'He always has a very good reason for everything he does.' He looked around the room as if he had never seen it before, turning back to her to burst out, 'For God's sake, I've scarcely been gone more than a month! When I left you didn't even know each other, much less *like* each other!'

'I wouldn't put it quite like that—' she protested weakly, clenching her hands over her roiling stomach. If Morgan had to choose between his son and his mistress she was wretchedly aware of who the loser would be.

'Then how *would* you put it?' he demanded crudely, backing her nervously against the bed. 'He's never actually moved one of his women in here before so I guess you must really have the hots for each other. Can't do without it at least once a day, huh? Or, knowing my Dad's mania for thoroughness—'

'*Mark*—!' Claudia was absolutely scarlet by this time. Mark had the grace to look slightly ashamed as he raked his hand through his hair and turned away.

'I used to think you were so…' He slashed the air with an expressive gesture as he paced away from her again in disgust. 'How *could* you, Claudia? For God's sake, he's old enough—'

'If you say he's old enough to be my father, I'll clock you one,' said Claudia, striving to regain her equilibrium with forced humour. 'For a start it's not true. He's *your* father, Mark, not mine. To me he's a mature, intelligent and…very exciting man.' Her voice thickened on the last words and Mark swung back to look at her, the hostility in his hazel eyes muted by curiosity. She perched weakly on the edge of the bed.

'But—*Dad*? I told you what he was like. Women are just another convenient form of relaxation, he *never* gets seriously involved. After all the agonies you went through with Chris I can't believe you'd let yourself be sucked into another situation like this. What security have you got now? When I spoke to your friend on the switchboard she said you'd even given up your job!' His look of horror was almost comical.

'I can always get another job, Mark.'

'What on earth have you let him *do* to you?' He sat heavily down on the bed beside her, trying to read her answer in her strained face.

'Nothing,' she murmured, her eyes as wise as they were unknowingly wistful. 'I've done it all to myself.'

The little she said was far too much. He sucked in a breath. 'Oh, my God—you're in love with him!' He sounded even more horrified than ever. 'Oh, Claudia, you *fool*!' His fingers tightened on hers as he asked quietly. 'How long do you think it's going to last?'

'It doesn't matter.' She shrugged, holding her head high. She mustn't let him think that she had any regrets, or blame his father for not being the man she wanted him to be.

'Yes, it does,' he said roughly, letting go her hands in order to pull her limp body close and hug her until her throat ached with unshed tears. Pulling back, his eyes fell to her unevenly buttoned blouse. He sighed, and began to match them up properly, with the brisk resignation of a parent tidying up an unruly child, and Claudia knew it was going to be all right. She was forgiven. 'Oh, Claudia, if you had to fall in love why couldn't it have been with someone who wouldn't ride roughshod over your feelings? Why in hell couldn't you have fallen in love with *me*?'

His arrogance was almost enough to make her smile. 'Because you're not in love with me.'

'Neither is he.'

The wounding words were spoken before he could call them back and as if he could apologise for their cruel truth Mark stilled his fumbling with her blouse and leaned forward to kissed her gently, passionlessly, on her trembling mouth.

Seconds later Claudia was staring into murderous blue eyes, a desperate shield between father and son as Morgan strode through the door.

CHAPTER TEN

'TAKE your hands off her!'

Mark, who had put his hands on Claudia's shoulders to steady her as they both guiltily jumped up from the bed, tightened them in automatic repudiation of his father's blistering order while she rushed into speech, gabbling out her reasons for being home early.

At her back Mark remained silent but his silence, like his hands on her shoulders, was a kind of clear physical taunt.

'And when I walked in,' Claudia finished awkwardly, 'I found Mark was home—'

'So I see.' The slowly enunciated words sent an icy chill down Claudia's spine as she stood nervously between the two men. Morgan prowled closer, bringing with him a strong aura of menace.

'I wondered why you had left the office again in such a rush,' he charged his son broodingly. 'Irene said that she told you I was across in the showroom. She thought it rather strange that you should take the trouble to call in on your way from the airport and yet not even bother to stay and say hello…'

'But *you* obviously didn't.' Mark's voice was as accusing as his father's. 'You knew exactly where I'd gone!'

Morgan stilled, his big shoulders flexing dangerously under his dark jacket. The two men were dressed in very similar business suits and Claudia felt like the tender meat in a brutally stylish sandwich.

'Why didn't you let us know that you'd moved your flight forward a week?' Morgan demanded bluntly.

A week? Claudia swallowed. Why hadn't he mentioned

Mark's imminent return if he had known about it? Had he intended, as Mark had claimed, to be rid of her before then?

'I thought I'd surprise you.' The murmur that stirred the hair on the back of Claudia's neck was supremely sarcastic. 'Instead, *I* was the one who got the big surprise.'

'I told you to take your hands off her.' Morgan's terse command was no longer an order, it was pure threat.

'Morgan, we were just *talking*—'

'Oh, is that what you're calling it now?' he interrupted Claudia with lethally soft sarcasm, reaching out a hand to toy suggestively with a button that Mark had failed to restore to its rightful place. Claudia shivered.

'I—I was changing—'

'Into something more comfortable...for Mark?'

'No, of course not,' she denied the silky suggestion frantically. 'He—I—we had no idea we were even going to see each other...'

'You're stuttering, Claudia. Are you nervous?'

'Of course she's nervous, with you standing over her like some brooding great tyrant!' Mark said angrily. 'What's the matter with you? Back off, why don't you?'

'Why don't *you*?'

Helplessly Claudia watched as the hand insistently nudging her button splayed flat in the air in front of her then curled into a savage fist.

'No, Morgan, don't—' She put both hands out and wrapped them protectively around the fist. She wouldn't be responsible for another angry estrangement between the two!

'Don't what? Give the boy what he wants?' he asked rawly.

'Don't be silly. This isn't what you think—'

'Mark *wasn't* kissing and undressing you on the bed? My bed? *Our* bed?' The blue eyes grew hotter, the voice thicker with each violent syllable.

Oh, God! Claudia felt Mark stiffen behind her, his hands

pressing even more deeply on to her shoulders. 'He was just being kind—'

'The hell he was!' With a gasp Claudia felt the fist move, powering out of her grasp, but instead of lashing past her it hooked around, spinning her out from under Mark's charge and dragging her back against him as he backed away, his other arm left free as a potential weapon.

'Damn you—!'

'No, Mark, don't—' Claudia held up shaking hands to stop him as he stepped aggressively forward. 'For goodness' sake, Morgan,' she pleaded to the man whose hostage she now was, 'think about what you're doing—'

'I know exactly what I'm doing. I'm making it very clear to everyone where they stand. You may have her friendship, Mark, but everything else is mine. She's mine.'

To illustrate the fact Morgan's free hand moved over her blouse, to find and cup her breast in a gesture that was as possessive as it was explicit.

Claudia tipped back her head to protest and found her mouth smothered with a ravishing, open-mouthed kiss that was every bit as explicit as the hand on her breast. He took his time and she was flushed with excitement and furiously embarrassed by the time he lifted his head.

After giving her one look of savage satisfaction Morgan focused his will again on his son. 'We've been lovers for weeks,' he said harshly. 'Accept it. Any hopes you had in her direction are dead and buried.'

His evident jealousy sent a wave of hope crashing over Claudia, quickly swamped by the despairing realisation that it was a purely sexual possessiveness.

'Claudia?' Mark's bewildered request made her gaoler shake her roughly within the prison of his arms.

'Go on, Duchess,' he ordered grimly. 'Tell him how much you enjoy my lovemaking. Tell him that this wasn't a one-sided seduction. Tell him that I'm the most important man in your life for the foreseeable future—'

In the ensuing, deadly silence Mark suddenly seemed to relax as he studied his father's stubborn belligerence. 'Why don't you let her go? You're hurting her.'

'No, I'm not. Am I, Duchess?' Without loosening his grip Morgan turned her tightly in his arms so that she was looking warily up at him. 'She likes me to be an aggressive lover.' He fitted his mouth over hers again, this time with lavish care. He kissed her with his whole body, tucking her intimately between his legs, his fingers splayed across her rounded buttocks and massaging them sensuously, uncaring of their deeply intrigued audience.

'Are we still having this conversation, or am I supposed to make my excuses and leave?' said Mark wryly, when it appeared that the other two had forgotten about him.

'Good idea,' said Morgan thickly, breaking off the kiss with extreme reluctance. 'Shut the door on your way out.'

'Morgan!' Claudia tried to squirm out of his seductive embrace but, feeling the familiar hardness stirring against her thighs, subsided blushingly. 'Mark—I'm sorry…'

'For what? Chosing a decrepit old man over a young and virile one?' He grinned. 'That's OK, honey. If you change your mind, you know where to find me.'

In the circumstances Claudia thought his flippancy dangerously misplaced, but Morgan didn't. His cynical smile was every bit as amused as Mark's cheeky one and infinitely more masculine.

'Stay away from her, son, if you value that virile, young hide.'

'Well, now, that's going to be fairly difficult to do,' Mark pointed out slyly. 'I live here, too, remember? Won't it be fun, the three of us in a ménage à trois…?' Wickedly he picked up Claudia's limp hand and raised it to his mouth.

'Mark—'

Claudia's warning was ignored.

'Come on, Dad, you've never quibbled at the idea of sharing before.'

Claudia's eyes widened with shock at the implications of that one, but Morgan was quick to counteract the mischief. 'Since we've never shared the same taste in women the idea was never any threat to my ageing masculinity,' he drawled pointedly, 'and, even if it had been, I never cared sufficiently to worry about it...'

'But with Claudia it's different?'

Claudia held her breath. She knew what Mark was trying to do with his clumsy probing. He was trying to help. But she would far rather he didn't stir up trouble...

'With Claudia the question doesn't arise. I think even your eager virility might draw the line at taking your pregnant stepmother for a lover.'

'Pregnant? *Stepmother*?' Mark looked pole-axed, as well he might!

'Didn't Claudia tell you while you were so busily...*talking* that she's decided to have my baby?'

Claudia, too, was stunned at the lengths to which he was prepared to go to cut his son out of her life.

'You're pregnant?' Mark's eyes fell to her flat stomach and then jerked frowningly to his father. 'You married her because she's pregnant!'

'I do seem to be making a habit of shotgun marriages, don't I?' Morgan drawled, unruffled by the suggestion, his glibness catapulting Claudia out of her state of suspended animation.

'*Stop* it! *Both* of you,' she demanded hectically. 'This is absolutely ridiculous! You can stop looking so appalled, Mark, of course we're not married.' She spat out the word as if it tasted vile.

'But we will be, by the time the baby's born,' Morgan said smoothly.

Claudia sucked in a cry as she wrenched herself out of his arms, pain and anger cutting deep into her heart. 'We don't even know if there is a baby!'

'Is that a no?' he asked evenly. 'Think before you speak,

Claudia, because I don't take rejection very well. I might not ask again.'

'You call this asking?' she choked.

'You want me to grovel for the privilege of making an honest woman out of you?' he had the gall to say coolly.

Her narrowed eyes glittered with golden spears of contempt. He wouldn't know honesty if it hit him over the head! 'The idea of having your face at boot-level has a very definite appeal at the moment,' she told him fiercely.

His eyes smouldered hotly in response. 'Or I could just throw you on that bed and strip you,' he threatened silkily. 'You never say no to anything I want there. Hell, a few minutes of foreplay and you're usually the one begging...'

'Er—Dad—'

Morgan didn't even look at him. His goading challenge was all directed at Claudia's scarlet face.

'Get out of here, Mark. This doesn't concern you. Well, Claudia, make your choice.'

'You mean you're actually offering me one?' she sneered, conscious of the deliciously familiar tension beginning to stretch inside her.

'Maybe I will go back to the office for a while,' murmured Mark gleefully as he edged out of the door. 'Er—congratulations, by the way...'

'How dare you imply that I'm so promiscuous that I'd carry on a sleazy affair behind your back with anyone who asked me, let alone Mark?' Claudia continued on the attack, only to gasp in shock as Morgan picked her up and tossed her effortlessly on to the bed, exactly as he had threatened. Fearful excitement raced through her veins as she remembered the next part of his erotic threat. 'Don't think you can—!'

The air puffed out of her as he came down heavily on top of her. Even fully dressed the contact was shockingly electric, shorting out her anger as he completed the live circuit with his wandering hands, pulling at her clothes and his own until they were both breathlessly naked and aggressively aroused.

'Don't think that this proves anything,' Claudia moaned as he gripped her strongly, shifting up and over her, parting her thighs and moving insistently between them, teasing her moist heat with his swollen body, withholding the fullness of him until she clutched at his hips with reckless impatience.

'It proves that you forgive me.' His tongue probed against a stiffened nipple as he deliberately aimed all the weapons in his sexual arsenal on his unresisting target.

'Forgive you...for...what...?' she laboured to remember.

'Anything...' He licked her nipple again. 'Everything...' He began to suckle with noisy intensity, at the same instant allowing her to pull him gloriously deep inside her, the satisfaction only fleeting as he slowly withdrew, to thrust even more deeply than before. The thick sounds of descriptive pleasure he made as he worked rhythmically over her sent tiny vibrating shocks thrilling through her moistly conductive flesh, slowly building to a powerful erotic pulsing that only he could transfer into the exquisite moment of perfect completion.

'Yes...oh, yes!' she whispered as she threw herself into the delirium of unrestrained loving.

'You forgive me for my unreasonable jealousy...?'

If she had been in her right mind she would have been delighted to hear him beg but as it was the words could no longer satisfy her. She welcomed the completeness of his possession. 'Yes...yes...'

'You're mine,' he rasped, the muscles in his arms cording with agonised tension as he supported himself over her writhing body, driving her harder, deeper into a sustained frenzy. 'Say yes, dammit, tell me you want to do this with me every day of your life...'

'Yes, yes, *yes*…!' she sobbed, and the explosive reaction that was her reward tumbled her into sweet oblivion.

When she woke, hours later, Morgan was gone. On the bedside table was the only proof, apart from her sweetly aching body, that it had not all been some wild and erotic dream.

> Had to go back to work. Don't believe in long engagements, especially in our case. I'll organise the licence, the trappings are up to you…

What made her heart tremble was not the written confirmation that his proposal had been real and not just the mockery of his jealous possession, but the casual signature.

> Love, Morgan.

Love?

In all the passionate words that had passed between them, love had been the only taboo.

But if it were true…?

She would sell her soul if it were true! Morgan had no need to marry her. Marriage would make him vulnerable, give her a public and private power over him which as his mistress she could never hope to achieve. So why would a rich, successful, attractive and powerful man such as Morgan risk the emotional and financial exploitation? Unless…

> Love, Morgan.

Claudia stared at the two words, her thoughts in a turmoil of anguished uncertainty. Her time had run out.

She rose and dressed swiftly, anxious for it to be over. If Morgan still wanted to marry her after she had told him about the reasons for her baby's death, well, she would know then that he *did* love her, with a strength that would last a lifetime.

She drove carefully, rehearsing her speech all the way, trying out the best phrases, cringing at the knowledge that there was no way she could soften the brutal impact of her confession.

At Morgan's office she was relieved when his secretary waved her in with a conspiratorial smile, not even bothering to check with her boss. After today there might not be too many more smiles coming her way around here.

He was sitting in his swivel chair facing away from the door, studying a slim file on his lap. Claudia hesitated in the doorway.

'Morgan?'

He froze, his head lifting like an animal scenting prey, but he didn't turn. Claudia stepped inside the office and closed the door, thankful for its cool support at her back. Without it she thought her knees might not hold her upright. She moistened her lips, frantically trying to remember her opening line.

'Morgan, I need to—'

'You *bitch*!' He came out of his chair and round the desk in a single stride. 'You sadistic, calculating, vindictive *bitch*!'

Stunned by his violently premature reaction, Claudia could only stand helpless and white-faced as he attacked her with his fury.

'Oh, yes, you might well look sick, you little—' He used a word which made her flush violently, then pale again as he continued with coruscating contempt, 'You are sick. You should be bloody well locked away! You let me believe that I was responsible for the *death of a child*!'

Claudia's mind went blank, all her careful defences devastated by the realisation that he already knew what she had agonised over telling him. Once again, she had failed him.

'What in the *hell* did you hope to achieve?' he ripped at her with white-lipped disgust. '*Revenge*? For what? Hurt pride? You admitted you never wanted Mark anyway so don't tell me I deprived you of your heart's desire. I was never a person to you at all, was I? I was an object, a convenient whipping post. You used me then, you bitch, to deny your own responsibility and you're still trying to use me!'

He towered over her, his remorseless fury battering her with a force that made his earlier display of temper a passing frown in comparison.

'And my God—what about this new child you professed to want from me?' he ground out pitilessly. 'Was that going to be just another pawn in your macabre game of "let's make Morgan suffer"? Or maybe there was never going to be a child. Maybe that was going to be your way of drawing out my guilt, torturing me with something you knew I'd never have. Well, you can rot in hell before I play any more part in your sick fantasies. Do you hear me, Claudia? You can rot in *hell*!'

And with that he threw the folder he was holding in her stricken face and walked away, sweeping a chair violently out of his path on his way. The cardboard file fell to the ground, papers fluttering out of it and she bent to pick it up, her body functioning purely on automatic. Her crabbed fingers stilled as she realised what it was she was gathering up.

'This is my medical file from the hospital...'

She had only whispered but he heard. He spun on his heel, visibly restraining himself from further violence.

'How did you get it?' she asked numbly. She had never dreamed he would find out this way, through cold, clinical details. 'I thought doctors didn't release this sort of information—'

'Yes, another amusing twist for your little tale of revenge,' he snarled, his fists clenched at his side as if he was fighting the temptation to use them on her. 'You'll laugh at this: I pulled some strings. I thought it might help for me to know…what sort of problems you might have bearing my child. I didn't want to put you through the trauma of trying if there was no possibility of carrying to term—'

Oh, God, he *had* loved her… 'But I told you—'

'You told me a lot of things, Claudia.' He cut her off with an angry swipe that deliberately sent a pen set crashing off his desk. Like the overturned chair it seemed symbolic of the devastation her lies had wrought. 'None of them worth sh—'

'Morgan, that's why I'm here. I came to tell you—'

'Did you?' he sneered cuttingly. 'How kind. What were you going to say? Hey, Morgan, guess what? You're not a murderer after all. I've been stringing you along all this time just for the pleasure of watching you squirm!'

The word *murderer* made her heart shrink to a tight knot in her chest. 'Morgan, please, won't you at least listen—?'

'To more lies? More self-serving half-truths?' he exploded, his eyes burning blue flames in a face that was a rictus of disgust. 'It was hard, but I could understand you lying about your baby's parentage. But this? *This*?' For a horrible moment he looked as if he was actually going to vomit but he swallowed the bile to utter harshly, 'I don't want to hear, Claudia. Not any of it. Get out! Get out of my office. Get out of my house. Get out of my *life*—'

'Morgan, I love you—' she began desperately and he swore, more vilely than before, smearing her with the taint of his violent loathing.

'Get out, Claudia, while you still can. If you don't then I won't be responsible for my actions. I could very easily kill you for what you've done to me—!'

Shaking, knowing that she had left it too late, that it had always been too late for them, Claudia turned, fumbling blindly for the elusive door-handle.

'And Claudia—you walk away from this relationship empty-handed. Understand? You take *nothing*!' He addressed her slender back with savage insolence. 'If you do I'll sue you for fraud and see you raped of every shred of reputation in open court. So leave the keys to the Corvette at the desk on your way out. You were a good lay but you didn't last long enough to earn the spare tyre, let alone the whole car!'

Claudia stiffened, goaded by the last, unforgivable insult into looking back over her shoulder at him with eyes that blazed with a rage that matched his. That car had been a symbol of their happiness together. She wouldn't let him take even her memories from her!

'Go to hell, Morgan Stone!'

She didn't remember the reckless drive back to the house on Marine Drive, only getting there in miraculously fast time and stumbling on her knees on the concrete drive as she fell out of the driver's door, her hand stinging with a burn from the hot tyre that she had momentarily propped herself against. She was still shaking like a leaf when she staggered into the house, automatically picking up the telephone in passing as it began to shrill upon her nerves.

'H-hello?'

A dead silence greeted her croaky greeting, then a guttural snarl. 'You're lucky to be alive, the way you took off from here!'

'You call this being alive?' she asked, with a hysterical sob of wretched black humour, and hung up on him.

She took the telephone upstairs with her, but he didn't ring back.

All night and for the next two days Morgan didn't ring. He didn't set foot in his own house, and Claudia didn't set foot out of it. She called the hotel and told them she had a virulent dose of summer flu and without a qualm diverted all her work to her replacement who had arrived from head office for his two-week familiarisation period.

Mark came home, crushing her with his concern and jabbing her with worried questions, but she wouldn't talk to him, couldn't explain the emotional numbness that smothered and protected her; could only sit and wait like a small, wounded animal in a trap, afraid to move, afraid to draw a predator's attention to itself...

On the third morning, before he reluctantly left for work, Mark finally pressed her more insistently, 'What are you going to do, Claudia? Dad's holed up at the hotel and blows a gasket at the mere mention of your name. You're sitting here like death warmed over. If...well, if you have to leave, where will you go?'

His worry pierced the thick grey envelope of her misery with a bright shaft of pain.

Leave Morgan?

She wondered if he knew she was still living in his house. No, if he had he would probably have hired some heavies to throw her out on the street by now.

'Go?' She didn't have anywhere to go, she realised in sudden panic. She couldn't stay at the HarbourPoint—her job there was nearly over and, besides, *he* was there. True to Mark's gloomy prediction of a few days ago she had managed to leave herself with nothing, *nobody*...

The shaft widened to become a shining path through the self-pitying murk that had buried her natural resilience. Claudia's dull brown eyes gleamed with a spark of resistance. After everything she had risked to be with Morgan, why was she giving up on him with so little fight? She had seen the way he respected those who stood up to him, even when he believed they were in the wrong. She had done a very great wrong, yes, but even the most hardened criminals were given their day in court. Now that Morgan's temper had had a few days to cool, might she not be able to approach him on a more rational level?

Would a man who hated her have made that angry phone call after their row? she asked herself. He hadn't asked about the car, he had been checking up to make sure she had got home safely. Even then, in the grip of a molten fury that cursed her very existence, he had been concerned enough to make that call...

What did she have to lose by confronting him again? She had nothing left to lose! But how, if he was so determined to avoid it? There had to be some way to lure him into a meeting. Her eyes narrowed as she suddenly remembered something he had threatened in the white-heat of the moment.

'Do you know any good lawyers, Mark?' she asked slowly.

He looked wary, startled by the sudden proud lift of her chin after several days of seeing it sunken on her chest. 'Sure. Why?'

Her eyes narrowed. 'I want to file an action for breach of promise.'

His jaw dropped. 'Breach of— You mean...*Dad*?'

'Nobody else has asked me to marry him lately,' she said grimly.

'But Claudia—my God, he'll never—my *God*!'

She refused to let his appalled jabber undermine the desperate act of a desperate woman. 'You were there,' she insisted. 'You heard him say he was going to marry me.'

Mark gulped. 'You want *me* to appear as your witness?' His voice squeaked like a girl's as he regarded her with awe. 'Claudia, he'd *kill* me—he'll kill us both!'

She looked at him with grave brown eyes that shimmered with the futile tears that she had refused to shed. 'Some things are worth dying for, aren't they?'

A grin of unholy amusement crawled slowly across his stunned expression as he contemplated her determined face.

'Yes. Yes, I guess they are. And I not only know a few good lawyers—some of them owe me favours. You just sit tight here, Claudia, and leave the fast-tracking to me!'

After he had gone, finding the whole thing far more entertaining than she thought was wise, or appropriate, Claudia allowed her confidence to collapse. Breach of promise? she thought sourly. That was a laugh! All that loving Morgan had ever promised her was heartache and he had delivered on that one with interest!

Having a vague idea that in the interest of profit lawyers always moved extremely slowly, Claudia consoled herself with the thought that she would have plenty of time to change her mind if her courage failed her. Meanwhile at least she could feel that she was making some attempt to take control of her life again.

For the first time in days she ate her breakfast and even managed a few nibbles of lunch, in deference to the despairing efforts of Morgan's very confused housekeeper.

In the afternoon, enervated by the heat and the effects of insomnia, Claudia smothered herself in sunscreen and sunbathed defiantly on the terrace in an effort to improve what she gloomily decided was her prison pallor.

A savage screech of tyres and the slam of a car door woke her from a light doze and she sat up woozily, aware of a painfully warm tingling in her skin and annoyed at herself for overdoing it. Was Mark home already? Checking to see she hadn't decided to slit her wrists? She really must tell him to stop hovering over her like a nervous parent. She got unsteadily to her feet and looked over the balcony, her eyes widening with horror as she saw the squat black car parked below, its tyres still smoking angrily.

At the same instant she heard her name echo through the house.

'Claudia? Claudia! I know you're here, Claudia, don't think you can hide from me!'

Frantically she looked around for something to put over her sleek yellow maillot but she hadn't brought her wrap out with her and she was contemplating snatching the tablecloth from under the remains of her alfresco lunch when

Morgan exploded up the stairwell into the sunroom and saw her.

'I thought I told you to get out of my house,' he rapped out. His eyes smouldered over her exposed limbs as he stepped out on to the deck and something flicked in his eyes. 'You're expecting me, I see.'

The sardonic murmur was such an unexpected turn-around that Claudia flinched. 'Don't flatter yourself!' she snapped, controlling the urge to cross her hands over her heaving breasts.

He was shaven but managed to project an aura of un-shaven haggardness, his eyes narrowed dauntingly in a face full of implacable straight lines. In a light grey three-piece suit and white shirt he made Claudia feel intimidatingly naked and ill-prepared.

'What else can a man think when he's so desirable women are driven to *court* his attention?' He tapped his palm with a tube of paper tied with ribbon.

'Do you know what happened to me today, Claudia?'

She shook her head helplessly, afraid to ask, mesmerised by the paper in his hand. Another medical file to beat her over the conscience with…?

'Two men—two very large, sullen-looking men accosted me in my showroom in the middle of an interview with a US Cable TV channel about the race…an interview that *you* helped set-up, incidentally…and served me with some legal papers which they were at pains to explain in very loud and explicit detail. Not only am I being sued for breach of promise, it seems, but my own son is apparently a willing witness against me and my own address is listed as the source of the complaint.'

'R-really?' Claudia didn't dare look him in the face. That lethal, silky soft evenness was totally unnerving. What on earth had Mark done? Even Claudia knew that no legal papers were ever drawn up this fast!

She watched through lowered lashes as the paper was

unrolled by hands which bore ominously white knuckles. 'Now, what kind of woman do you suppose does something this stupid?'

A woman in love.

The silence stretched. Claudia swallowed. The warm tingling in her skin had become a scalding heat. To her horror she could feel his eyes crawling over her body again, and her breasts begin to swell and ache with remembered hunger.

She put her hands around her waist, unconsciously deepening the cleavage of the low-cut bathing suit as she jutted her jaw with an aggression to match his. 'An angry one?'

His hard, arrogant expression didn't change.

'Angry?' His voice was still as soft as the rest of him was hard. He reached out with the offending papers and scraped the edge of one corner tauntingly over the dark circle of her nipple revealed by the paleness of her costume. 'I don't think so, Claudia.' His nostrils flared as her nipple instantly contracted. 'You do know, don't you,' he said, scraping the paper slowly back and forth with cruel deliberation, 'that this breach of promise isn't worth the paper it's written on?'

Claudia trembled. 'Morgan, I—'

'Don't.' He stopped her with a clipped monosyllable. 'Don't lie to me. Not again. Not ever again!' Having slapped her in the face with breathless hope, he struck her again with another terse demand. 'Are you pregnant?'

'What?' She blinked at him, dazed.

'This suit, it mentions my abandonment of you in a…delicate condition…'

Oh, *Mark*!

She looked at him, clear-eyed, not even tempted. 'No.'

If he wanted her, it was going to be for herself, alone!

'How can you be so sure? Your period isn't due until next week.'

She would never, *never* get used to his crude frankness

at the most delicate of moments. Blushing, Claudia caught at the paper that was teasing her breasts, crumpling it like the irrelevancy they both knew it was.

'I—I'm sure I'm probably not,' she said firmly.

'"Sure" and "probably" are a contradiction in terms.'

'Is that what you came here for, to talk terms?' she flared, stung by his cold formality.

'You called and I came,' he told her.

'I didn't—'

'Claudia, this suit is so much trash.' He illustrated his claim by taking it out of her nerveless fingers and throwing it over the balcony. 'It's a paste-up job, a mishmash of legalese that amounts to out-and-out blackmail. I don't know who your lawyer is but I'm going to see that he gets disbarred. And as for those two loud-mouthed goons he used as process servers—!'

'I—that was Mark...I only suggested it this morning—I wasn't really going to go through with it...' She didn't mean to cry, she really didn't, but his crookedly mocking smile was too much for her. 'I hate you,' she whispered as he gathered her against his chest.

'And I hate you.'

He kissed her, to show her how much, and the tears flowed even faster. Was this execution or absolution? She still didn't know.

'I'm sorry, I'm sorry, I'm sorry...' she murmured brokenly into his mouth. 'I was mad—you were right, I was temporarily insane when I lost the baby, but even when the insanity passed I was afraid to face what I'd done. I just wanted to forget it—all of it...' She shuddered with the memory. 'And...and then when we met again I was—I still couldn't make myself do it. I knew you would be disgusted—you were right to be, because there's no excuse. But I really was going to tell you that day...that was why I followed you to the office. I would never, ever have married you letting you think...'

'That I was a murderer of babies?'

'No, oh, no—don't say that…' She cupped his face and looked deep into his eyes, shocked to see that the glorious blue was veiled by rain-drenched clouds. 'I'm so sorry,' she repeated helplessly, aching for him. 'I'll never forgive myself. I—I'll understand if you can't either—'

His gaze held her wavering one steady. 'No, you won't.'

She bit her lip, caught out in yet another lie. 'I'll try to understand…I'll do anything you want to try and make it up to you…'

'Anything except go away and leave me in peace.'

His bitter irony was almost too much to bear. She closed her eyes. 'Even that…'

'And what if you really are pregnant?'

Oh, God, he was relentless. She opened her eyes, accepting her punishment with fatalistic calm. 'Whatever you want.'

'An abortion?'

Pure shock congealed the blood in her veins at the prospect of such a fitting revenge for what she had done to him. '*No*!'

'Not quite *anything*, then.' How could he savage her like this, with such cold mockery, yet hold her so warmly and intimately in his arms? Was this to be her eternal punishment?

'No, not quite anything,' she admitted wearily.

'I told you not to lie to me, Claudia.'

'I'm *trying*!' she cried thickly, tortured by being able to touch him, yet knowing she was not touching him at all.

'Try harder.' With the same grim intensity he asked, 'Do you love me?'

She clenched her teeth, the admission bitter. 'Yes!'

His hand cupped her chin, holding it still for his ruthless interrogation. 'Do you imagine that I love you?'

And aching silence. Not think—*imagine*… A cruel distinction. What was the truth here and what was the lie? She looked at him, filling her heart and mind and senses with his essence.

'Yes,' she said huskily. 'Otherwise you wouldn't have let me goad you into seeing me again. But that doesn't mean I'll take advantage of it—'

A fugitive gleam of laughter darted like summer lightning across his eyes. 'I can see that you believe that right now, Duchess, but I have no doubt that's going to turn out to be another bold-faced lie. You'll take shameless advantage of my every weakness—'

'Loving isn't a weakness, Morgan,' she protested earnestly, trembling with exquisite relief. 'It makes you strong.'

'Strong enough to conquer the black demons of doubt,' he agreed, smoothing his hand across her sun-warmed bare back. 'Even when I hated you, Claudia, I never doubted that you were mine to hate—'

'Morgan—'

'No, let me say this, so there can be no misunderstanding, so that we can put it behind us.' His finger touched her lower lip, slightly swollen where she had bitten it and drawn blood. 'I would very much like for you to be pregnant with my baby, but, whether you're pregnant or not, I still want to marry you. I chased you, I caught you; I won't give you up easily. We can't change the mistakes of the past but we can definitely shape a better future for ourselves, if both of us are willing. In the last few days I worked out that there was quite a bit of injured pride keeping my angry feelings of betrayal on the boil. I've spent the last few days drunk and thinking ugly thoughts, sulking because life wasn't fair, but then who said it ever was?

'This morning I started to function in the real, unfair world again. And in the real world I found that I still had the same choice I had before I picked up that medical file: life with Claudia and life without Claudia. The same choice…and the same Claudia.

'I know you quite well, you see, and one of your flaws is an annoying habit of protecting yourself from unpleasantness by ignoring it—like pretending to be tough and mercenary and blasé about sex when you're really a diehard romantic who would no more fall into bed with a man she didn't love than hurt him if she did.' He lowered his mouth towards hers and his tongue briefly touched the tiny, throbbing wound in a gesture of exquisite gentleness.

'You didn't want to hurt Nash so you agreed to marry him although you had doubts; you didn't want to hurt Mark, so you didn't tell him how I insulted you; you didn't want to hurt me so you tried to protect me as long as possible from a knowledge that would, you suspected, cause me more pain than it alleviated—'

'I truly am sorry, Morgan—'

'I know. So am I. For the time we've wasted. You probably would have allowed yourself to be seduced by me a great deal sooner if you hadn't had a guilty secret to protect,' he murmured, enjoying her blush, and the tentative reblooming of her feminine confidence at the casual acceptance implicit in his teasing. 'When I got served those damned papers I lost my temper and nearly punched out those guys, until I realised that you *couldn't* be serious…not my passionately soft-hearted Claudia. You were telling me that you hadn't run away. That you were still there for me if I wanted you. *If*?'

His forehead rested against hers, moving back and forth to smooth away the last ruffles as he kissed her nose. 'Whatever wrongs you've done, you taught me a very valuable and necessary lesson two years ago: that life is fragile and every moment we are given is precious to us and to the people who love us. It's due to you that I rediscovered myself and my son…and my capacity for love.

'I love you, my darling Duchess, and that's a cause for celebration, never apology. So marry me, and let's enjoy our lifetime of precious moments together. I promise you that I'll make you feel so well-loved that you'll forget there was ever anything but trust between us...'

She was feeling beautifully well-loved already, his mouth cherishing hers, his hands moving skilfully under the thin fabric of her maillot, reviving her spirit and coaxing her heart and body into his caressing care.

Their celebration was personal and private but it did indeed have a very lasting and notably public effect.

Nine months later, almost to the very day, little Sarah Stone was delivered upon an unsuspecting world in the awkward confines of a classic Corvette parked crookedly outside a Wellington hospital, her tiny, enraged cry announcing that she had her panic-stricken father's temper and her embarrassed mother's talent for attracting his attention!

READER SERVICE™

The best romantic fiction direct to your door

Our guarantee to you...

The Reader Service involves you in no obligation
to purchase, and is truly a service to you!

There are many extra benefits including a free
monthly Newsletter with author interviews,
book previews and much more.

Your books are sent direct to your door
on 14 days no obligation home approval.

We offer huge discounts on selected books
exclusively for subscribers.

Plus, we have a dedicated Customer Care team
on hand to answer all your queries on
(UK) 020 8288 2888
(Ireland) 01 278 2062.

Historical Romance™
4 brand new titles each month
...rich, vivid
and passionate
Available on subscription every month
from the Reader Service™
GEN/04/RS2